C0-ANZ-795

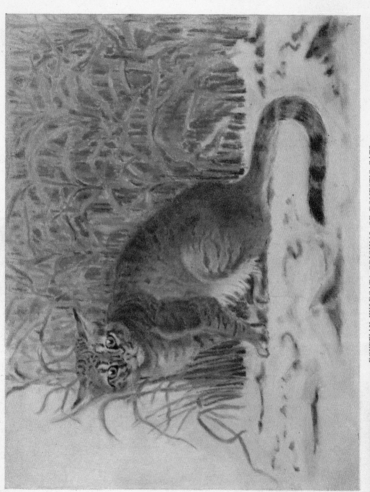

EGYPTIAN WILDCAT: ORIGINAL OF DOMESTIC CATS

THE LIFE OF ANIMALS

THE MAMMALS

BY

ERNEST INGERSOLL

AUTHOR OF "WILD NEIGHBORS," "AN ISLAND IN THE AIR,"
ETC., ETC.

*WITH FOURTEEN FULL-PAGE COLOR PLATES
AND MANY OTHER ILLUSTRATIONS*

SECOND EDITION, ENLARGED

STUDENTS LIBRARY
CONCORDIA TEACHERS COLLEGE
RIVER FOREST. ILLINOIS

New York
THE MACMILLAN COMPANY
LONDON: MACMILLAN & CO., LTD.
1907

All rights reserved

Copyright, 1906, 1907,

By THE MACMILLAN COMPANY.

—

Set up and electrotyped. Published May, 1906.
New edition, with additions, April, 1907.

Norwood Press
J. S. Cushing & Co. — Berwick & Smith Co.
Norwood, Mass., U.S.A.

QL
706.I5
1907

23823

It is possible to make natural history entertaining and attractive as well as instructive, with no loss in scientific precision, but with great gain in stimulating, strengthening, and confirming the wholesome influence which the study of the natural sciences may exert upon the higher grades of mental culture; nor is it a matter of little moment so to shape the knowledge which results from the naturalist's labors that its increase may be susceptible of the widest possible diffusion.

— ELLIOTT COUES.

ACKNOWLEDGMENTS

A PREFACE is needless for a book of this kind, which needs no explanation and could be saved by no excuses; and I may substitute for it an Acknowledgment of Gratitude due to those who have helped me, much to the advantage of the reader.

Foremost among them is Mr. George P. Brett, President of The Macmillan Company, who has placed at my disposal every facility for, and put no obstacles in the way of, my making the best book within my power. If I have not succeeded, it is not the fault of my publishers.

Next I wish to recognize gratefully the important service rendered the book by Dr. W. D. Matthew, Associate Curator of Vertebrate Paleontology in the American Museum of Natural History in New York, in giving me the benefit of his eminent knowledge of extinct mammals and in supervising those pages of the book relating to them. The reader and myself are similarly indebted to Professor Henry F. Osborn, Curator of Vertebrate Paleontology in the American Museum of Natural History; to Dr. Daniel G. Elliot, Director of the Field Columbian Museum, Chicago; to Mr. William T. Hornaday, Director of the New York Zoölogical Park, Dr. C. B. Andrews, of the British Museum, and to certain others, for the criticism and approval of parts of the work in which they were especially interested and well informed.

The liberality of the New York Zoölogical Society has enabled me to place before the reader many of the original and admirable pictures of animals made by the Society's Photographer, Elwin R. Sanborn; while other excellent illustrative material in this extremely difficult branch of photography has been derived from the private collections of the Duchess of Bedford and Mr. H. W. Shepheard-Walwyn, in England; and of Messrs. L. W. Brownell, Silas M. Lottridge, Clarence Lown, W. H. Fisher, and others in the United States. In each case the negatives have been taken personally by these accomplished amateurs.

Lastly, I desire to mention the aid given by my daughter, Helen Ingersoll, who drew ten of the fourteen colored plates and many of the smaller illustrations in the text.

E. I.

NEW YORK,
May 1, 1906.

PREFACE TO SECOND EDITION

THE principal features in this new edition are the addition of several important animal photographs to the list of illustrations, and the correction of a few minor errors.

I am glad of this opportunity to express my grateful appreciation of the extraordinary welcome which this work has received from a wide circle of scientific critics and literary reviewers, both in this country and in Great Britain.

Another source of gratification is the fact that the book has not only been approved of for young readers, but is *liked* by them, and is taking its place as an enjoyable as well as useful tool in the field of education.

E. I.

NEW YORK,
April 1, 1907.

CONTENTS

			PAGES
INTRODUCTION			16
MAN AND THE APES	*Primates*	. .	. 7–57
BATS AND FLYING FOXES . . .	*Chiroptera*	. .	58–67
SHREWS, MOLES, AND HEDGEHOGS	*Insectivora*	. .	68–77
PRIMITIVE FLESH-EATERS . . .	*Creodonta*	. .	78–81
BEASTS OF PREY	*Carnivora*	. .	82–229
MARINE CARNIVORES . . .	*Pinnipedia*	. .	. 230
HOOFED ANIMALS	*Ungulata*	. .	231–385
ELEPHANTS AND DINOTHERES . .	*Proboscidea*	. .	386–399
MANATEES AND SEA COWS . .	*Sirenia*	. .	400–403
WHALES, PORPOISES, ETC. . . .	*Cetacea*	. .	. 403
GNAWING ANIMALS	*Rodentia*	. .	404–468
SLOTHS, ARMADILLOS, ETC. . . .	*Edentata*	. .	469–484
PANGOLINS AND AARD VARKS . .	*Fodientia*	. .	485–487
MARSUPIAL ANIMALS	*Marsupialia* .	. .	488–520
DUCKBILL AND ECHIDNAS . . .	*Prototheria* .	. .	521–526
AUTHORITIES CITED			527–538
INDEX OF AUTHORITIES CITED			539–541
INDEX			543–555

LIST OF COLORED PLATES

EGYPTIAN CAT . . . . *Frontispiece*

FACING PAGE

AMERICAN MONKEYS 40

JAGUAR AND TAPIR 100

HYENAS 158

RATEL AND ICHNEUMON 176

FOX AND JACKAL 208

BEAR 214

ANTELOPE HEADS 268

HARNESSED ANTELOPE 270

SABLE ANTELOPE 274

OKAPI 296

FALLOW DEER 308

GOPHERS AND GROUND SQUIRREL 426

SUGAR SQUIRREL 502

THE LIFE OF MAMMALS

INTRODUCTION

THIS is to be a book upon the mode of life, the history and the relationships, of the most familiar and important class of animals — the Mammals. It is the class, indeed, to which we ourselves belong, as well as do most of our domesticated servants and pets. From it we derive an enormous amount of aid and material. It furnishes us with a large part of our clothing and bedding; it supplies the principal element of our food; it provides materials for making a multitude of things of daily use; and were it not for the aid of these animals the farmer could hardly raise his crops, nor the merchant dispose of his wares, nor the rest of us enjoy many of our ordinary comforts and pleasures. And yet the surprising circumstance remains, that we have no popular name for this extremely important group.

If I had announced this simply as a book on "animals," without any descriptive subtitle, a reader might have understood in a general way what it was to be, yet he could not be certain; for any living creature is an "animal," and a book under that title might properly include the whole range of zoölogy. Hence a distinctive name is required if the author's purpose is to become clear. One cannot say "quadrupeds" with accuracy, for that would include four-footed reptiles and amphibians, while it would exclude man, who has only two feet, and such marine members of the class as have no limbs

at all. Similarly the terms "beast" and "brute" are inaccurate or wrong; and so we are driven to borrow a term from the Latin to supply the need. This is the word "mammal" —
Name. a word easy to remember, definite in meaning, which ought to come as commonly and properly into use as "bird" or "fish," since, like them, it stands for its whole class and for nothing else. This term expresses the one great distinction which separates mammals from all other animals, namely, the feeding of their young upon milk, a nutritious liquid, rich in sugar and fats, secreted by the mother's system in glands or milk bags from which the milk is sucked out by the little ones, whose stomachs, at first, can make use of no other kind of food. These milk glands are called in Latin *mammæ*, whence the technical class name *Mammalia*, and also our English word "mammal" — an animal that suckles its young.

This fact alone, had we no other means of judging, would show us that the mammals stand highest in the scale of animal life. The simply organized animalcules, the lowly worms, shellfish, and insects, grow up without any parental attention — are simply turned loose to shift for themselves. Very few fishes or reptiles take any special care of their little ones, and none feed them. In the case of many birds the young are able to run about and pick up their own living as soon as they emerge from the eggshell; and where they remain in the nest for a time and are cared for by the parents the food brought them is usually the same as that of the old ones. This state of things shows progress; and in a general way the rule holds that the higher the organization of the animal the more helpless are its young, and the more they need parental care, time to mature, protection, and special food. Hence the peculiar provision of the mother's milk in this class is a sure indication of the high rank of mammals as a group; and the infants of the superior members of it depend upon their milk diet much longer than do the inferior members.

Another distinctive peculiarity of the mammals is their hairy covering — something that belongs to no other class of animals, and which gives an immense advantage.

A hair is a threadlike outgrowth from a minute nipple sunken in the skin, which continues to secrete the horny substance at its root, **Hair.** as the hair wears away at its point. Hairs vary in form and structure and consequently in appearance, giving such differences in pelage as the velvety fur of the mole, the long wavy coat of the skunk, the bristles of the pig, the spines of the porcupine, or the scale armor of pangolin and armadillo. All of these are modifications of hairs, and it seems likely that claws, finger nails, and sheath horns are of similar structure.

The purpose of the hairy coat is mainly protection from the weather; and those mammals (of cold climates) which have a close woolly under fur, usually have also an outer thatch of longer, coarser hairs to shed the rain. Hair makes a warm covering, not only because of the air with which it is filled, but because of the air entangled among it. Watch a muskrat swimming. You will see that his body is covered with glistening bubbles held between the under and outer fur, and that he comes out of the water with a perfectly dry skin. Thus hair not only keeps dampness and cold out, but the bodily heat in, as you well know who wear this covering at second-hand in the form of "furs"; and the coats of mammals vary in character and density not only with the climate in which they dwell, but with the season, the heavier winter coat loosening and falling out in the spring, but growing again in the autumn. A semiannual shedding of the hair is characteristic of most northern animals, at least, as is familiarly shown by horses and dogs. This quality of warmth in the hair is probably the secret of the supremacy attained by the mammalian race. Its beginnings were early in the Mesozoic or Secondary age of geologic history, when dry land was gradually rising out of the seas and swamps into extensive areas, and the climate of the world was slowly cooling. At that time the ruling animals

3

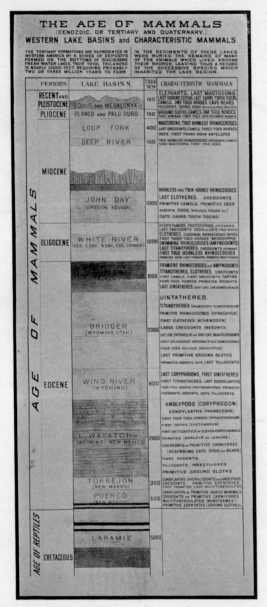

on shore were reptiles, covered with a leathery or scaly hide, and having cold blood. Now when a kind of small creature arose among them whose skin sprouted *hairs* instead of scales, it seems to have profited so much by this novelty that nature enlarged and improved on the model. Its great advantage was in the *warmth* of the new covering, which as it became perfected induced a steadily increasing warmth of blood, and this promoted activity,

AGE OF MAMMALS.

Museum chart prepared by Prof. H. A. Osborn and Dr. W. D. Matthew. By permission of the American Museum of Natural History, New York.

followed, of course, by advancing ability and developing brain. At any rate before long — geologically speaking — we find that the hairy mammals became numerous, and that the reptiles correspondingly decreased, till finally the dinosaurs, pterodactyls, and other cool-blooded, sluggish, massive land reptiles had died out, and the earth was ruled by warm-blooded, active mammals and birds.

The traceable history of mammals extends back to the Triassic, the oldest of the three divisions of the Mesozoic era, but only three or four Triassic specimens have been discovered, and these are so imperfectly preserved that they give little information. Just preceding that time there flourished a group of reptiles, the Theromorpha, which were large terrestrial forms with skull, teeth, and fore limbs surprisingly like those of mammals, and which fill an intermediate place between the highest amphibians of that time and the lowest of the mammals; "and it is altogether probable that from amongst some of their number . . . the Mammalia arose." But this by no means clears up the problem, for the solution of which future information must be awaited. **Theromorpha.**

It is not doubted, however, that true mammals, — though few and very small and inconspicuous, as they would need to be in a land filled with ravenous reptiles, — existed throughout the whole Mesozoic era; and before its close the two grand divisions of Mammalia, Prototheria and Eutheria, had become established; and the two primary divisions of the latter, the Marsupials and Placentals, had already been separated. Then came the time when the mammals began to go ahead and possess the earth, — a process pictured by Prof. W. B. Scott: —

"The passage from the Mesozoic to the Tertiary was marked by widespread and very important changes in the physical geography of the northern hemisphere and by an extraordinary change in the life of the earth. Vegetation had attained almost its modern state. . . . The huge and bizarre reptiles of the Mesozoic had all disappeared, while the mammals came to the front in an astonishing outburst, as it may be fairly called [so that the Tertiary is styled Age of Mammals]. Henceforth the mammals were to be the dominating type, taking the place of the dethroned species.

"Much of mammalian history has been preserved in the fresh-water deposits of Tertiary age in various parts of the world, but in no region yet **Age of** known with such fullness as in the western part of the United **Mammals.** States, where are found deposits covering almost the whole of Tertiary time. These great rock masses, of different dates, cover thousands of square miles, and were laid down in various ways. Some were accumulated in lake basins, others were spread by sluggish streams over their flood plains, others may have been heaped up by the winds in semi-deserts. The rocks thus accumulated entombed the bones of innumerable animals, the fossil remains of which are not only extraordinarily abundant, but are preserved in a degree of completeness found in very few other parts of the world." [119]

NOTE. — The small raised figures in the text refer to the enumerated List of Authorities at the end of the book.

Technical (specific) names will be given, so far as it seems desirable, in the Index.

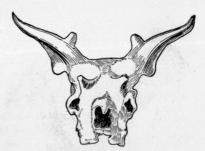

SKULL OF SIVATHERIUM.

MAN AND THE APES — Order, PRIMATES

THE most perfectly organized animal, and the one best known to us, is man; and a book of zoölogy which omitted him would leave out the standard by which, in a certain sense, all others are measured. He is readily classified, apart from intellectual attainments, at the head of the highest order of mammals, the Primates, which includes with him the manlike, or anthropoid, apes, the monkeys, and the lemurs. All these have five fingers or toes (digits), each covered at the tip by a flat nail; and in most cases the thumb or great toe, or both, are "opposable" — that is, may be bent around opposite the other digits so as to form a grasping organ. The higher the Primate in the scale of organization the more perfectly are its fore limbs and hands adapted to seizing and handling objects, and its hind limbs to supporting and moving the body; and the whole sole of the "plantigrade" foot rests upon the ground instead of the toes alone, as in the case of the "digitigrade" dogs, cattle, and the like.

These and other characteristics fit the Primates for life in trees, where nearly all spend their time; and the peculiarities of the skeleton and system of muscles are such as follow from this mode of existence. The number of young, as a rule, is no more than two annually, and they are born in a helpless condition, often almost naked of hair, toothless, and with the eyes shut; hence they must for a period be nursed and carried about by the mother. The food consists almost wholly of fruit and other soft or easily digested vegetable materials, insects and eggs, and the teeth are of nearly even size and ordinarily thirty-six in number.

Man is distinguished from his fellow-Primates mainly by his erect walk, the roundness of his skull, caused by the indrawing **Man as a** and general lessening of the face, and by the ex-**Primate.** pansion above and behind the ears of the brain case; by his power of articulate speech; and by the absence of a hairy covering. This statement takes no account of that vast superiority of mind which chiefly distinguishes him; but it may be noted here that the differences in size and complexity of the brain — the seat of the mental faculties — between him and the greater apes are no greater than exist between some men and other men.[1]

As to his faculty of speech, that seems a mental accomplishment rather than a physical peculiarity, largely due to early men having caught the idea of making and using articulate sounds, and having perfected the art by practice. The vocal organs in the human throat do not differ materially from those of other vertebrates, nor are they remarkably advanced in perfection. The shape of the human mouth and teeth, the more refined form and mobility of the lips, tongue, etc., undoubtedly aid in controlling the voice, and in pronunciation of sounds that have become the symbols of ideas, and therefore must be imitated exactly and repeated on demand. The ability to do this depends, however, on the possession of an educated ear, as is plain from the fact that persons totally deaf are also speechless, although their vocal organs are perfect, and may be taught to pronounce words; and one who has not a fair sense of melody in his ear is usually unable to learn to sing.

Nearly all of man's physical peculiarities are the result of his gradually acquired erectness, which has caused his spine to assume an elastic, S-like curve, rounding out at the shoulders and in at the waist, which forms a sort of spring, easing the jar of stepping or jumping, and also makes a better brace for exerting the strength of the limbs, while it adds flexibility to the body. The pelvis, greatly broadened, falls into an upright position, so as to bring the legs directly under the trunk, whose weight they must support without help from the arms. This duty, gradually enforced, has strengthened, straightened, and nearly equalized the bones of the legs, extended the heel, and enlarged and arched the instep to bear the weight of the whole frame; while the toes, useful now only to help the foot in holding its place, and in pushing and balancing the body, when a step forward is taken, are short and strong, with the great toe squarely alongside the others. The arms are shortened, the hands extremely flexible and become the most perfect grasping organs, due mainly to the greater length and freedom of the thumb, for whose control have been developed one of the very few novel muscles possessed by man alone. To his hands, next to his brain, man owes the possibility of his great advancement.

It is in the head, however, that the most striking human feature is seen, apart from the erect posture and accurate balance of the body upon its pillarlike legs. The skull is a dome poised beneath its center **The Human Face.** instead of aft of it, as in the apes and lower creatures, and it contains twice as much brain room as does that of any other Primate. The frontal bones have been shortened and contracted until in the best examples the face protrudes little if any beyond the front line of the comparatively lofty brow.[2] The jaws have become semicircular in shape, the teeth small and crowded, the canines never much larger than the others, the chin is well filled out, the nose narrow but prominent and well separated from the mouth, and the eyes deeply set in comparatively small, bony sockets, which do not enlarge inward, as in lower animals, to obstruct the brain case; while the ears are small, low, and set close to the head. Several of these features may be seen separately in various apes and monkeys, but their combination is perfected in man, and gives to his head a dignity, and to his countenance an expression, unmistakably his own.

Man's brain may be compared properly only with the brains of the anthropoid apes. "The human brain differs from that of the manlike apes," says Forbes,[3] "in regard to its convolutions and their separating grooves, only in minor characters; but in weight, as in capacity, very greatly. The weight of a healthy, full-grown human brain never descends below thirty-two ounces; that of the largest gorilla, far heavier than any man, never attains to more than twenty. Yet 'the difference in weight of brain between the highest and the lowest men is far greater relatively and absolutely than between the lowest man and the highest ape.'"

Some fossil bones found in 1894 in Java by Professor Eugene Du Bois are of extreme interest, because they represent a creature between man and the highest apes which lived in the early

Pliocene epoch next preceding the Glacial epoch. Only the top of the skull, a thigh bone, and two teeth are known;
Pithecan- and they indicate an erectly walking animal, about
thropus. five feet and six inches tall, which in general appearance, and in having a brain capacity almost equal to that of the earliest known human beings (the cave dwellers of the Neanderthal in France), was much nearer man than is any modern ape. This creature is truly, as Professor Haeckel puts it, "the long-searched-for missing link," in other words, represents the commencement of humanity.[4] It is named *Pithecanthropus erectus.*

The rude, chipped-stone implements found in the red clay on the chalk downs of southern England,[67] and in similar Pliocene deposits in neighboring parts of France and Belgium, denote the existence of, in that region, "Eolithic man," a being capable at least of making these objects contemporary with Pithecanthropus in Java; but no fossil bones of Preglacial man in Europe have been recovered.

Chimpanzees, Gorillas, Orang-utan, and Gibbons

The chimpanzees, gorillas, orang-utan, and gibbons or "anthropoid apes," differ from mankind principally in the form of the skull, and in the great length of the arm as compared with the leg. The foot is more handlike, too, a tree-gripping rather than a ground-stepping organ. Nevertheless, all can stand or even walk fairly erect upon the ground, balancing themselves by outstretched arms; when they are in haste, however, and, indeed, ordinarily, they rest their weight upon their long arms and closed hands, the knuckles touching the ground, and so progress on all fours or swing along somewhat like a man on crutches. The spine of the chimpanzee alone among them shows much approach to an S-like curve, and the skull, which is longest fore and aft, is set on the neck well forward of its center. The skull is thick, ridged along the crest, and unites into a solid globe much earlier than do the skulls of our own infants, putting an end much sooner to the possible expansion of the brain. The forehead is sloping, the jaws are very massive and protruding, and the 32 teeth are large, the canines becoming formidable tusks in old males. Bony ridges over the eyes give a frowning expression, especially to the gorilla. The brain is much smaller than that of man, where it is never less than 55 cubic inches, while in the chimpanzee it is, on the average, $27\frac{1}{2}$ cubic inches, in the gorilla 35 inches, in the orangutan 26, and in the gibbons far less.

The chimpanzees are the best known, having been exhibited alive in Europe at least as early as 1641. Previously to that **Chimpan-** narratives of travelers to the Guinea coast, where **zee.** the Portuguese already had trading stations, had contained a fair account of these "men of the woods," published in such books as "Kingdom of Congo" (Frankfort, 1598) and "Purchas His Pilgrimes" (London, 2d ed., 1625). Since then books relating to equatorial Africa have abounded with stories about them, but much has been hearsay, or vague and exaggerated.

Copyright, N.Y. Zoöl. Society.   Sanborn, Phot.

YOUNG CHIMPANZEE "POLLY."

Many young chimpanzees, however, have been kept captive and some of them closely studied, so that we are fairly acquainted with this ape's character and intelligence when tamed, though still in the dark as to the limit of its capacity for education.

Sifting out the truth as well as we can, it appears that there are at least two species of chimpanzee, — the "common" one and the bald one. The former and more familiar one is the larger, and has a coat of straight, silky, brownish black hair, which falls smoothly away from a parting in the middle of the head and forms bushy whiskers. The face, great outstanding ears, hands, and feet are naked, much wrinkled, and dull flesh-color, growing darkly reddish with age. The latter species has hair of deeper black, but the growth ceases above the ears, leaving the whole crown of the head bald, and this hairless skin, with that of the face and ears, fingers and toes, is deep black; the ears are even broader and flatter than in the other species, and the features noticeably different. A variety of this bald ape is represented by Du Chaillu's [6] "koola-kamba," and by the female Johanna, which was bought from the Lisbon "Zoo" by the Barnum-Bailey Circus Company, when two years old, and was exhibited in the United States and in Europe from 1894 to 1897, but died in Nuremberg in 1900 when approaching seven years of age.[121] Sally, of which more is to be said presently, endured the northern climate longest, living in the London Zoölogical Gardens eight years (1883–1891). Then there was brought to the Zoölogical Garden at Dresden, Germany, in 1875, a young female ape which was most interesting and puzzling to naturalists by its combination of the characteristics of both chimpanzee and gorilla. It was named Mafuka, and proved a wild, unmanageable creature, which was carefully described and pictured by Hartmann,[7] whose book on the anthropoid apes is the most comprehensive account of them we have. The general opinion is that Mafuka was a mongrel between a chimpanzee and a male gorilla. Koppenfels says other examples are known.

Chimpanzees belong to the forests of all equatorial Africa west of the great lakes, but the bald species seems limited to the Gaboon Valley.

They are rarely found in open country, although they spend much of their time on the ground, hiding in thickets in family groups, and are nowhere numerous. Mated pairs **Habits.** seem to remain together permanently; and more than one missionary has been disconcerted, when he tried to show the Africans the wrongness of having several wives, by their disgusted reply that they did not wish to be like apes. They show great affection for their families, the father often taking the baby from the mother and carrying it, especially in dangerous places; and they seek to assist one another when hurt or in trouble. The grief shown when one loses its mate in captivity is real and touching. When at rest they usually sit with their backs against a tree, and ordinarily move about on all fours, their gait when walking erect being weak and uncertain, so that then they feel unsafe. They are secretive and timid, and will run away from a man or woman if allowed; yet when cornered they prove themselves ugly fighters, striving always to bite off the fingers or toes of the foe — usually another ape. The only quadrupeds they need fear are leopards and crocodiles.

There is no good evidence that they arm themselves with sticks as weapons, but the Niam-niams told Schweinfurth that in a fight with a negro one would if it could wrest the spear from the man's hand and use it vigorously. The Manyema hunters, on the other hand, assert that a captured spear is simply broken and thrown away. Both reports may well have been true. Dr. Livingstone writes[8] of battles between the sokos, as he calls them, and the Manyema negroes west of Lake Tanganyika, who frequently organized hunts for these pillagers of their plantations, and drove them into nets, where they would become entangled and could be killed with assagais. They hunted them similarly for the sake of their flesh; and the missionary suggests that the cannibalism of these negroes might have grown out of this taste. The Manyema seemed to regard the animal on the whole as an extremely keen, cunning, mischievous sort of "good fellow," fond of scaring persons alone in the forest, or of picking up a child and pinching it to hear it squeal, but meaning no great harm by its pranks.

The chimpanzee families move about a great deal, mostly at night and in search of food, and now and then gather about a village in such numbers as to work great damage, especially to young bananas. Their food consists almost wholly of the softer forest fruits, varied by grubs, eggs, and fledgelings of birds, lizards, and the like, and in captivity they become very fond of meat, and cleverly catch live birds put into their cages.

It is to obtain such food that the apes climb the trees, and the German explorer Schweinfurth describes [9] how prevalent and secure they are in the forests northwest of Albert Nyanza, where the trees grow one above the other in stages, the upper springing from seeds implanted in the top branches of those beneath them, and forming "galleries" so dense that it is difficult for the wiriest of climbers to penetrate them, and "bowers in which perpetual darkness reigns."

To such a leafy stronghold the ape retreats at night, and builds a rude platform of branches on which his family lie down for rest, while he may curl up in a crotch beneath its shelter; but no such a roofed hut as Du Chaillu portrayed seems ever to be constructed.

Their feeding time is mainly evening and early morning, and it is then that these apes are most active and noisiest, uttering the cries, shrieks, and howls which have impressed all travelers, and whose loudness is due to air sacs and an arrangement in the throat resembling that of the South American howlers. Hence we read of troops of hundreds, but in reality eight or ten chimpanzees together make a "crowd," and it usually consists mostly of young ones, who make as much sport as possible out of the occasion, and are particularly fond of drumming on resonant logs or hard earth with sticks. That this simplest of possible employments of an instrument or tool should be the only one achieved by the highest of the apes, is striking testimony to the wide distance between it and the lowest human savage.

The next of the great apes — the West-African gorillas — are the biggest, fiercest, and yet most anthropoid of them all; the most repulsive of all beasts, perhaps, because **Gorilla.** so like humanity devoid of every attractive quality except mere physical strength. A gorilla is of so massive a frame as to weigh more than twice as much as any man of similar height. In relative shortness of arms and length of legs it stands nearest man, but its brain is no larger than that of a four-year-old child. The face is naked and black, very wide, with a huge protruding mouth, nostrils broad and flat, and the eyes overhung by bony ridges. To a prominent ridge on the skull, running from the forehead back to the nape, are attached thick masses of temporal and neck muscles. The canine teeth are formidable tushes, and the whole face, crowned by reddish hair, and set closely above the shaggy, massive shoulders, expresses brutal savagery. The coat consists of blackish or reddish bristles, with an under fur, and it becomes gray with age. The arms reach down to the knee when the gorilla stands erect, as it will readily do, for its feet are big and have a prominent heel; and, as might be expected of so heavy a creature, it spends much time on the ground, and sleeps there on beds of weed stalks, etc., or, more often, perhaps, makes "nests" in trees for the night. It seems to be less timid than the chimpanzee, probably because it has nothing to fear but an occasional leopard.

Until recently only a single species, the original *Gorilla savagei*, was known, and it was believed to be restricted to the forested coast hills between the Kamarun and **Western** Kongo rivers; but since 1903 other specimens of **Species.** huge size have been shot in the interior of the French Kongo (State), and also near Lake Albert Edward. In *La Nature* for July 29, 1905, Dr. Hamy reproduces photographs and descriptive notes of a male killed far up the Sanga Valley, at Ouassu (or Uesso), which measured 2.3 meters (nearly $7\frac{1}{2}$ feet) tall and 1.5 meters across the shoulders. This is, at least, a foot taller than any coast gorilla recorded. In the same year a large gorilla was killed between Lakes Albert Edward and Kivu, described as *Gorilla beringeri* by Matschie. Both these are now regarded as species separate from each other and

A FEMALE GORILLA WALKING.

from the coast one; but further information may modify that opinion. Little, in fact, is known of the living nature and habits of any wild gorilla. The cabbage, or terminal bud, of the oil palm, bananas, pawpaws, and plantains are the favorite fare, often obtained by raiding plantations. Various hard nuts are also eaten, some of which the coast gorilla is said to crack with a stone; but on this, as on most other points of behavior, contradictory reports exist.

Du Chaillu's thrilling accounts of ferocious fighting with men have been completely discredited, and Winwood Reade, who visited the Gaboon Valley directly after him, and other well-informed persons, assert that Du Chaillu never saw a living gorilla. "That a huge arm descends from a tree, draws up and chokes the wayfarer, must be false," declares Lydekker, "for intelligent natives have confessed to knowing no instance of the gorilla attacking man. . . . But we must believe that this ape, if provoked or wounded, is a terrible foe, capable of ripping a man open with one stroke of the paw or of cracking the skull of a hunter as easily as a man cracks a nut. There is a tale of a tribe that kept an enormous gorilla as executioner, which tore its victim to pieces, until an Englishman, doomed to meet it, noticing a large swelling near its ribs, killed it with a heavy blow or two on the weak spot."

There is little doubt, at any rate, that this is the least intelligent and most savage of all the great apes. Only one of the several young ones that have been sent to Europe have lived more than eighteen months; and the single one brought to the United States (in 1893) survived only five days. Hornaday says this is due to the fact that "they sulk, often refuse food, will not exercise, and die of indigestion." A second baby, imported in 1905, died on the voyage.

The third of the anthropoid apes is the orang-utan, or "man of the woods," whose home is Borneo and the eastern lowlands of Sumatra. In Borneo it inhabits the swampy for- **Orang-**
ests between the coast and the interior mountains, **utan.**
to which it retires in the dry season. It is more often seen than the others, and has been well studied by Brooke,[29] Wallace,[31] Hornaday,[30] Beccari,[209] and other naturalists in its native woods, and when dead by many anatomists. The Dyaks call it "mias," and distinguish several varieties.

The orang-utan spends its life more exclusively in the tree tops than does either the gorilla or chimpanzee, rarely descending to the ground except to get water, and then it moves slowly and awkwardly by swinging its body along between its long arms used much like a pair of crutches. In the trees, however, the orangs travel with the certainty and ease of practiced gymnasts. Too heavy for leaping, they reach out and grasp with their hooklike hands a limb or a bunch of twig ends, swing underneath to the next hold, and so on at great speed, as an athlete travels hand over hand beneath a tight rope. Usually they go singly; or a female may be accompanied by an infant, which clings astride her waist, and also, perhaps, by an older offspring, for the young stay with their mother until two years old, and do not mature until twelve or fourteen. At dusk each old one weaves together broken branches into a sleeping-plat-

form, making a satisfactory couch in two or three minutes, usually not above twenty-five feet from the ground. Such nests are found so numerously that probably a fresh one is built every night; and Hornaday describes the animal as sleeping on its back, with one or more hands hooked around an adjacent branch.

Copyright, N. Y. Zoöl. Society. Sanborn, Phot.

YOUNG ORANG-UTAN "DOHONG."

Captive orang-utans always grasp the head of the bed or the bars of the cage when asleep, even though lying on the floor.

"The orang-utan," says Forbes, "is of a very shy and uncertain disposition; if captured when full grown it is wild and ferocious; when young it is easily trained, but never lives in captivity to attain maturity. When attacked and hard-driven by human enemies, and it gets to close quarters with them, it can be a formidable and dangerous antagonist, and has been known to fatally injure its assailants." A Dyak hunter told Wallace: "The mias has no enemies. No animals dare attack it but the crocodile and the python. He always kills the crocodile by main strength, standing upon it, pulling open its jaws, and ripping up its throat. If a python attacks a mias, he seizes it with his hands, and then bites it and soon kills it." Almost every specimen taken, however, shows scars of fighting among themselves. It will rarely unprovoked attack a man. In one case, as Dr. A. R. Wallace has recorded, a female mias on a durian tree kept up for at least ten minutes a continuous shower of branches and of the heavy spined fruits, as large as thirty-two pounders, which most effectively kept every one clear of the tree she was on. She could be seen breaking them off and throwing them down with every appearance of rage, uttering at intervals a loud pumping grunt, and evidently meaning mischief. This durian is the vile-smelling but delicious fruit which in its season forms the favorite food of men and animals alike. Otherwise these apes live on leaves, buds, nuts, and soft fruits.

This Malayan ape is smaller and weaker than its African cousins, males standing not more than four feet six inches, and weighing 160 pounds, while the females are smaller. The body is bulky, the belly protuberant, and the legs very short, while the arms are so long that the fingers hang down to the ankle. The coat is a variable dark brick-red and long, forming a beard in old males. The head is short and high, with the bony crest of the skull and the ridge over the eyes less prominent than in the gorilla; while the nose is insignificant, and the jaws are large and protrusive, with a long smooth upper lip. The eyes have a pleading expression, the ears are small and closely appressed, and many of the older males have the cheeks greatly and distinctively broadened by flat callosities. Lastly, although its brain is most like that of man, the orang-utan is inferior, in general, to both the gorilla and the chimpanzee.

The fact that it is confined to these Eastern islands, so far removed from its relatives, is singular but explainable, for fragmentary fossil remains of manlike apes (especially one named Dryopithecus), none older than the Miocene Age, have been found in southern Europe and eastward to China, showing that in past time such animals existed throughout the warmer parts of the Old World. Some of these fossils are evidently of existing species, which appear by their present restricted habitats to have nearly come to the end of their career, — for species rise and flourish and decline as do individuals, — and all the anthropoids are doubtless doomed to speedy extinction.

As has been said, none but young examples of these great apes have been kept in captivity (except at Calcutta) where they could be under scientific notice; but chimpanzees ten or a dozen years old have been seen in Europe. The little ones of all species seem much alike, gentle and playful when kindly treated, affectionate toward their friends, and safely allowed to run loose on shipboard or in villages, but likely to fly into a rage when teased, and to grow sullen and revengeful toward those who have injured them, and this viciousness increases as they grow older and learn the measure of their strength.

One of the most interesting ever shown in the United States was the chimpanzee Crowley, who traveled three or four years with a circus, and in **Anthropoids in Captivity.** winter was lodged in the Central Park Menagerie, in New York. When he came to us in June, 1884, he was only about a year old and weighed only 15 pounds; in June, 1886, he weighed 57 pounds, and two years later 110 pounds. He died of tubercular phthisis in August, 1888, when his total height was 4 feet and 4 inches. His skeleton and mounted skin may still be seen in the American Museum of Natural History. Another noted chimpanzee shown in the United States in 1890 was Chiko. Dohong and Polly were in the New York Zoo in 1903.

The youngsters of all three species are about equally capable of being taught simple tricks, and come to understand many human words, and to make their cries express various emotions comprehended by their keepers; but they are sedate as compared with the vivacity of the mischief-loving monkeys. Circuses abound in trained young chimpanzees and orang-utans which will wear clothes, sit at table, and eat all sorts of things with knife, fork, and spoon, drink from tumblers, smoke a tobacco pipe, use pen and paper, and do many quaint "stunts" with a comical resemblance to a little old man. In these feats the chimpanzee shows himself the most nimble in wits as well as in body. As a London keeper told Lydekker: "The orang is a buffoon; the chimpanzee a gentleman." Of the many excellent accounts of these young apes one of the fullest is that in "Cassell's Natural History," Vol. I, where Sayers, Broderip,[15] and other writers are quoted extensively.

Gibbons. Lowest of the anthropoid ape family stand the gibbons, — slender, monkeylike forms of the Indo-Malayan region having wholly arboreal habits, in flocks, and feeding on fruit, leaves, insects, spiders, birds' eggs, etc. They have arms so long that when they stand upright the finger tips touch the ground. The jaws and nose are prolonged into a snout,

Copyright, N. Y. Zoöl. Society.   Sanborn, Phot.

A SIAMANG.

and the canines are very large in both sexes, while the brain is simple. The largest is the Sumatran siamang, which stands three feet tall and is shining black; and it, like the orang, has distensible air sacs in the throat, connected with the larynx, yet its howling is no louder than that of the other gibbons which have no such sac. The cry of the siamang is described by a correspondent of *The Field* (Oct. 18, 1879) as precisely like the howling of dogs: —

"One might almost fancy that the various voices were arranged with a view to a concert effect. There is always one old gentleman with a very deep bass, who jerks out his howl after a swinelike fashion; the baritones, contraltos, and sopranos expressing their feelings in prolonged notes. There seems also to be some kind of competition between the siamangs and the onkas, for no sooner does a music party of the larger species assemble, than a miserable spider-legged onka plants itself in an adjacent tree and gives full play to its powerful lungs. The cry of the onka beats that of the jackal and laughing hyena clean out of the field, and at times nearly drives one to distraction. It is exactly like that of a suffering child, only four times as strong."

Among the most distinctive gibbons are the hoolock, of the Himalayan foothills, which is brown or black relieved by a white band across the forehead; the lar, or reddish-faced, white-handed gibbon of the Malay Peninsula; the wau-wau of Java, Borneo, and the Sulu Islands, which is ashy gray, with whitish eyebrows and black cap, fingers, and toes; and the Sumatran onka, or agile gibbon. All these are much alike and frequent mountain forests up to about four thousand feet. They are remarkably adept at climbing and leaping — will, for example, rush end over end down hill slopes "by grasping bamboos or branches that bend beneath their weight, and allow them to drop until they can seize the ends of other bamboos and branches lower on the slope, and take another mighty swing downward "almost like a flock of birds."

However, when they do occasionally come to the ground, they show themselves able to walk erect and more human-like than any other ape, setting the foot down flat upon the sole, holding the long arms gracefully above the head, and so taking a rapid and funny gait, which would recommend them to Delsarte or an American cake-walk expert. Forbes had a tame siamang that used to accompany him every evening about the village plaza, leaning elegantly on his arm, to the admiration of all the people; and a French writer describes how one would walk down the length of a table without disturbing a dish.

All the gibbons are peaceable among themselves, gentle, cheerful, easily tamed when caught young, and show a quick affection toward man. One of the most complete and illuminating studies of the group is that by Haeckel.[28]

Baboons, Monkeys, and Marmosets

It has already been said that all the Primates fall into one of two groups: (1) the broad-nostriled or Old World apes and **Monkey Types.** monkeys; and (2) the New World, narrow-nostriled monkeys and marmosets. A part of the former group (man and the manlike apes) have been considered. Now we are to take up the remaining families of Primates, only three in number, which comprise

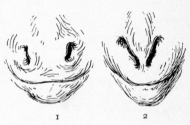

I   2

TYPES OF NOSTRILS IN MONKEYS.

1. Platyrrhine.   2. Catarrhine.

the baboons, macaques, langurs, capuchins, howlers, marmosets, and others popularly recognized as "monkeys."

One of the most singular and interesting things in zoölogy is the deeply cut line separating these two groups of animals, which at first glance seem so much alike. The compressed noses of the Old World apes and monkeys, to which they owe their group name Catarrhina, contrasted with the widely separated, outward-flaring nostrils of the Platyrrhina, or New World families, give only one of several distinctions. The former are, as a whole, of larger size than the latter. Their anatomy differs; thus while the catarrhines (including man) have only thirty-two teeth, the platyrrhines have thirty-six — four extra premolars. The catarrhines generally have those patches of hard, hairless, brightly colored skin on the buttocks, termed ischial callosities, never present in the American forms, for the latter do not sit up upon their haunches. Some Old World monkeys boast long tails, but these never show the slightest tendency toward that prehensibility so characteristic of our platyrrhines. Again, no American monkey possesses distensible folds inside of the cheeks, called cheek pouches, characterizing many foreign species. These distinctions have existed forever, apparently, "since no fossil remains of monkeys at all intermediate have so far been discovered"; and this is another evidence of the very early time at which South America became isolated, as shown by the singularities of its fauna. The Old World catarrhines are the superior in organization, and must receive first notice.

All the Old World monkeys, apart from the anthropoid apes, belong to a single family, Cercopithecidæ, divisible into two sections: (1) small, agile, long-tailed forms (Semnopithecines) without cheek pouches; and (2) larger, short-tailed forms (Cercopithecines) with cheek pouches.

The semnopithecines seem to have the higher organization, as is shown especially by the complicated stomach, in the first chamber of which may be stowed a large amount of the leaves that constitute the bulk of their food, to be slowly passed on to the truly digestive sac. These monkeys may therefore pick and swallow the materials for a meal with great rapidity, and then go to some safer place for its slow digestion, thus keeping out of danger a much larger part of the time than if they had to eat long and slowly; nor do they need the pouches in their cheeks which the other group uses for a similar economy of time and risk. All dwell in trees, and the group includes the small African guerezas and the Asiatic langurs, —

Langurs. the latter best known by the sacred monkey, or l'entelle of India, venerated by the Hindoos because it represented Hanuman, the Monkey-god who assisted Rama, one of the mythic heroes. Hence no faithful Brahmin Hindoo will harm one (though delighted to see another man drive them away or even kill them), and they come fearlessly about villages, raiding gardens and orchards, and pilfering from shops and food stores, making themselves where numerous a great nuisance. The pious have thrown a similar protection over other species, so that in some parts of India all monkeys are safe from molestation, and become intolerable. J. L. Kipling [11] and Felix Oswald [120] tell entertaining stories of their too familiar ways. Sometimes a community will capture a band and ship them away, but if they do not come back others will take their places, and their thieveries must be guarded against incessantly. Near Simla there is a famous " monkey temple," on Jakko Hill, said to be presided over by a queer, fanatical fakir who is by birth and education a European.

Like most monkeys these Indian langurs abominate the tiger, and a troop racing overhead and "slanging " the king of

ENTELLUS MONKEY OR HANUMAN.

the jungle has many a time led to the downfall of his striped majesty; therefore tiger hunters join with priests in defending the little gray mischief-makers, laughing at their black faces and well-brushed whiskers as they peer saucily down through the foliage.

Some twenty-five or thirty other species of leaf-eating langurs are scattered wherever forests occur, from the snowy heights of Kashmir to Borneo, and many most interesting things are related of them by Blanford, Jerdon, Hose, Wallace, Blyth, Swinhoe, Hornaday, Forbes, and other writers familiar with that part of the world. Some of them are gay with black, white, chestnut, yellow, and other tints. All feed mainly on leaves, flowers, and young shoots; utter loud, not unmusical cries, and move about in troops. Their long slender bodies and long limbs, resembling those of the American spider monkeys, give them vast leaping powers, and astonishing flights will be made by a band, one after another, from some lofty tree top to a lower one, maybe thirty feet away. One trick is to spring upon a limb in such a way that in its recovery from the pressure of their fall it will lift them up to where they can seize another and so go on. Often the mothers carry a clinging young one in these perilous leaps, and the accuracy with which they calculate the distance and other facts of the case is wonderful.

AN OLD MALE NOSE MONKEY.

One notable species is the large wanderoo of Ceylon, so fully described by Tennent,[17] and the **Nose Monkey.** object of quaint superstitions; but the most remarkable of all is the nose monkey of Borneo, which the Dyaks laughingly call "white man," and which many naturalists place in a separate genus. This is of large size, is brown with gray rump, limbs, and tail, cheeks yellow, and a nose that gradually elongates with age, until in old ones it is a bulbous, wagging proboscis that hangs down below to the chin, and gives a most comical caricature of a human countenance to the face. They are nowhere common and rarely seen, though their cry, like a deep tone from a bass viol, is a familiar sound beside the rivers of Sarawak.

The remaining semnopithecines (genus Colobus) are African and differ from the Asiatic langurs by the absence of any thumb. The ten species are found in equatorial Africa, and may be called guerezas, after an Abyssinian one long known. They vary in length of body from twenty-one to about thirty inches, and have tails a tenth *Guereza.* or more longer than the body and more or less tufted at the end. Their habits are similar to those of the langurs, and it has rarely been possible to bring one away from its native hills. Their dense, long-flowing, beautifully colored hair, however, has made their skins highly valued by

THE MOUNTAIN GUEREZA.

the natives and so much in demand in Europe that all these monkeys are likely soon to be exterminated. Some are shining black, some white and black, some bay or a mixture of these tints. The guereza proper is a most striking little animal, for its head, body, and limbs are covered with jet-black hair, while on each side of the back there arises a line of long white hair which hangs down below the flanks, forming a kind of mantle of pure white; and the dark face is surrounded with a fringe of white hair which forms long Dundreary whiskers on each cheek. With these skins the Masai and other East African warriors decorated themselves for battle and covered their shields. A variety inhabiting the lofty mountains east of Victoria Nyanza has the tail heavily fringed with long white hair that glitters like spun glass, and it is said by the Arabs to take great pains to keep this plume and its mantle perfectly clean. H. H. Johnston [18] says that besides making headdresses from the skin the Mandara warriors affix the flowing yaklike tails behind their belts as if they grew there. These pendent white fringes serve their wearers as a screen against the annoyance of insects when they lie asleep in the tree tops; and they choose sleeping places among the hanging moss where they are practically invisible, in spite of their contrasted black-and-white coats.

Turning now to the other group, we meet the common monkeys of Africa, about forty species, many of which are familiar in menageries, such as the tiny talpoin, the ascagne, hocheur, malbrouck (French names), green monkey, patas, mona, and Diana of West Africa, and the East African grivet, so

THE DIANA MONKEY.

commonly depicted in the old Egyptian wall paintings. All are small, slender, long-limbed, and muscular, and have long tails and round heads usually adorned with whiskers and beards of formal cut. Their fur is thick and soft, and in most species each hair is ringed with different and often brilliant colors; and while the predominant hue is blackish or olive-green, sometimes bright, the coats of many are gayly marked with blue black, red, chestnut, tawny, golden green, bright yellow, white, or jet-black, often in quaint spots or stripes, so that they are the most ornamental of all the monkey tribe. None, perhaps, exceeds in prettiness the mona and Diana, with white fronts and well-combed hair and beards.

The guenons, says Forbes, are entirely confined to Africa, where they live entirely in the forest regions, herding together in large troops. "They can move from tree to tree with great rapidity, and can climb even on vertical surfaces with surprising quickness. They are **Guenons.** abrupt and energetic in their movements, restless and noisy, incessantly chattering and making grimaces. . . . Their food consists of leaves, birds' eggs, and honey, but preëminently of fruits, while they are especially destructive to the ripe grain fields of the natives near the woods in which they live. . . . The guenons are not only restless but very inquisitive; they are, therefore, when young very easily tamed and as a consequence they are frequently to be seen as performers in circuses and exhibitions. When aged they are unreliable in temper, and often very ill-dispositioned. They are said also to repel with missiles any intruders into the region in which they are established in any numbers."

The mangabeys are a smaller group of West African monkeys, intermediate between the guenons and the macaques, but their hairs are not ringed. The half a dozen species are blackish or brownish with white markings, the eyelids invariably white.

The cercopithecines form a group of rather large, short-tailed Old World monkeys, represented by the macaques and baboons, whose special mark is the possession of cheek pouches.

All the macaques are Asiatic except one, — the magot or Barbary ape, to be spoken of later. Seventeen species are recognized, scattered from Baluchistan to northern China and Japan, and southeastward to Timor, **Macaques.** some widespread, others restricted to a narrow habitat on some single island, mountain range, or bit of coast. They vary in size from thirteen inches (nose to root of tail) to nearly three feet, and the males are always much larger than the females, and have bigger canine teeth. The tail is long in a few, but short in most, and many have a distensible sac in the throat.

They go about in flocks of both sexes and all ages, and are active, noisy, like to scramble about rocks, and some swim and dive well. Blanford,[19] who describes them extensively, says that their food is varied, most or all eating insects and snails, as well as seeds, berries, fruits, etc., while one kind feeds entirely on crabs and the like gathered at low tide. In some parts of India they do great damage in gardens, where they have occasionally been seen to devour lizards and frogs. All cram the food into their cheek pouches and then hide away to chew it at leisure. Their doglike teeth and strong nails are capable of inflicting severe wounds, so that old ones are well able to defend themselves in the warfare of the jungle.

The Malayan pig-tailed macaque has been taught for centuries in the East Indies to climb trees and throw down ripe cocoanuts, avoiding green ones. The "little, graceful, grimacing rilawa, or bonnet macaque of Ceylon," says Tennent, "is the universal pet and favorite of both natives and Europeans. Tamil conjurers teach it to dance, and . . . carry it from village to village, clad in a grotesque dress, to exhibit its lively performances." Of the rare leonine macaque of upper Burma, which is black, and has a great horseshoe-shaped mane about its head and shoulders, a specimen named Sally lived in the London "Zoo" in 1869 and showed extraordinary cleverness. She walked upright with little effort, and carried things thus, and would drink out of a bottle or smoke a pipe — relics of her education on shipboard. The dried flesh and bones of a Chinese macaque form a material for medicine; and the Chinese of Formosa invariably chop off the tail of the single Formosan species, because, as they explain, it is an insulting caricature of their cue. One of their old books informs its readers that the macaque has no stomach, but digests its food by jumping about and so shaking it up until it is absorbed by the system. The monkey which appears so numerously in Japanese bronzes and pictures is a macaque peculiar to Nippon, where it ranges farther north than any other monkey known, and is careless of cold and snow.

Of all this group the best known is the widespread little yellowish Bengal or rhesus monkey, which abounds in northern India and eastward to China, some living in the high northern mountains, where they have acquired a thick undercoat of wool to resist the cold. This monkey is rarely molested by the Hindoos, so that around certain temples hundreds will come at the call of the fakirs to get rice and peas; and it is the common juggler's trickster of northern India. The lion - tailed macaque is kept tame in large numbers by the natives of the western coast of India, where it is considered the luckiest thing in the world to see one of them the first thing on awakening in the morning; hence their owners carry them about with them when travel-ing, even upon a railroad train.

Copyright, N. Y. Zoöl. Society.   Sanborn, Phot.

AFRICAN RED-HEADED MANGABEY.

There remains only the Barbary ape, or magot, which dwells in Morocco and Algeria, especially about Constantine, and is preserved in a small free band on the Rock of Gibraltar; but nobody knows whether it is indigenous or, as is more prob-able, was carried thither long ago. The authors of "The Gardens and Menageries of the Zoölogical Society" of Lon-don, written about 1830, mention that this ape "has even estab-lished itself on the Rock of Gibraltar, where it is said to have become extremely abundant." It is about two and a half

Students Library
Concordia Teachers College,
RIVER FOREST, ILL.

feet long, light brown, with the naked parts pinkish, and no tail. These apes are interesting historically as furnishing the

"subjects" used for anatomical study in the old days when Aristotle, Galen, and other early naturalists and surgeons were forbidden to dissect human bodies.

This brings us to the most repulsive of all the Primates, yet of much scientific interest, — the **Baboons.** baboons. They number about a dozen species, all African and Arabian except one, — the jet-

GIBRALTAR APE.

black, wood-ranging, fruit-eating baboon of the forests of Celebes and Betchuan, which, as its habits would suggest, stands somewhat intermediate between them and the macaques. Its lone presence in the East (recalling that of the single African macaque) is an example of the many likenesses between the faunas of the Africa-Arabian and the Indo-Malayan region, and a reminder that in a former era these faunas were one, supposedly continuous on lands now lost in the Indian Ocean.

The African baboons present striking peculiarities in appearance, and all are much alike. In size they vary from the bigness of a spaniel to that of a mastiff, and a comparison with dogs is apt, for these apes go about habitually on all fours, their limbs are stout and of about equal length, and their heads and muzzles are canine; hence the ancient name *cynocephali*, dog-headed. In some, as the mandrill, the naked nose is swollen at the sides like a hog's snout, thrown into ridges and colored black, pale pink, or blue and purple; while the great callosities on the stern are of the same or contrasted colors.

When the beast is enraged or otherwise much excited, these colors glow with great brilliancy. It has been observed in the cases of all the apes so colored that the red hinder end is a subject of great pride, and that they will turn it toward an animal or person with whom they are pleased, or toward a mirror when one is placed in their cage. Darwin has much to say on this curious circumstance in his "Descent of Man"; and I recall how one of his Arab friends told Burton,[54] during his adventurous journey to Mecca, that the Arabian apes catch and kill kites by exposing the pink stern and concealing the remainder of their bodies: the bird pounces upon what appears to be raw meat, "and presently finds himself viciously plucked alive." To our eyes, however, these gaudy naked parts only add to the ugliness of all baboons, which their overhanging eyebrows, small eyes, ferocious disposition, and filthy habits intensify.

The fur of the baboons is blackish or greenish or a yellow-ish gray, grizzled by the fact that every hair is ringed with various colors; or the coat may be party-colored, the drill, for example, having whitish beard and cheeks, and the gelada a brown mane and gray chest with a black body.

Baboons, unlike other monkeys, are denizens of open country rather than of forest, and lovers of rocks and deserts, where they travel about in large bands. "I shall never forget," remarks Alfred Evans, writing in *The Field* (London) of the chacma of South Africa, "the first time I came across a troop of them."

"This was on an undulating stony range of hillocks, where the spek-boom (elephant tree) luxuriates, and the rough spinous crimson-crested aloe rears its head to a height of some ten or fifteen feet, often mistaken at a distance, by one unaccustomed to their peculiar erectness, for human beings, having the appearance of solitary sentinels keeping guard in the unbroken stillness of a vast wilderness. This is the natural home of the baboon; here he finds his most delectable food, succulent roots and bulbs, beetles, scorpions, centipedes. His living prey, his tit-bits, he hunts and rummages for amongst the myriads of loose stones that lie about in every direction; these he cautiously and gently rolls over with one hand, then pounces on his unsuspecting victims with the other. His sight is so keen and his grasp so unerring that nothing escapes — not the minutest larva or most agile insect.

"In times of drought, when driven by hunger, I have known them do a vast amount of havoc among young lambs and kids . . . his object is not meat, but milk. His method of procedure is this: Finding a lamb or kid curled up asleep, as is their custom on a windy or sunny day after a good swig at the maternal fount, he secures him in his merciless grip, at once lays hold of the stomach, and with a wrench of his powerful arms tears it open."

The sense of smell in this species is amazingly keen, especially for hidden water springs in the desert. It is recorded that the Bushmen of the Kalahari plains used to train captives to help them search for water when famine was impending; and undoubtedly the observation of what roots, etc., these animals were accustomed to eat, taught the earliest human venturers into these regions what might be found there in the way of food. Le Vaillant, a French naturalist who wandered and wrote in South Africa from 1781 to 1785, had a tame chacma whose intelligent and amusing behavior he ascribes at length in his "Voyage." He says: "When he found any fruit or roots unknown to my Hottentots, we never touched them until my dear Kees [the chacma] had first tested them; if it refused them, we judged them to be either disagreeable or dangerous, and threw them away." One method Kees had of uprooting any plant which resisted an ordinary pull was to seize the tuft of leaves with his teeth as close to the ground as he could, then throw his heels over his head, giving a jerk that always succeeded. The favorite food on the southwest coast is that extraordinary plant, the Welwitschia. Baboons also eat lizards and the like, and are fond of honey and certain gums. With these habits it is not surprising that they are everywhere exceedingly harmful to plantations, tearing up or trampling down more than they consume, and destroying a field in a night. Hence they are hated and persecuted by white and negro farmers

Chacma.

MANDRILL.

alike, and baboon hunts are a regular thing among the colonists.

As to their courage and fighting prowess, various accounts are given. They go in bands, sometimes exceeding one hundred individuals of all ages, and choose for their lairs cliffs and rocky ridges full of crevices and thickets, such as the extraordinary Black Rocks of Angola, where the yellow baboon dwells in thousands, and subsists mainly on lichens. Yellow Baboon. In such places they are safe against any enemies except leopards (which the old males are said to be able to vanquish), and the larger serpents or birds of prey; and these can make away only with the young now and then. Dogs dare not attack full-sized baboons, which have been seen again and again going fearlessly to the aid of some little one that dogs have "treed" on a rock. G. A. Henty, whose stories have been the delight of so many boys and girls, and who accompanied the British Expedition to Abyssinia in 1868, has written in his "March to Magdala" amusing accounts of their battles with dogs and other doings. Although the negroes, especially the women, have an inordinate fear of them, trustworthy evidence of their ever having attacked a man, except in defense of their young, is not at hand. A band will, however, roll or throw stones or anything else they can get hold of against intruders, and their aim is distressingly true.

In Volume I of "Cassell's Natural History," where Professor P. Martin Duncan has given an extended account of all the baboons, including much history and odd fable, the following paragraph occurs in reference to the big, lion-maned geladas (Theropithecus) of southern Abyssinia: —

"They descend and sometimes rob the farmers with impunity, and return after having committed a vast amount of mischief. But it happens that the great dog-faced troops are out on the same errand, and the two sets of thieves speedily disagree. A fight ensues, and the geladas roll down great stones which the others try to avoid, and then they all rush together to close quarters, making a great uproar, and fighting with great fury.

Some of these gallant geladas had the audacity to stop a Serene Highness (a Duke of Saxe-Gotha) in his travels in Abyssinia . . . by rolling down stones in such quantity and of such a size that not only had the firing party to retire, but the passage of the caravan was stopped."

Some of these baboons are as tamable and teachable as other monkeys, but as they grow old they become unruly and **Sacred Baboon.** subject to dangerous fits of rage. Professor Duncan's treatise just referred to, and the books of Broderip,[15] Blanford,[23] and others record the feats of various learned baboons in menageries and elsewhere. They were tamed and trained anciently in Egypt, where a religious sect held the shaggy Arabian species (*C. hamadryas*) to be sacred to Thoth, — a deity who held a similar place in their pantheon to that occupied by Hermes or Mercury among the Greeks or Romans, as god of the moon and patron of letters.

"Sometimes," we are told by Wilkinson,[58] "a cynocephalus, placed on a throne as a god, holds a sacred ibis in his hand; and in the judgment scenes of the dead it frequently occurs seated on the summit of a balance, as the emblem of Thoth, who had an important office on that occasion, and registered the account of the actions of the deceased. The place where this animal was particularly sacred was Hermopolis, the city of Thoth. In the necropolis of the capital of upper Egypt a particular part was set apart as the cemetery of the sacred apes." A very full and critical account of what the ancient Egyptians, and after them their European conquerors, knew and thought of these baboons, and of many other apes and monkeys trained by them, is contained in Anderson's "Zoölogy of Egypt." [55]

The sacred baboons are large, with a straight, long, ridged muzzle, deeply set eyes, the face and other naked parts flesh-pink, and the coat ash-gray. The males have a heavy mane on the shoulders and long thick whiskers. Ehrenberg asserts that the style of wearing the hair common to the ancient people of the lower Nile and to the Abyssinians and Sudanese of to-day, was copied, as a sign of adoration, from the mane of this beast; and that the monumental structure in the desert near Cairo, the Sphinx, is modeled after the same animal god.

In the monkeys of America we have, as has been stated, a broad-nosed type differing from their relatives of Africa and Asia; and it is a more ancient and an inferior type. **American** The group is divisible into two families, — the Hapa- **Monkeys.** lidæ, or marmosets, with thirty-two teeth, and the Cebidæ with thirty-six teeth. "The former include the marmosets (Hapale) and the tamarins (Midas). The latter comprise the capuchins (Cebus), which may be taken as the representative genus of American monkeys, the woolly monkeys (Lagothrix), the spider monkeys (Ateles and the allied Eriodes), the howlers (Mycetes), the sakis (Pithecia and Brachyurus), the night monkeys or douroucolis (Nyctipithecus), and the squirrel monkeys or saimiris (Chrysothrix) with the allied Callithrix."

The forests of equatorial South America are the headquarters of the tribe, and the exclusive home of many species, some of which are restricted to narrow areas; the great rivers often acting as impassable boundaries. No monkeys ascend high in the Andes, or reach the West Coast; and none is found south of the forests of Brazil or north of south-central Mexico. Fossil remains of monkeys are rare everywhere, and known in the New World only from the Santa Cruz Miocene formations of Patagonia; and they show no more kinship with Old World types than do the existing species.

American monkeys are all small, the largest having a body no more than twenty inches long, while some are no bigger than young kittens. One baby is born to each pair each year as a rule. All are very hairy or woolly, and none has naked callosities. Adapted to a continuous life in trees, most of them are provided with prehensile tails — that is, the tip is muscular and almost automatically curls around whatever it touches.

"This prehensile tail," wrote Waterton, "is a most curious thing. It has been denominated very appropriately a fifth hand. It is of manifest advantage to the animal either when sitting in repose on the branch of a tree, or when in its journey onwards in the gloomy recesses of the wilderness. You may see this [spider] monkey catching hold of the branches with its hands, and at the same moment twisting its tail around one of them as if in want of additional support; and this prehensile tail is sufficiently strong to hold the animal in its place, even when all its four limbs are detached from the tree, so that it can swing to and fro and amuse itself solely through the instrumentality of its prehensile tail, which, by the way, would be of no manner of use to it did accident or misfortune force the monkey to take up a temporary abode on the ground."

Nevertheless, as Dr. Lydekker remarks, since the teetees have no prehensibility in the tail, and others, as ooakaris, lack a tail of practicable length, it is clear that the prehensile organ must be regarded as a kind of luxury. "Indeed," as he observes, "the whole question as to the reason why some monkeys have long tails, others short tails, and others again no tails at all, is involved in great obscurity." But that is true of many other features of animal structure and economy more important than tails!

Copyright, N. Y. Zoöl. Society.   Sanborn, Phot.

A CAPUCHIN.

The most familiar and characteristic of the American monkeys are the capuchins or sapajous of the genus Cebus, eighteen species of which are catalogued between Paraguay and Costa Rica, though none wanders throughout this wide range, and only one is known in Central America; but they are so closely alike in structure and habits, and so variable in color, that nobody knows how many true species really exist. The body is rather stout; the head round and the muzzle short, giving a miniature and somewhat pathetic caricature of the human countenance; the hair is not woolly, and it **Capuchins.** stands up over the forehead like a monk's cowl, but sometimes forms a crest; and the tail is long and prehensile, but not naked on the under side of the end. The color is usually a variable dull brown, but one is reddish, and several have more or less white about the shoulders.

These monkeys go in small, orderly troops, led in single file by an old male and remain mostly in tall trees, sometimes one hundred and fifty feet above the ground. Bates,[25] whose "Naturalist on the Amazons" is a storehouse of information on these and other animals of that region, describes how, when the foremost of the flock reaches the outermost branch of a tall tree, he springs forth into the air without a moment's hesitation, and alights on the dome of yielding foliage belonging to the neighboring tree, maybe fifty feet beneath, all the rest following his example. "They grasp, on falling, with hands and tail, right themselves in a moment, and then away they go along branch and bough to the next tree." A Chilean species will hang by the tail from a branch at a dizzy height, balance itself with all four limbs stretched out, then drop twenty or thirty feet and stop by seizing another branch with its tail. They usually have a settled sleeping-place, whence they issue every morning to explore the near-by trees for fruits, tender shoots, insects, eggs, young birds, and other edibles; and go and come by regular routes through the woods. Bananas are their mainstay, but oranges are a favorite delicacy, and these are opened by tearing the rind, too bitter for their taste, with the nails, and then scooping out the pulp with the forefinger. Their fondness of sweets is taken advantage of by the forest people to entrap them. The pulp of a gourd is dug out through a small hole, sugar is placed inside, and the trap is set out and watched.　Presently a monkey discovers it, thrusts in his hand, and soon gets so busy and so much enjoys his feast that he will suffer himself to be caught sooner than forego the handful of sugar which he cannot pull out so long as his fist is closed. Precisely the same plan, with a cocoanut for a trap and rice for bait, is used to catch monkeys and other animals in the Far East.

When captured old, capuchins are likely to mope, refuse food, and die; but the young become tame and interesting. They are hardy, and most of the organ grinders' monkeys of both continents belong to this group and are mainly "weepers," whose fur is golden brown, with a blackish line extending backward from the nose to the shoulders, and the face and fore parts generally pale yellow.　They are greatly attached to their masters and to any animal friends; and in Paraguay are usually brought up with a young dog on whose back they ride half the time.　Their intelligence and quickness to learn is great; for instance, they contrive, after the surprise of a failure or two, to open an egg and eat it without spilling a drop. But like most monkeys they are filled with a spirit of mischief and are expert thieves.　An excellent anecdote was recorded by Professor Cope, who had two of these monkeys in his house in 1872, and had the temerity to call them "Jack and Jim, the sons of Cebidæ."

"Jack displays a thousand traits of monkey ingenuity.　He is an admirable catcher, seldom missing anything, from a large brush to a grain, using two hands or one.　His cage door is fastened by two hooks, and these are kept in their places by nails driven in behind them.　He generally finds means sooner or later of drawing out the nails, unhooking the hooks, and getting free.　He then occupies himself in breaking up various objects and examining their interior appearances, no doubt in search of food.　To prevent his escape, I fastened him by a leather strap to the slats of the cage, but he soon untied the knot, and then relieved himself of the strap by cutting and drawing out the threads which held the flaps for the buckle.　He then used the strap in a novel way.　He was accustomed to catch his food

SOUTH AMERICAN MONKEYS

VARIEGATED SPIDER-MONKEY   GEOFFROY'S TAMARIN
                    SMOOTH-HEADED CAPUCHIN
RED-FOOTED NIGHT MONKEY   RED HOWLER

(bread, potatoes, fruit, etc.) with his hands, when thrown to him. Sometimes the pieces fell short three or four feet. One day he seized his strap and began to throw it at the food, retaining his hold of one end. He took pretty correct aim, and finally drew the pieces to within reach of his hand. This performance he constantly repeats, hooking and pulling the articles to him, in turns and loops of the strap. Sometimes he loses his hold of the strap. If the poker is handed to him he uses that with some skill in the recovery of the strap. When this is drawn in he secures his food as before.

"Here is an act of intelligence which must have been *originated* by some *monkey*, since no lower or ancestral type possesses the hand necessary for its accomplishment. Whether originated by Jack, or by some ancestor of the forest who used vines for the same purpose, cannot be readily ascertained."

Their smart doings as pets, and individuality, are the theme of innumerable stories. Belt [26] descants upon the human-like behavior of a white-fronted capuchin he kept a long time: —

"He had quite an extensive vocabulary of sounds, varying from a gruff bark to a shrill whistle; and we could tell by them, without seeing him, when it was he was hungry, eating, frightened, or menacing; doubtless one of his own species would have understood various minor shades of intonation and expression that we, not entering into his feelings and wants, passed over as unintelligible."

Closely related to the capuchins are the barrigudos, caparros, or woolly monkeys, which are of bulky form and clothed in a woolly under fur; the tail is long, prehensile, naked beneath, and exceedingly sensitive. They are slow, exclusively frugivorous, are eaten by the Indians with great gusto, and "are great favorites, from their grave countenances, which resemble the human face more than those of any other monkey, their quiet manners, and the great affection and docility they exhibit." Some rare species of southeastern Brazil connect them with the next genus, — the spider monkeys.

These light, slender, exceedingly active and agile monkeys, called "coaitas" by the Brazilians, are among the most wide-

spread and familiar of all the American tribe, and are regarded
as the most advanced in organization. The prehensile tail
Spider here reaches its highest perfection, as well as all other
Monkeys. organs which adapt the animal to a purely arboreal
existence. Bates [25] has much to say in support of this view, and
tells many interesting things of them — among others how fond
the Indians are of them as pets. "The disposition of the coaita,"
he says, "is mild in the extreme; it has none of the painful

BLACK SPIDER MONKEY.

restless vivacity of its kindred, the Cebi, and no trace of the
surly, untamable temper of its nearer relatives, the Mycetes,
or howling monkeys." Of the ten species of spider monkey,
the two best known in South America are the variegated, whose
coat is a handsome mixture of black, white, and orange-yellow;
the red-faced black one, so common as a pet in the Guiana
villages, and often taken abroad; and the large white-whiskered
one, the eating of which is so graphically described by Humboldt [66]; but all the kinds are a favorite flesh with the Indians
and enjoyed well roasted by most white men: Bates found it

like beef, but sweeter and richer. From the Isthmus of Panama to northern Nicaragua one sees everywhere in the tops of the forest trees Geoffroy's varicolored spider monkey rushing about in bands and hunting for insects and fruit. One of the trees most frequented is the "nispera," a gutta-percha-yielding kind which bears a round fruit about the size of an apple, hard and heavy when green. When Belt was living in Nicaragua he soon learned to avoid these trees when monkeys were there.

"Sometimes they lay quite quiet until I was passing underneath, when, shaking a branch of the nispera tree, they would send down a shower of the hard round fruit; but fortunately I was never struck by them. As soon as I looked up, they would commence yelping and barking and putting on the most threatening gestures, breaking off pieces of branches and letting them fall, and shaking off more fruit, but never throwing anything, simply letting it fall. [Other observers have recorded that they *threw* sticks, etc.] . . . Sometimes a female would be seen carrying a young one on its back, to which it clung with legs and tail, the mother making its way along the branches, and leaping from tree to tree, apparently but little incumbered by its baby. A large black and white eagle is said to prey upon them, but I never saw one." [26]

A closely similar species is common in Guatemala, and northward as far as San Louis Potosi in Mexico. The howlers, arguatoes, or alluates are the largest and most powerful of South American apes and the dullest, and are peculiar in having no thumb or only a rudimentary one, and in having the hyoid bones in the throat (of males only) widely enlarged and cavernous, so as to form a curious hollow organ, by which their voice is so increased as to be audible two miles. Their colors are usually blackish or brown, although one is brick-red; but there is much variability, and in some of the half-dozen species the sexes differ from one another in dress, and the young from both. They feed chiefly on leaves and fruit, and are seminocturnal in habit, wandering about in small parties and giving their "harrowing roar" late in the evening and again early in the morning, or when rain impends; sup-

Howlers.

posedly to intimidate their enemies, such as wild-cats, tree serpents, and such birds of prey as the harpy eagle, but there is no evidence that any one of these is at all frightened by the noise. Humboldt and other early writers believed that big bands must assemble and howl in chorus; but Wallace showed by his own studies, and by the unanimous testimony of the Indians, that one individual alone makes the roar, which he describes as of remarkable depth and volume. Waterton vividly portrays the effect on the traveler's mind as he lies in his hammock in the forest and listens to these unearthly cries. The Indians hate the howlers, finding them too dull and sullen to tame, and so kill them for food, to sell their hides to white traders, or for the sake of the long hair, which is twisted into cordage and otherwise utilized.

Coming to the sakis and ooakaris (or "yarkees"), we find a group with non-prehensile tails and the incisor teeth inclined **Sakis.** forward. The sakis (Pithecia) have long, bushy tails, the hair on the head long and parted in the middle, and a thick beard; the body is not large. They are very delicate, so that it is rarely one can be kept long alive, nor is it often

attempted, for they are uninteresting and likely to be cross as captives. Of the five species none are very well known; the largest is the black cuxio, and the most striking is the rare white-nosed saki,

BLACK SAKI, CUXIO, OR SATAN MONKEY.

whose face is scarlet except the white end of its nose.

The three species of ooakaris are quaint little monkeys with very short tails, and their light-colored silky coats set off by a scarlet face, which in one — the bald ooakari — extends into a very high forehead; but this one has a black face. All are diurnal, scrambling about the high tree tops of the forests of the upper Amazons, and nowhere numerous.

Still another group embraces the related night monkeys, teetees, and squirrel monkeys. All these are "small and elegant animals, covered with long hair, and having long, **Night** bushy tails, which are not prehensile, although they **Monkeys.** can be curled around a branch." The night monkeys, owl monkeys or douroucolis (Nyctipithecus), have a short, thick body, clothed with prettily varied fur, a round head and roundish face encircled by a whitish ruff; and their enormous yellow eyes, betokening their nocturnal habits, give an owlish expression to the countenances. "They sleep all day long in hollow trees," to quote Bates again, "and come forth to prey on insects and fruits only in the night; . . . [and] are aroused by the least noise, so that when a person passes by the tree in which a number of them are concealed, he is startled by the sudden apparition of a group of little striped faces crowding a hole in the trunk." Alston [114] was informed that the Central American species (*N. trivirgatus*) lived in small parties or families which remained concealed in the tops of the trees during the day, often hidden in heaps of sticks and dead leaves which are perhaps collected by themselves. At nightfall they come forth to feed, but seldom seem to wander far, returning regularly to the same places, especially in search of the fruit of the guava. During the darkness they continually utter a low cry sounding like *douroucou*, feebly pronounced. They are not often kept as pets, but are interesting and gentle when carefully treated, as may be seen by reading the experience of Olive Thorne Miller, related in *Harper's Magazine* for July, 1886. The cries of all these night monkeys are like those of a cat, and they hiss when angry.

The teetees (Callithrix), on the other hand, although differing from the night monkeys in little except in having bristly hairs among the fur, smaller eyes and more bushy tails, are "diurnal animals, arboreal and gregarious, noisy and agile, living on fruit, insects, birds' eggs, and even small birds. They range all over South America, from Panama to the southern limits of the forested regions." They are dull-witted and rarely tamed. There are a dozen or so species, mostly grizzled red or else black with red and white markings.

The squirrel monkeys, or "saimiris," are a small group much like these teetees, — looking truly like squirrels, — and very nu-**Teetees and Squir-rel Mon-keys.** merous from Costa Rica to Bolivia. The commonest one is only about ten inches long, but its tail measures fourteen inches; and is yellowish gray with a dark head and a comical little black-and-white face with tufted white ears. Baron Humboldt thought no other monkey had so much the physiognomy of a child; its sudden changes from joy to sorrow, and *vice versa*, were very infantile, and when seized with fear its eyes became suffused with tears. One that Humboldt had was extremely fond of spiders and insects, and would try to pick up figures of wasps, etc., when shown them in a book, although uncolored. The same story of eager recognition of a picture is told of the silky tamarin by Geoffroy St.-Hilaire. They will steadfastly watch the mouth of a person speaking, and if allowed to sit on their master's shoulder will frequently touch his lips, tongue, or teeth. They live in large flocks, and in a rain sit huddled in close groups, with their tails wrapped around each other, and are so miserable that then the Indians have no difficulty in shooting them with their small poisoned darts.

This brings us to the end of the family Cebidæ, and there remains only the small family Hapalidæ, characterized dis-**Marmo-sets.** tinctively by having only thirty-two teeth, and including the tiny tamarins and marmosets, which are hardly separable and connect the monkeys with the lemurs.

There are a large number of kinds, showing considerable variety in color, from silvery gray to black or white and black, or yellowish or reddish tints, and in several the long, almost bushy tail is ringed. The fur is soft and the general look is that of a kitten, but some have manes, or mustaches, resembling balls of cotton, or long whiskers brushed straight back, or ears prettily fringed. Their actions are much like those of squirrels, but they can rarely be seen or studied wild in the dense forest, for they stay in the high tree tops. Most of what we know of them, therefore, has been gained by their captivity, where they make charming but exceedingly delicate pets. South Americans carry them about sometimes in the folds of their hair.

The Indians get them by trapping, or else by shooting the mother with blow-gun darts, and finding two or three babies clinging to her fallen body. The one best known and most often exported is obtained only in the island of Marajo, at the mouth of the Amazon. None exceeds a foot long, and the pygmy marmoset is the smallest known monkey, its body measuring only six inches. All writers on South American zoölogy have much to say of these attractive little creatures, especially Bates; and in *The Field* (of London) for April, and May, 1881, will be found an entertaining as well as valuable series of articles by Dr. Arthur Stradling on the habits of these and of many other Brazilian monkeys. William T. Hornaday, Director of the New York "Zoo," gives the following authoritative advice as to the care of monkeys in captivity: —

"The temperature should be 75 degrees, kept as even as possible. *Food:* boiled rice or tapioca, baked or boiled potatoes, ripe bananas or apples; a little raw meat, finely chopped; dried or parched sweet corn that is easily chewed; a little stale bread; occasionally a small raw onion. Permit no teasing; feed regularly, water frequently, and keep the cages clean. When monkeys become ill, carefully ascertain their trouble, then treat them the same as one would sick children."

In the late Tertiary formations of various parts of Europe have been found remains of several extinct monkeys and bab-
Fossil Pri- oons, ancestral to those of the present day; and in
mates. Madagascar occur fossil lemurs, one of which (Megaladapis) was as large as the gorilla, with limbs remarkably massive and powerful. The early Tertiary rocks of North America have yielded various extinct Primates (Adapis, Notharctus, Anaptomorphus, etc.), more or less intermediate between monkeys and lemurs, and indicating that these two great divisions of the Primate stock were not then widely separated. Then as now this stock was adapted to arboreal life, and distinguished from the contemporary ancestors of carnivores and insectivores by the opposable thumb and great toe, nails instead of claws upon fingers and toes, and by various dental peculiarities. But the divergence was by no means so great as now, and in the preceding Cretaceous all three no doubt were merged in a single primitive stock.

Lemurs and their Kin

The second and inferior division of the Primates is that of the lemurs (*Lemuroidea*), a large group of queer, interesting little animals now found only in Madagascar, tropical Africa, and the Orient. This widely scattered distribution is so peculiar that it could not be accounted for until paleontologists began, about 1860, to report the discovery of fossil remains of lemurs not only in Africa, Europe, and northern India, but in the rocks of the western United States, showing that at the beginning of the Tertiary period the progenitors of these animals were scattered all over the globe, which was then much warmer in climate than now. Those forerunners of the group show many resemblances to the primitive Insectivora. Change of climate and other reasons caused them to become extinct, in most parts of the world, and at last to survive only in the two tropical regions mentioned, especially Madagascar, where the stock seems to have originated, and where they have never had many active enemies.

Lemurs are distinguished from the monkeys (*Anthropoidea*) by the openness of the bony socket of the eye, the elongated jaws, giving a foxlike aspect to the face, the sim- **Malmag.** plicity of the brain, and other anatomical features betokening a lower grade of structure and intelligence. The group falls very naturally into three families: Tarsiidæ, Chiromyidæ, and Lemuridæ, of which the first and second contain only one species each, and the third and lowest all the remainder, *i.e.* the lemurs proper, or "half-apes."

MALMAG, OR TARSIER.

The spectral tarsier, representing the first family, is a most extraordinary little creature, inhabiting the lowland forests of the islands from Sumatra to the southern Philippines, where it is called "malmag." It is no larger than a small rat, is light brown, has a large head with immense brown eyes, a short muzzle, pricked-up ears, and a comical grinning expression on its broad face. The tail is long and tufted. The hind legs are longer than the front ones, owing to the greatly lengthened heel bones (tarsi); and these and all the paws are hairless, and terminate in long bony digits which have pads beneath their ends. By these pads the animal is enabled to climb smooth bamboos, like a tree frog, which it resembles in its way of sitting, and in its gait on the few occasions when it descends from the tree tops. It lies hidden during the day in some hole in a trunk or under the roots of a tree, and at night hunts for insects or lizards, especially the latter. Cumming [39] kept one in a cage and found it gentle, affectionate, extremely cleanly, and with many pretty ways; and when its single young one was born it carefully concealed the baby from view, when it was nursing it, and carried it around in its mouth like a cat.

The malmag's nearest relative is the even more extraordinary aye-aye of eastern Madagascar, alone representing the family **Aye-aye.** Chiromyidæ, and having much the appearance of a small, big-eyed squirrel with a weasel's face. The teeth are curiously squirrel-like, too, there being no canines, and the incisors large and of continuous growth; while the

THE MADAGASCAR AYE-AYE.

total number is only eighteen. Its fur is long and blackish, with yellowish white about the face, chest, and under parts. The hind feet are monkeylike, but the hands terminate in long bony fingers with birdlike claws, and the fourth finger is much more slender and elongated than the others. This curious finger aids it in pulling grubs out of holes, scooping out the pulp of fruits, and keeping itself clean — a process to which captive specimens devote much time, hanging by their hind legs to make their toilet conveniently. It is entirely nocturnal and arboreal in its habits, which have been most fully described by Baron[40] and by Lydekker.[65] One of the most interesting facts is, that the female constructs in a tree a special and elegant globular nest as a nursery for the care of her single offspring. Nothing whatever is known of the ancestry of this remarkable little creature, but it is evidently a survivor of a very ancient type.

The lemurs proper (family Lemuridæ) are characterized by thick woolly fur, a doglike muzzle, and the form of the teeth. In the center of the upper jaw there is always a toothless gap, or diastema, on each side of which the teeth are arranged according to the following formula: I. $\frac{2}{2}$, C. $\frac{1}{1}$, P. $\frac{3}{3}$, M. $\frac{3}{3}$, = 36.

This formula is the customary way of stating mammalian dentition, and it means that on each side of the jaw there are, of incisors (I.) two above and two below; of canines (C.) one above and one below; of premolars (P.) and molars (M.) three and three; — that is, eighteen teeth in all on one side of the face, or thirty-six for the total dentition.

The endrinas, however, have teeth: I. $\frac{2}{2}$, C. $\frac{1}{1 \text{ or } 0}$, P. $\frac{2}{2}$, M. $\frac{3}{3}$, = 32 or 30 in number. In the upper jaw the incisors are small and perpendicular; but in the lower, where they are long and narrow, they protrude horizontally in front. The forty-five species in the family are separable into four groups: (1) the endrinas, sifakas, avahis, and woolly lemurs; (2) the "true" or typical lemurs; (3) the chirogales; and (4) the pottos, aye-aye, and loris.

The endrinas number five species, all of Madagascar, and the largest species, called "babakoto," is one of the best-known animals on the eastern coast, where the traveler hears its "doleful, doglike howls" from morning **Babakoto.** until night — an unusual thing among these secretive animals. It has a head shaped like that of a miniature bear, the face naked, and, like its paws, brownish black; its dark upper parts often reddish; while the whiskers, forearms, rump, small tuft of a tail and ankles, are white. It rarely comes to the ground, spending its time moving about in high trees with its fellows and living principally on fruit and leaves, yet often catching birds in order to eat their brains. The silky-haired, monkey-like sifakas, which are white with reddish and black markings, are more generally distributed over Madagascar, and are exceedingly pretty, but delicate, inactive, and morose in captivity.

True or typical lemurs (Lemurinæ) have rounded heads, fox-like muzzles with thirty-two teeth, small ears, and a soft, thick, and woolly fur often elegantly tinted. They range in size from that of a cat to that of a squirrel, vary much in color, and are confined to Madagascar. These run about on the limbs of trees on all fours, but on the ground walk erect on their hind legs, and are capable of very agile jumping. Nearly all are diurnal but most active toward evening, and very noisy. Only one or two young are born at a time, and these are carried about by the mother, at first clinging to her breast, but later riding on her back. Lemurs

Copyright, N. Y. Zoöl. Soc.   Sanborn, Phot.

RUFFED LEMUR.

are easily kept, readily breed in menageries, and one of the most interesting is the ring-tailed, or "Madagascar cat," gray, with the long tail ringed in black and white. Like the others, it is not scattered generally over the island, but lives only on the slippery seaside cliffs, scrambling about rocks where not even barefooted men can walk, its long, smooth, leathery palms, channeled with suckerlike grooves, enabling it to go safely. The ruffed lemur of northeastern Madagascar is the largest of this race, in some of whose species the males are black while their mates are red. The hattocks, gentle lemurs, and sportive lemurs are allied genera.

Next come the galagos and their relatives, widely distributed in central Africa, but unknown in Madagascar. They are small, have a rather short muzzle, large, membranous, **Galagos.** folding ears, small eyes set close together, fingers and toes very long and slender, thick, soft grayish fur, and a bushy tail. The night is their hunting time, for they sleep by day in holes in trees or in leaf nests, differing in model with the species. Every one comments on their power of folding or crumpling their batlike ears. Sir John Kirk says of the great galago, or "palm-rat" of the Mozambique coast, that the rapidity and length of its leaps are extraordinary, and that it adheres where it alights "as if it were a lump of wet clay." An examination of the pads beneath the balls of its toes would have shown Sir John why. It has a great fondness for palm wine, and whenever it can get at an open jar of it will get ingloriously tipsy; and many are arrested and condemned to jail in some dealer's cage following such a spree. As pets, however, they are entertaining only after dark, hiding during daylight in their sleeping boxes. Mr. Bartlett [41] turned a galago loose in his room one evening, and learned something.

"Judge my utter astonishment to see him on the floor, jumping about *upright* like a kangaroo, only with much greater speed and intelligence. The little one sprung from the ground on to the legs of tables, arms of chairs, and, indeed, on to any piece of furniture in the room; in fact, he was more like a sprite than the best pantomimist I ever saw. What surprised me most was his entire want of fear of dogs and cats. These he boldly met and jumped on at once, and in the most playful manner hugged and tumbled about with them, rolling over and over, hanging on their tails, licking them on the head and face. . . . He was delighted with a little wooden ball which he rolled about and played with for a considerable time, carrying it in one hand while he hopped and skipped about in high glee. He eats fruits, sweetmeats, bread, and any kind of animal substance, killing everything he can pounce upon and overpower."

The mouse lemurs, dwarf lemurs, and fat-tailed lemurs are groups of many diminutive species closely allied to the galagos, but confined to Madagascar. They have been particularly described by Forsyth-Major,[42] Grandidier,[43] and other students of the curious zoölogy of that great and ancient island. One very peculiar thing about them is their habit of going into a dormant state during the hot and dry seasons, curled up in their nests just as a northern animal does in its hibernation. They go in very fat, subsist by absorption of this stored tissue, and when the rainy season awakens the tropical world, they come out thin and weak to enjoy renewed life. The act and its cause are thus the same as the winter sleep of northern animals.

Lastly, something must be said about the "slow" lemurs (Lorisinæ), of which two species, the angwantibo and potto, **Pottos and** are West African, and two, the slender and the slow **Loris.** loris, are East Indian. Both are small (eight to fifteen inches long), have soft woolly fur variously colored, a triangular face with very large and staring eyes close together, almost no tail, and strangely misshapen hands and feet. They are nocturnal and, in strong contrast with most of their race, are perhaps the most sluggish of all mammals — the very embodiment of seeming laziness. They live in trees, climbing about with extreme caution and deliberation, in search of insects, leaves, fruits, birds' eggs, and similar food; but old Bosman evidently exaggerated when he wrote in 1704 of the potto of the Gold Coast: —

"Some Writers affirm that when this Creature has climbed upon a Tree, he doth not leave it until he hath eaten up not only the Fruit, but the leaves intirely; and then descends fat and in very good case in order to get up into another Tree; but before his slow pace can compass this, he becomes as poor and lean as 'tis possible to imagine: And if the trees be high, or the way anything distant, and he meets with nothing on his journey, he inevitably dies of Hunger, betwixt one tree and the other. Thus 'tis represented by others, but I will not undertake for the Truth of it. . . . I know nothing more of this Animal, than that 'tis impossible to look on him without Horrour, and that he hath nothing very particular but his odious Ugliness."

In the evening a loris will sometimes get up energy enough to rise on its hind legs and then fall forward on an insect; and one placed on the ground may be forced into a wavering kind of trot. The Oriental slow loris chatters when angry, and when pleased utters a short though tuneful whistle thought by Chinese sailors, who take them to sea, to denote the coming of wind.

Lemurs are all perfectly harmless, yet their big eyes, weird actions, and often loud and strange cries in the dark woods, have led to their being partly reverenced and partly **Fear of** feared by the natives of their countries. The very **Lemurs.** name "lemur," given them by Linnæus, means "ghost." In Madagascar, where they are the most characteristic animals of the forest, none is intentionally killed by anybody. Travelers are told that if a person sleeps in the forest an aye-aye will bring him a pillow — if for his head the person will become rich; if for his feet he will either die or become bewitched. Hence if an aye-aye is accidentally caught in a trap the owner will usually set it free, after smearing it with grease to render it harmless. Some Malagasies believe that their ancestors were changed after death into the great babakoto, and that the trees in which these clamorous lemurs dwell supply infallible remedies against otherwise incurable diseases. Forbes,[3] after reading the works of French explorers, writes: —

"The people say it is very dangerous to kill these lemurs with spears, because if a spear is hurled against one of them it seizes the spear in its flight without being in itself hurt, and in its turn stabs with certain aim those attacking it. They also relate that when the female has borne a young one, she takes the little creature in her arms and tosses it to her mate, who is seated on a neighboring tree, and that he throws it back to the female. If the little one does not fall to the ground after being subjected to this exercise for a dozen times, the parents bring it up with the greatest care; but if the contrary event happens, they abandon it, not even troubling to pick it up."

This is an excellent example of the sort of material with which the pages of "natural history" books were formerly loaded, as serious information, not, as here, as the credulous say-so of childish savages; and recent developments in literature seem to show that modern readers would accept the same sort of wonder-tales as confidingly as did our grandfathers.

Copyright, N. Y. Zoöl. Soc.   Sanborn, Phot.
SLOW LORIS.

Similar superstitions attach to both species of Oriental loris. Thus, the curious emaciated "slender" loris of southern India and Ceylon is brought in large numbers to the markets of Madras, because, as Jerdon [44] explains, their big eyes are a favorite remedy among Tamil doctors for ophthalmic diseases; and Tennent [17] reports that the Singhalese compose from their eyeballs love potions and charms. The Malays of Sumatra told Stanley Flower [45] that the "slow" loris is always unhappy because it is forever seeing ghosts, and that is why it hides its face in its hands — an instance of the way in which acute observation of specific habits and manners is frequently mingled with gross mistakes and most illogical beliefs and superstitions. Never stopping apparently to think of the little animal as he really is, a Malay will in good faith account to you for the commission of an unpremeditated crime by asserting that some enemy "had buried a particular part of a loris under his threshold, which had, unknown to him, compelled him to act to his disadvantage." Even the little malmag is feared in Sumatra, where the appearance of a pair in a rice field is supposed to presage misfortune, or even death, to the farmer.

BATS AND FLYING-FOXES — Order, CHIROPTERA

No animals would seem more dissimilar from monkeys and lemurs than the bats, yet there are so many points of resemblance in structure that some of the older zoölogists classified bats among the Primates, and modern ones rank them next to them in an order *Chiroptera* — the "wing-handed" creatures. No fossil remains have been discovered bridging the gap between these and the lemurs, on the one hand, or the Insectivora on the other; and no one is yet able to explain the steps in acquirement of the power of birdlike flight which so sharply distinguishes bats from all other mammals. In fact, at first bats were classed with birds, regardless of their fur and teeth and of the fact that their young were born and suckled like those of other mammals; and this egregious error was not authentically corrected until refuted by John Ray, the father of modern zoölogy, who was born in England in 1628 and died in 1705.

Bats are simply flying mammals, necessarily small, with the bones of the fore limbs light, hollow, and greatly elongated, the middle finger in some cases exceeding the total length of the body. These lengthened digits (1st to 4th, for the thumb is short and remains outside) support between themselves and the hinder limbs a membrane which opens and closes much like an umbrella. Most bats also have a membrane between the hind legs and the tail, supported by a bony process from the heel, and useful in steering. The expanse of these leathery wings is far greater than that of most birds relative to the size of the body, but the muscles are weaker; and the exterior thumb with its strong claw, and in some cases a sucker, by which bats scramble about rocks and trees, recalls the similar organ in that primitive, lizardlike bird, the archæopteryx. The body is small, with a capacious chest to contain the very large lungs and heart, and to support the wing muscles; and the breast-bone is keeled. The skull is almost as large as the chest, with wide nostrils and ears but minute eyes (except in the fox bats), and the mouth has thirty-eight teeth of the usual four kinds, but

LITTLE BROWN BAT OF THE EASTERN UNITED STATES.

all with very sharp cutting edges and the canines frequently long and needlelike. The pelvis, on the contrary, is weak, and the hind limbs are small, while the knee bends backward because of the outward twist of the limb. This makes the foot almost useless for walking, but fits it, with its peculiarly strengthened ankle, to be extended straight backward, and serve as a means of hanging the body, head downwards — the bat's ordinary attitude in rest or sleep.

The wing-membrane is the most striking feature of bats, and their chief reliance not only for moving about, but for information, since its surface is so exquisitely sensitive that apparently the animal becomes **Wing** aware of the nearness of a solid object approached in utter dark- **Membrane.** ness, when the eyes — which at best are minute and buried in fur — could not perceive it. Indeed, in the often-quoted experiments by Spallanzani,[47] it was shown that blinded bats could fly swiftly about in a room full of dangling strings and other obstacles without touching one, alight easily where they pleased, and apparently travel without any inconvenience. Schöbl and others have verified these disclosures, and have explained them by microscopic examinations of the wing membrane. Schöbl found that it consisted of a double layer of skin, one continuous with the hide of the back, the other with that of the abdomen, fused together. Within these fused skins are embedded two layers of elastic muscles, blood vessels, and nerves, the last in an extremely complicated system, with innumerable branching fibrils extending nearly to the surface; also a vast number of bulblike ends, each situated at the root of one of the microscopically minute hairs with which the surface of the wing is covered. To these hairs and bulbous underlying "end organs" are attributed the bat's exalted sense of touch, while another set of fibrils seems to report sensations of temperature, pain, etc.

Many bats are aided, furthermore, by membranous outgrowths about the ears and nose, similarly formed and equally or more sensitive. These in some families reach an extravagant size, and give the face a most comical or perhaps hideous aspect; and they are larger in males than in females.

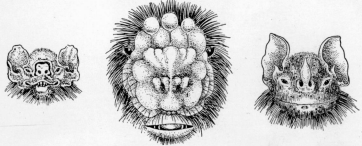

EXAMPLES OF MEMBRANOUS GROWTHS ON THE FACES OF LEAF-NOSED BATS.

The bats fall into two divisions, — the small and nocturnal *Microchiroptera*, and the large and diurnal *Megachiroptera*.

The former division is the higher in respect to organization, and contains the greater number and variety of bats, scattered all over the world, even to the Arctic Circle, Cape Horn, and remote sea islands. There are five families, — the Phyllostomidæ and Emballonuridæ of the Tropics generally; the desert bats (Nycteridæ), the nose-leaf bats (Rhinolophidæ) of the warmer parts of the Old World; and the Vespertilionidæ, which have no nose leaf, are represented in all quarters of the globe, and are by far the most numerous of all.

The first-mentioned is an extensive family of rather large bats with well-developed eyes, large ears, nose leaves, and three phalanges in the middle finger. They are scattered over tropical America, and the most of them feed wholly upon insects, others on a mixture of insects and fruit, while two species have become world-famous as "vampires," — a name recalling the superstition rife in Europe in the Middle Ages as to foul, blood-exhausting fiends, which were fabled to lull their victims into unconsciousness by the slow flapping of their wings, and then deprive them of life. The foremost of these vampires is a small reddish species (*Desmodus rufus*), whose front teeth are like keen daggers, while the cheek teeth have disappeared, having nothing to do, since the animal subsists wholly on a liquid diet (blood), and the digestive organs are extremely modified; indeed, no other mammal known shows so great a departure from the type in its mouth and stomach as does this. To quote Professor Flower:[16] —

Vampire.

"Travelers describe the wounds inflicted by the large, sharp-edged incisors as similar to those caused by a razor when shaving: a portion of the skin being shaved off and a large number of severed capillary vessels thus exposed, from which a constant flow of blood is maintained. From this source the blood is drawn through the exceedingly narrow gullet — too narrow for anything solid to pass — into the intestinelike stomach, where it is probably gradually drawn off during the slow process of digestion, while the animal, sated with food, is hanging in a state of torpidity from the roof of a cave or the inner side of a hollow tree.

"They appear to be confined to the forest-clad parts, and their attacks on men and other warm-blooded animals were noticed by some of the earliest writers. Thus Peter Martyr (Anghiera), who wrote soon after the conquest of South America, says that in the Isthmus of Darien there were bats which sucked the blood of men and cattle when asleep to such a degree as to kill them. Condamine, a writer of the eighteenth century, remarks that at Borja (Ecuador) and in other places they had entirely destroyed the cattle introduced by the missionaries."

Although many of the old stories of harm done to men and women were exaggerated, it is true that vampires attack sleeping persons, and without awakening them withdraw an annoying quantity of blood.

For the many curious adaptations and habits of the hundreds of other kinds of bats, the reader must be sent to the larger zoölogies, and to the writings of Dobson,[46] the leading authority on the group. A capital account of bats and the superstitions about them has been written by Dr. Oswald.[120] In general, the bats of this division are night flyers, and retire during the day to dark places, such as hollow trees, caves, and the crevices and chambers of old buildings and of ruins. There they hang by their heels to the rocks and walls, sometimes in compact masses which burst into a cloud of frightened creatures when the haunt is invaded; and the acrid odor of their bodies, and of the deposits of their valuable coal-black guano (which has become an article of commerce), is almost overpowering. The rock tombs and temples of India, and the tombs and pyramids of Egypt, are thronged with various bats.[55]

Brownell, Phot.

A BAT IN A SLEEPING POSITION.

Tomb Bats. Egypt seems peculiarly well suited to bats, by its warm climate and clear sky at night, and the bat guano from certain caves is valuable in agriculture. In warm countries these retreats are occupied the year round; in colder countries some species regularly migrate to the South in winter, as is the practice of some bats of the United States, but most sleep away the cold months when no insects are flying.

The food of most bats consists of insects caught on the wing at dusk and dawn, and they do us much service by their agile industry; or tropical species may take a mixed diet, and such have peculiar, brush-tipped tongues. The fur is usually some hue of brown or gray, but a few Orien-

BRUSH-TONGUED BAT.

tal species are mottled or variegated with orange, bright yellow, black, and so on, most strikingly displayed in the painted bat of Ceylon, which is deep orange with varicolored wings. It haunts the forest, says Jerdon, hiding by day in the folded leaf of a plantain, and when disturbed in the sunlight looks more like a butterfly than a bat.

One would think such a gaudy dress dangerously conspicuous, but it will not do to pronounce upon such a matter until we are thoroughly acquainted with the wild habits of the wearer. Mr. Swinhoe, a diligent and sagacious naturalist long resident in China, informs us that in fact the colors are highly protective. He describes **Conceal-ment by Color.** one of these brilliant bats, native to Formosa, as resorting almost exclusively to the longan tree. "Now this tree is an evergreen; and all the year through some portion of its foliage is undergoing decay, the particular leaves being in such a stage partially orange and black. This bat can therefore at all seasons suspend from its branches, and elude its enemies by its resemblance to the leaf of the tree. It was in August when this specimen was brought me. It had at that season found the fruit ripe and reddish yellow, and had tried to escape observation in the resemblance of its own tints to those of the fruit." Dobson reaches the same conclusion regarding the red hue of the Indian fox bats; and other instances are quoted by Dr. Dallas, who has given an extensive and interesting account of the bats of the world in "Cassell's Natural History," Vol. I.

In the United States we have about eighteen species of bats (See Allen's [49] and Miller's [50] monographs), nearly all of the family Vespertilionidæ, half a dozen of which are familiar in the east and several others on the Pacific coast; and entertaining accounts of their habits are given by Bachman,[90] Godman,[91] Merriam,[48] Fisher,[51] and others; while much about those of the West Indies will be found in Gosse's [53] book on Jamaica.

One extraordinary sub-family contains the large carnivorous "false vampires" of India (Megaderma), which kill and feed upon small animals, chiefly frogs. In respect to the obscure breeding habits of our North American bats, Stone and Cram [52] offer the following information: —

"Awake, at the most, some four out of every twenty-four hours of their drowsy little lives, they never make any nests or even attempt to fix over the crannies where they hide and where the little bats are born. These helpless things are not left at home at the mercy of foraging rats and mice. When the old bat flits off into the twilight the youngsters go with her from the first, clinging about her neck, swinging away over the tree tops, and along the foggy water-side, while she chases the numberless little flying things of the dark. When there are twins the he bat takes his share of the responsibility, and carries them about with him until they are able to look out for themselves.

"One summer two little bats were discovered hanging close together on the branch of a low tree on the lawn; during the day-time the parent remained with them, folding her wings about them, but at dusk she generally left them while she foraged for food. After a couple of days, however, they disappeared, doubtless transferred to some other spot safe from prying eyes."

The fruit-eating bats (Megachiroptera) must have a few words. Some fifteen genera and seventy species are distributed from South Africa to Japan, Australia, and Polynesia. **Fruit Bats.** None has expanded ears, or nose leaves, or membranes between the tail and the thighs. The smaller species (one weighing only an ounce) are often very peculiar, — as the harpies, whose nostrils protrude as tubes; the strange hairless bat of Borneo, which, having no hair to which a baby could cling, carries its young in an abdominal pouch; or the larger West African hammerhead, whose muzzle is swollen into a grotesque form. A well-known species is the Egyptian rousette, which abounds in the orchards of the Nile delta, and gorges itself on the fruit of the doleb palm. The ordinary fruit eaters, however, are those forty or more species of Madagascar, India, and eastward, suitably named "fox bats," for some of them, as the Indian flying-fox or the Malayan kalong, are almost as big as foxes, the latter species reaching a length of eighteen inches and measuring five feet across the outstretched wings. They are clothed in fox-red fur, have long, pointed muzzles, sharp, upright ears, and big eyes, giving them a terrierlike look.

EAST INDIAN FLYING-FOX.

These bats feed on all sorts of soft fruits except acid ones, such as oranges; are especially fond of figs and guavas; and are a destructive pest to orchards and gardens. In some parts of Java, for example, no delicate fruit can be raised except by protecting the trees with nets and fighting off the nightly forays of bands of kalongs. They live and travel in vast companies, roosting by day on chosen trees, where they hang by one hind leg, each protected from the sun's glare, and from rain, in the closely wrapped mantle of its wings, and large branches frequently break under the weight. At sunset they fly away to their feeding grounds, scattering over a wide area. Where a **Riotous** fig tree attracts a crowd, the roughest fighting begins **Living.** over coveted plunder, each one screaming, clawing, biting, and struggling to seize something and get away to a secure retreat to enjoy it. "There he hangs by one foot, and, grasping the fruit he has secured in the claws and opposable thumb of the other, he hastily reduces it to lumps, with which he stuffs his cheek pouches until they become distended like those of a monkey." Later he chews and swallows this food at leisure. At dawn all return to their roosts, and, says Tickell, "hook themselves along the branches, scrambling about hand over hand with some speed, biting each other severely, striking out with the long claw of the thumb, shrieking and cackling without intermission." No doubt these squabbles are rendered more violent by the disgracefully dissipated habits in which the bats indulge during their nocturnal expeditions, for, according to Dr. Francis Day and other observers, "they often pass the night drinking the toddy from the chatties in the cocoanut trees, which results either in their returning home in the early morning in a state of extreme and riotous intoxication, or in being found the next day at the foot of the trees, sleeping off the effects of their midnight debauch."

The larger fruit bats are eaten by the natives of their countries, and liked by white men when carefully skinned and cooked; nevertheless the bat pronounced unclean food by Mosaic law (Deut. xiv. 18; Lev. xi. 19) was of this kind. They are sometimes tamed as affectionate pets.

Few animals have acquired a worse reputation among the ignorant and superstitious than bats, — and less deserve it; nor is it likely that those of America or Europe would have produced such an impression of gloom and terror as the Oriental bats seem long ago to have done.

"That the ancient Greek and Roman poets, furnished with exaggerated accounts of the animals infesting the remote regions with which their commerce or their conquests had made them acquainted," remarks Bell, in his classic "History of British Quadrupeds,"[93] "should have caught eagerly at those marvelous stories and descriptions, and rendered them subservient to their fabulous but highly imaginative mythology, is not wonderful; and it is more than probable that some of the Indian species of bats, with their predatory habits, their multitudinous numbers, their obscure and mysterious retreats, and the strange combination of the character of beast and bird which they were believed to possess, gave to Virgil the idea, which he has so poetically worked out, of the Harpies which fell upon the hastily spread tables of the hero and his companions, and polluted, whilst they devoured, the feast from which they had driven the affrighted guests. But that the little harmless bats of our own climate, whose habits are at once so innocent and so amusing, and whose time of appearance and activity is that when everything around would lead the mind to tranquillity and peace, should be forced into mystery and horror, as an almost essential feature in the picture, is an anomaly which cannot be easily explained."

At any rate, while the graceful pinions of a bird have been given to their angels of light, the leathery and angular wings of the bat have always been used by painters and sculptors to signalize the forms of fiends from pits of darkness. This is simply the old primal contrast of light and darkness, day and night, for which the nocturnal and elusive bat has furnished a ready symbol.

LYRE BAT (MEGADERMA).

SHREWS, MOLES, etc., — Order, INSECTIVORA

THE next order of mammals to be considered is that of the *Insectivora*, — a collection difficult to define, of small-sized and plantigrade, but otherwise very unlike animals, which feed almost wholly on insects or worms. They are found in all parts of the world except Australia and South America, but near relatives are sometimes widely separated, the insectivores of the West Indies, for example, being closely allied to those of Madagascar. Some are subterranean, others aquatic or arboreal. Deep-seated distinctions in structure correspond to these variations in mode of living, and strengthen the evidence from fossils that this group represents "little altered survivors of some of the most primitive placental mammals."

There is a good deal of evidence, direct and indirect, that the insectivores were once a far more abundant and important group. So far as we can tell from the rare and fragmentary jaws and tiny teeth, the order is of immense antiquity, being traceable far back into the Age of Reptiles, during the Jurassic period. At all events, they were a numerous and varied group in the Eocene, including arboreal, terrestrial, and aquatic types, some of considerable size, and several species very abundant, besides many minute forms comparable to the moles and shrews of the present day, and very likely ancestral to them. At the beginning of the Tertiary, they are indistinguishable from the earlier of the creodonts, but the latter soon branched off, becoming adapted to a predaceous life, while the insectivores retained more nearly their ancient mode of living and failed to keep progress with the higher groups, so that in the later Tertiary epochs they diminished rapidly in numbers and variety. To-day only a few survivors are left, protected from their enemies by some unusual defense, as in the case of the hedgehogs; by a subterranean mode of life, as the moles; by their agility, minute size, and unpleasant odor and taste, as are the shrews; or, finally, by their living in some remote corner of the world, as Madagascar, Cuba, or South Africa, where their more highly organized and intelligent enemies and rivals have not yet searched them out and hunted them into oblivion.

This antiquity, and their pretension of primitive generalized characteristics, account for the otherwise puzzling resemblances shown by some of them to bats and lemurs (especially the aye-aye), and make it very difficult to place the order in a true relation to the other orders. Whether, indeed, the insectivores have not descended from several primitive stocks, instead of only one, is still undecided.

THE SHORT-TAILED SHREW.

One of the most out-of-the-way forms is the

Colugo. colugo, or kaguan, an animal of the Oriental forests, which is about the size of a cat and has a very voluminous "patagium," or extension of furry skin, so that it looks and sails through the air like a flying-squirrel; but the patagium more resembles that of a bat, while otherwise the creature is so lemurlike that it is often called in books the "flying-lemur." It feeds on leaves, is nocturnal, rests during the day by clinging, head downward, to a shady trunk, sails from tree to tree by long leaps, and is familiar from Siam to Java, while a smaller species lives in the Philippines. Wallace[31] and Horsfield[57] have written most about it; and its genus represents a suborder *Dermoptera*, while all the remainder of the order are called *Insectivora*, or true insectivores.

Of these latter the highest are the shrews, — small, mouselike animals, with long, pointed heads, slender jaws filled with sharp,

Shrew. red-tipped teeth, the incisors long, forward-pointing, and curved, a flexible, bewhiskered nose sometimes much prolonged, close, rounded ears, and a musky smell. The fur is soft and the tail scantily haired. Shrews are found in most parts of the world, and in spite of their littleness are

COMMON EASTERN LONG-TAILED SHREW.

wonderfully hardy, existing in far northern regions and on high mountains. Even our eastern long-tailed shrew, the smallest mammal known in the world, since it is not bigger than the end of one's little finger and weighs but a fraction of an ounce, is able to run about in the snow, or to burrow through it, even when the mercury stands twenty degrees or more below zero.

All the shrews are ceaselessly active, wandering about underneath leaves, old grass, and logs, and boring their way into loose loam or the punky wood of decayed stumps, in search of earthworms, grubs, beetles, slugs, and similar prey, including young mice and the fledglings of ground-nesting birds, and varying this fare by bites from soft-shelled beechnuts, tuberous roots, etc. They are astonishingly quick of hearing; are bold, pugnacious, and fierce, often killing and eating other shrews; difficult to keep alive in captivity, utterly untamable, and easily frightened to death.[87] All kinds exhale from glands near their armpits a musky odor which no doubt is protective, since most hawks, cats, foxes, etc., do not eat them unless excessively hungry; but owls and weasels "appear to be well pleased with such flavors, and catch and devour them in large numbers." This odor reaches its maximum in the great musk shrews of the warmer parts of the Old World, one of which is the misnamed "musk rat" of India, familiar to every villager, for it enters houses at night and ransacks them for insect vermin. Many long-nosed shrews are aquatic in their habits, dwelling in bank burrows and swimming, diving, and even walking with ease on the bottom of streams where they find their food. All have some modification or other of feet and tail to adapt them to these methods of work.

One of the most extraordinary things in natural history is the fact that ancient superstitions cling to these little creatures in Europe, and are now and then heard of even in America.[87] Gilbert White [62] gives us a hint of them in his well-known account of the shrew ash at Selborne. Another old writer,

WESTERN SHREWMOLE.

the Reverend Edward Topsell, "clearke of the king his most excellent maiesties closet," at the opening of the seventeenth century, in his rare "Historie of Four-footed Beastes," printed in London in 1607, says of the shrew that "it is a ravening beaste, feigning itself gentle and tame, but, being touched, it biteth deeply and poysoneth deadly. It beareth a cruel minde, desiring to hurt anything, neither is there any creature that it loveth, or it loveth him, because it is feared of all."

The shrews are connected with their relatives, the moles, by various mole shrews, and by the large, web-footed, long-snouted aquatic "desmans" of the Pyrenees and of Russia, whose silky coat is so much valued by the peasants of the Volga Valley.

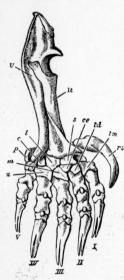

BONES OF FOREARM AND MANUS OF MOLE.

C, cuneiform ; *ce*, centrale; *l*, lunar; *m*, magnum ; *p*, pisiform; *R*, radius; *rs*, radial sesamoid (falciform); *s*, scaphoid ; *td*, trapezoid; *tm*, trapezium; *U*, ulna ; *u*, unciform; *I-V*, the digits.

The moles belong to the northern hemisphere alone, and differ from shrews in their greater size and wholly subterranean habits. The head is small, pointed, and almost continuous with the thick, tailless body, from which the limbs project very little, so that the animal has the shape of a round, pointed wedge; ears and eyes have almost disappeared and the sense of smell is mainly depended upon for such information as the creature requires. The fur is soft, short, and lies equally well either backward or forward ; and the mouth has forty small, sharp teeth. The most striking adaptive change, however, has occurred in the fore limbs, to fit them to the work of digging. The breastbone, collar bones, and arm bones are all shortened, set forward (giving a great leverage), twisted outward and enormously strengthened, and terminate in a massive "hand," whose fingers bear spadelike claws, supplemented by a special "sesamoid" bone, outside of the thumb, which really forms a sixth finger. The hind limbs are little changed.

The mole passes its whole life underground, only occasionally coming out upon the surface at night. Its enormous strength enables it to force its way through compact soil, though it naturally prefers the looser sort near the surface, and on this account, as well as because such places are richer in worms, it infests gardens and lawns, where its course is marked by the heaved-up soil beneath which it has passed, and by the hillocks of earth which it now and then comes to the surface to throw out. For the most part, however, it simply loosens the soil with its powerful diggers, crowds it beneath and behind it, and glides on, leaving no proper tunnel, since it does not mean to go back that way, but is merely wandering about in search of the earthworms, grubs, and other flesh to which it is guided by its delicate scent. In winter the moles dig

Brownell, Phot.

A GARDEN MOLE.

below the frost line and do not hibernate. Each family has, however, a central home, or burrow, which is the true "mole hill," and here are a series of connecting galleries, a living chamber with an opening to the surface, and regular tunnels leading off toward the customary hunting grounds. Wood [63] and Bell [93] have pictured this as a complicated "fortress," said to show very high engineering intelligence; but this seems exaggerated, and certainly is not true of the American mole, which, also, does not gather in colonies as do those of Europe. An interesting fact is mentioned of the latter by Beddard, namely, that a German naturalist believes he has evidence that it stores up worms for consumption during the winter, biting off their heads to prevent their crawling away.

Our common mole has webbed hind feet as if aquatic, as also have the eastern hairy-tailed mole and Townsend's mole of the

Pacific coast; but none of these is so likely to be found in marshy ground as is our quaint star-nosed mole, which, as Stone and Cram say, is a creature almost as well fitted for a partially aquatic life as the otter and mink, and, as a matter of fact, does **Star-nosed** pass most of its time about the water, pushing exten-**Mole.** sive tunnels through the black peaty soil of swamps and along the borders of little brooks and ponds. "The soft, black loam is thrown up in frequent heaps, a foot more or less

STAR-NOSED MOLE.

in diameter, the opening of the burrow being under the bank, and as often beneath the water as above." This mole is easily recognized by the fact that its piglike snout ends in a circlet of fleshy pink tentacles. It feeds on worms and insects, but like its relatives varies this with such fish, fish eggs, reptiles, and other flesh as it can get. A learned treatise on American moles has been written by Dr. Frederick W. True.[7]

In South Africa dwells a group (Chrysochloris) of moles called "golden," because of the unique and lovely iridescence of their fur; but they interest us chiefly because the bones of the fore limb are modified in a totally different way from the typical, and by their likeness to the Australian marsupial mole. Africa also contains the elephant or jumping shrews, which take their first name from the proboscislike extension of the snout, especially marked in the Algerian species, or "rat á trompé," which is tamed as a funny pet; and take the second name from the elongated and half-naked hind legs, which give them much the look and the leaping gait of jerboas. Many kinds are known, all as big as rats, or larger, and dwelling in crevices of rocks and like places, whence they go abroad at nightfall in search of insects.

Tropical Shrews.

Much like them in structure and in the flexible trunk are the pretty tupaias or tree-shrews of India and eastward to the Philippines; otherwise they so closely resemble squirrels in appearance, food, and but manners that in the case of one species at least "one has to look at the teeth" to distinguish them. This has often been adduced as a case of "mimicry," which is very rare among mammals; but it seems to me rather an instance of "convergence," that is, the result of two animals coming to be like one another because they have followed the same manner of life under identical circum-

stances. The likeness of the jumping shrews to jerboas is another instance. Some of these tupaias are very numerous and familiar in India and Sumatra, running freely about houses when allowed, and even scampering over the table to pick morsels of food from the plates.

A rarer oddity is the river

ELEPHANT SHREW.

shrew of West Africa, which looks and behaves like a small otter, though its tail is compressed like a muskrat's. Then there are the almiquis of Cuba and Haiti, which suggest ground-traveling opossums, and their cousins, the ancient race of tenrecs of Madagascar. Among many curious peculiarities, the tenrecs have that of spines along the back or mixed with the hairs, and an ability to partly roll themselves up.[48] These qualities show a likeness to the hedgehogs, which are widely distributed in the Old World but unknown in the New, for our "hedgehog" is a porcupine.

The common European hedgehog is a queer little animal, about ten inches long, covered with an armor of short, stiff, and sharp gray spines, and trotting on small legs and feet which scarcely lift it off the ground. It pokes its piglike snout into all sorts of places likely to harbor prey, and is careless of enemies, since it is guarded as well as is an armadillo or tortoise in its shell. Thus protected and

Hedgehog.

doing good rather than harm to garden or orchard by its visits, it survives numerously in the midst of civilization, and few animals have been so closely watched or so well "written up." The following is from Maunder's "Treasury": —

"When molested, it instantly rolls itself into a sort of ball and presents but its prickles to the foe; and the more the animal is irritated and alarmed,

EUROPEAN HEDGEHOG.

the more firmly does it contract itself, and the more stiff and strong does its bristly panoply become. Thus rolled up it patiently awaits till the danger is passed: the cat, the weasel, the ferret, and the marten soon decline the combat; and though a well-trained, wire-haired terrier or a fox may now and then be found to open a hedgehog, it generally remains impenetrable.

"The hedgehog is strictly nocturnal, remaining coiled up in its retreat during the day, and wandering about nearly all the night in search of food. It generally resides in small thickets, in hedges, or in ditches covered with bushes, making a hole about six inches deep, which it lines with moss, grass, or leaves. The hibernation of the hedgehog is undoubted; although it lays up no store for the winter, it retires to its hole, and in its warm, soft nest of moss and leaves it lies secure from the rigors of the frost and the violence of the tempest, passing the dreary season in a profoundly torpid state. The female produces from two to four young ones early in the summer, which at their birth are blind and covered with soft white spines which in two or three days become hard and elastic. The flesh of these animals, though generally rejected as human food, is said to be very delicate."

Although the little animal feeds mainly on slugs, snails, insects, etc., and its services are constantly requested in country kitchens infested with cockroaches, it also eats birds' eggs, mice, frogs, toads, and even snakes, and its eagerness to attack and devour vipers compensates for occasional depredations upon outlying nests of game birds and poultry. When it discovers a viper it will pursue it, smell at and lick it, not minding the "striking" of this poisonous serpent, and at last will seize and bite it all along the back, breaking the bones in many places, and then proceed to devour it. Almost as many fables and errors are current among the peasantry in regard to the hedgehog as to the shrew.

In the Malayan region is found a related genus (Gymnura); and fossils show that the hedgehog family (Erinaceidæ) is one of the oldest known among mammals, and has undergone very little change since the Miocene era, which illustrates how when nature hits upon a good thing it preserves it!

HEAD AND PALM OF FORE FOOT OF AMERICAN GARDEN MOLE.

By permission of the American Museum of Natural History.

A CREODONT FEEDING UPON THE HEAD OF A UINTATHERE.

78

PRIMITIVE FLESH EATERS — Order, CREODONTA

SOME of my younger readers may have asked themselves by this time how the order of the larger groups of our subject is determined, — why the Insectivora followed the Primates, the Carnivora are to come next, then the Ungulata, and so on. The reason is, partly, that their ancestors, so far as we know them as fossils, seem to have been related in a way which indicates such a succession. It is scarcely more than an indication, however, for although in describing them, or making a list, we must set the animals in a row, naturalists long ago ceased attempting to show that any linear arrangement of that kind represented the reality. The present variety among mammals (as in other classes) is the result of development along different lines from one or more points of beginning, so that any proper picture of the growth and arrangement of any class would be that of a spreading fan, with sticks of unequal length; or that of the branches of a tree — some reaching farther than others and themselves dividing again and again into twigs.

Data for Classification.

"One of the most striking and significant results of the study of the later Mesozoic and earliest Tertiary mammalian faunas," says Professor Scott, "is that the higher or placental mammals are seen to be converging back to a common ancestral group of clawed and carnivorous or omnivorous animals, now entirely extinct, to which the name of Creodonta was given by Cope. The creodonts are assuredly the ancestors of the modern flesh eaters, and, very probably, of the great series of hoofed animals also, as well as of other orders. From this central, ancestral group the other orders proceed, diverging more and more with the progress of time, each larger branch dividing and subdividing into smaller and smaller branches, until the modern condition is attained."

It is plain, then, that to understand the history of the modern mammals we must learn something of the Creodonta. Professor E. D. Cope tells us that in the overflowing mam- malian fauna of the early Tertiary there was nothing which could be classed with the Carnivora of the present, which order did not appear before the Oligocene period. All the predatory beasts of that time differed from the Carnivora in various points of structure. Their brains were dispropor- tionately small and but little convoluted, indicating low intelli- gence. Their limbs were shorter, and the wrist and ankle joints less compact and strong; the feet less perfectly adapted to chasing and seizing; five-toed as a rule, and resting the heel upon the ground; and the tail was long and muscular. The teeth in most cases were of that small and primitive type still seen in the mouths of the Insectivora, adapted to feeding on insects and miscellaneous small things, both animal and vege- table. The smaller and more primitive creodonts, indeed, are almost indistinguishable from the contemporary insectivores. In their later and more advanced races we find certain teeth becoming more and more specialized for a flesh diet, but in only one family, the Miacidæ, are these specialized teeth (car- nassials) the same ones as in the modern Carnivora. This likeness, with others, shows that our Carnivora are descended from the Miacidæ. The remaining families of creodonts could not compete with the miacids, because of their inferior equip- ment, and have left no descendants.

The creodonts must have been big-headed, savage-looking animals, with jaws and teeth disproportionately large and long: short-legged, and long-tailed, resembling nothing in our world so much as the Tasmanian wolf and Tasmanian devil of Aus- tralia, to which, however, they were only remotely akin. Some were terrestrial, others dwelt and hunted on trees or in the water; and they equaled in size and doubtless in ferocity the biggest modern cats and wolves. Along with these strictly predacious creodonts were some that mimicked the bears, and others (Mesonychidæ) whose massive teeth were adapted to bone crushing and carrion chewing, so that their habits were probably those of hyenas. Some of these last equaled, or exceeded in size, the largest modern beasts of prey, and one of them is represented in the accompanying illustration.

Contemporary with the Mesonyx was a more strictly live-flesh-eating creodont named Patriofelis, which was nearly as big as a lion, and remarkable for its extremely massive proportions and broad splay feet. The short jaw and catlike teeth of this animal — and of its smaller predecessor, Oxyæna, of the Lower Eocene — caused the fragmentary fossil remains first examined to be mistaken for the bones of ancestors of the cats; but fuller knowledge has shown that this was an error.

The hyænodons, whose skeletons are obtained from the Oligocene formations of Europe and America, represent the last surviving branch of the Creodonta, and they presently gave place to the more intelligent and better adapted true Carnivora (descended from the Miacidæ), which arose side by side with them and won in the competition for food and success.

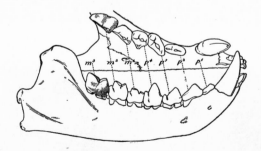

UPPER AND LOWER TEETH OF A CREODONT (HYÆNODON).

Shows the carnassial teeth (second upper and third lower molar).

BEASTS OF PREY — Order, CARNIVORA

THE story of the creodonts tells of the rise of the powerful modern order, Carnivora, — the beasts of prey, whose food is flesh of other animals which must be killed day by day. Hence they are equipped as hunters and fighters, and their armament is carried to a very high degree of perfection, so that almost every kind of living thing may be preyed upon by one or more sorts of carnivores, and each may defend his quarry and himself against rapacious rivals. All (except the bears) walk upon the under surface of the toes — are "phalangigrade."

There always has been and always will be in every department and rank of animal life a class which thus lives by preying upon its neighbors. From the beginning, certain kinds of animals have discovered, by accident or example, that some, at least, of their associates were eatable and within their power; and have thereafter depended upon them for food. Hence men long ago divided the animal kingdom into those living wholly on a vegetable diet (herbivorous — herbivores), or wholly on flesh (carnivorous — carnivores).

Now this is an economical arrangement by nature in two ways. In the first place, it permits a double use of a larger part of the available and always limited food supply. The vegetable eaters gather and digest the raw materials, so to speak, which are so abundant and persistent that they afford subsistence for a very great number of animals in most parts of the globe; and every sort of growing thing, from microscopic diatoms in the water and the scanty lichens on arctic rocks to luscious fruits or solid timber, is utilized by some creature. In short, the vegetable world could support, generally speaking, no more animals than are now feeding upon it, and there the population of the world would come to its limit but for a second circumstance: the eating of a meal of grass or the like does not put an end to its usefulness as food. This raw material, as I have termed it, is simply changed by the processes of digestion and assimilation into the substance of the eater's flesh, which contains all the nutriment of the original, but is freed from its large proportion of useless, innutritious matter, discarded as waste. It is therefore in condition to be eaten again and support another animal; and so two may exist where one lived before. Moreover, the second consumer will have the advantage of using the material in a far more compact and refined condition. A lion can swallow in five minutes the elaborated equivalent in nourishment of what it had taken the antelope all day to gather. The better the food, the better the animal; and this is one good reason why the carnivores as a class are superior to the herbivores.

The other way in which the arrangement serves the economy of nature is that the beasts of prey, in catering to their appetites, really serve also the interests of the other half of the animal world by keeping the ever growing population of vegetable eaters within proper bounds, so that the ratio of numbers to food supply is maintained. Without some such check all the small rodents, not to speak of the antelopes, deer, etc., would so swarm in a few seasons as speedily to destroy the herbage and foliage of the world, and bring poverty to all and starvation to many. An idea of what would happen may be gained by recalling the way the rabbits have overrun Australia, where they had little to fear from "nature's police."

It is evident that the practice of gaining a living by preying upon live creatures, perhaps protected by an armor, or secretly hidden, or able to escape swiftly, or to defend themselves vigorously, calls for an organization very different from that of animals with nothing to do but to crop herbage peacefully, gather leaves and fruit, or dig for unresisting roots. This difference is most strikingly shown in the teeth, which here are adapted to seizing, holding, biting, and cutting, in contrast to the nibbling and grinding requirements of herbivorous animals. The characteristic features of the dentition in the Carnivora are the length and strength of the canines, and the angular, knife-edged form of the cheek teeth; while the incisors are small and feeble, useful for little more than to scrape a bone. On the other hand the canine, of little importance in other groups, here becomes of prime importance, — **Dentition.** a dagger and hook in one, — an instrument by which both to disable and to hold the prey. Naturally it is most fully developed among dogs and bears, which have little other means of seizing an animal, whereas the cat has the efficient aid of its claws. But after a predatory animal has killed its victim the tough flesh must be cut into pieces small enough to be swallowed, and an instrument well suited to this has been gained in the alteration of the elsewhere blunt fourth premolar in the upper

jaw, and the first molar in the lower jaw, into thin, sharp, three-pointed fangs, shutting down past one another like a pair of scissor blades. These are called the "sectorial" or "car-

DENTITION OF A CARNIVORE (FOX).

c, canine teeth; *s*, sectorial teeth, or carnassials.

nassial" teeth, and they are often larger and more prominent than either the knifelike or conical ones in front of them, or the robust molars behind them, whose crowns are studded with tubercles, definite in number and arrangement.

The classification of the Carnivora has been a puzzling task, on account of the "generalized" character of many of the fossil species, and the constant disclosure of facts

Families. disconcerting to previous conclusions; but the prevailing view now is that the order should be divided into families arranged as follows:—

I. LAND CARNIVORA — FISSIPEDIA

Cats (Felidæ)	Cosmopolitan.
Saber-Tooths (Nimravidæ)	Extinct.
Civets (Viverridæ)	Old World.
Hyenas, etc. (Hyænidæ)	Old World.
Weasels, Badgers, etc. (Mustelidæ)	Cosmopolitan.
Dogs (Canidæ)	Cosmopolitan.
Bears (Ursidæ)	Cosmopolitan.
Raccoons (Procyonidæ)	America.

II. Sea Carnivora — Pinnipedia

Sea Bears or Fur Seals (Otariidæ) . . . . Eastern Pacific.
Walruses (Trichechidæ). . . . . Subarctic Oceans.
Hair Seals (Phocidæ) . . . . Cosmopolitan.

All of these families were well separated long before the present geological era, and some of them go back to the dawn of the Tertiary, when the Carnivora were beginning to take definite characteristics as a great branch of animal development. In speaking of the Creodonta it was said that that order had disappeared at the close of the Mesozoic, but that there were indications that in one direction — that led by the family Miacidæ — descendants might be traced in the next succeeding era, the Eocene. The remains of Eocene **Evolution.** carnivorous mammals, however, are very few, and often of doubtful identity; and at best there exists a long gap in structure as well as in time between them and their supposed ancestors among the creodonts. Their fossil skeletons combine in a puzzling manner features that afterward become distinctive of separate families, *i.e.* they are synthetic, or generalized, types.

More material has been obtained from the Miocene formations, but the specimens still show a generalized condition, in which doglike and civet-like features seem most prominent, leading to the conclusion that the canine type is the oldest and most central stock, whence the modern diversity has gradually branched off. Thus one of the oldest-known fossil carnivores is the European Cynodictis (in several varieties), which has been called a "viverrine dog" because it is such a combination of civet and fox. This shades off into the many species of Galecynus, and of Amphicyon, planti-grade animals existing in all parts of the Miocene world, and varying in size from that of a small fox to that of a long-bodied bear, — a huge com-bination of wolf, mungoos, and bear! Others of the same or a later time are more nearly typical civets, or stand between such and the linsangs, or connect civets and weasels; while at the beginning of the next, or Pliocene, period, there appears a curious animal, the ictithere, which completely unites the civets with the hyenas.

Amphicyon was plantigrade and had other bearlike characteristics. Beside it, as we know from Miocene fossils, lived another animal (Hemicyon), which was more dog than civet, plus bearlike features; and later we find Hyænarctos still more ursine, so that these represent a line of change from bearlike dogs into doglike bears, and connect the Amphicyon stock with the true bears and raccoons. In a similar way fossil forms of the Upper Eocene and Lower Miocene connect the civet stock with the apparent ancestors of the fur-bearers (weasels, badgers, otters, etc.). It is not, indeed, until the late Miocene, near the end of the Tertiary period, that the groups of Carnivora as we now see them became distinctly set apart from one another by the dying out of the old intermediate stock forms.

Saber-Tooths and Other Ancient Cats

The cats, although not the oldest, stand as the most perfected or specialized of all the kinds of carnivores, and probably of all kinds of animals, not excepting man. This splendid and very compact series first definitely appears in the Oligocene era, from an unknown ancestor among the creodonts. Somewhere in its early history arose a divergent branch, starting in the Oligocene with such forms as Pseudoælurus and Archælurus, which developed amazingly throughout most of the Tertiary period, and to which Cuvier gave the name of "saber-tooth cats." They were especially numerous and powerful in the Americas, yet abounded throughout the Old World. From the first these beasts showed a tendency toward enlarging the upper canines, until finally in such genera as Smilodon, as restored by Wolf, they became huge tusks. Dr. W. D. Matthew, who has made a particular study of these creatures, has given me the benefit of his conclusions in the ensuing account: —

"Our prehistoric ancestors could have told us of an animal much larger and more powerful than any lions or tigers known to us, — the great saber-toothed tiger Smilodon, — **Smilodon.** which seems to have realized very completely the idea of the King of Beasts as portrayed in mediæval tradition. This great carnivore equaled the largest polar or Kadiak bear in size. It was related to the large cats, but distinguished by its enormous upper canine teeth, enlarged into curving, sharp-edged, flattened fangs, projecting seven inches below the jaw. No record or tradition of it has survived, but its petrified bones have been found in caves and river gravels of the Quaternary period, with those of the mammoth, megatherium, and other extinct giants, and associated with the relics of the primitive men. In the pampas of the Argentine Republic, a rich store-

By permission of the American Museum of Natural History.

THE GREAT SABER-TOOTHED TIGER SMILODON.

Restoration drawn by Wolf, under direction of Dr. Daniel G. Elliot.

house of fossils, two entire skeletons have been recovered, one of which is mounted in the American Museum of Natural History in New York.

"The restoration of an extinct animal might be supposed to be largely a matter of conjecture; but in fact, when a perfect skeleton is at hand, and the artist has a knowledge of anatomy and of the form and habitual attitudes of its relatives, great certainty is possible. The general proportions can, of course, be accurately followed in the outline; the form of the head, position and size of the eyes and ears, the shape of the muzzle and width of the mouth, may be closely inferred from the characters of the skull; while the size and shape of the muscular attachments on the bones enable the artist to reconstruct the muscles of the body with a fair degree of exactness. Even the coloring is not wholly guesswork, for it is governed very largely by the habits and mode of life of the animal, judged by its living kindred.

"The smilodon had short, muscular limbs and broad, padded feet, with retractile, catlike claws; but its general appearance could not have been very catlike, for the shape of the head, the high shoulders, short, deep trunk, and small hindquarters were much more like a hyena. The tail was short and stumpy. The most noticeable peculiarity is the huge, saberlike, upper canine teeth.

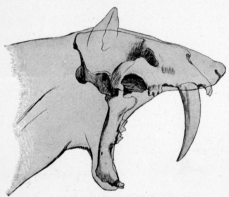

HEAD OF SMILODON.

Outline restoration drawn by Charles R. Knight. (By permission of the American Museum of Natural History.)

"The modern great cats kill their prey usually by biting it in the neck so as to break the spinal column. They pursue as a rule the long-necked, thin-skinned ruminants, which are the most abundant herbivores of to-day, seldom molesting the short-necked, thick-skinned pachyderms such as the rhinoceros and the elephant. The saber-tooth appears to have used his great canine fangs in a quite different method of attack; the whole structure of the animal indicates that he struck them forcibly into the side of his prey, the mouth gaping wide meanwhile, and then presumably withdrew them with a ripping, tearing stroke, leaving a great gash whereby a large animal would soon bleed to death. The whole head is adapted to such a method of killing. The

Methods of Killing Prey.

mastoid neck muscles, serving to draw the head down, are so excessive in size as to make a noticeable fullness beneath the neck, and were evidently far more powerful than are those of any cat, indicating that this animal could strike its head downward with enormous force. Again, while the cat's lower jaw has a wide gape, and can swing back on its hinges to an angle of over 90 degrees, a smilodon could open its mouth at least 30 degrees more, thus giving room for full play by the long tusks. With the head thrown back, the lower jaw lying back almost upon the throat, it was able to strike its daggers deep into its victim, and then, pulling backward, rip a deadly gash in the flesh.

"It is fair to infer that the saber-tooth preyed upon creatures much larger than himself, for his means and methods of attack would be ineffective and unnecessary in the case of a small animal. Moreover, his heavy build and short wide feet show that he was not agile or swift-footed, and the smaller animals had probably little to fear from him. On the contrary, he was the chief or only enemy of the big pachyderms of his time, lying in wait for them, perhaps at their watering places, springing upon their backs, and gashing and bleeding them to death before they were able to shake him off and gore or trample upon him.

"An animal of such habits might fulfill the legendary requirements of the 'King of Beasts' more nearly than does the lion. It would be bold and fearless of the most powerful, and it might well be thought to **Heraldic** exercise a 'magnanimous' forbearance toward the small and **Lion.** weak ones, since they were neither feared by it nor were its natural prey. It is curious to note several of the characters of the heraldic lion in the saber-tooth, — for instance, the vast mouth, long head, huge forequarters, and widely spreading claws. Surely one might fancy the designer of these horrifying creatures must have had some inspiration from an instinctive recollection of the smilodon as it appeared to our prehistoric ancestors."

By the time this saber-toothed race had disappeared there had risen into prominence, corresponding with the rise of the long-necked, thin-skinned horses, cattle, antelopes, and the like, which superseded the pachyderms as they dwindled, the race of true cats, endowed with qualities better fitted to the new conditions — among others, better brains. These forms concentrated during the early Miocene into the genus Felis, which **Rise of Cats.** has outlasted its saber-toothed cousins and flourishes to-day. "According to present knowledge," remarks Woodward, "they [the Felidæ] seem to have gradually evolved in the Old World, first migrating to North America at the close of the Pliocene period, and thence eventually reaching South America." Many extinct species are to be found in all the later deposits, some of which lasted until exterminated by man, *e.g.* the "cave lion," whose bones lie in the caverns and river gravels of Europe, sometimes bearing marks of human weapons; but it was probably not different from the African lions of to-day. In the western United States, about the same time, there roamed several tigerlike cats, in whose killing the Stone-age men of this country may have had a part. They were the equal or perhaps the superior of the lion, at any rate were far more formidable than our modern pumas or jaguars.

Puma, Jaguar, and Tiger Cats

No better example of this splendid feline race could be taken than our American puma. Until the invasion of his domain by civilization, he possessed the whole continent from near Hudson Bay to the Strait of Magellan. No other land animal whatever has so great a north-and-south range; and when one thinks of the wide contrasts in climate and conditions generally to which it must accommodate itself, one would expect to find a bewildering variety of forms. On the contrary, it would be hard to find a species so uniform as this. There is little or nothing by which any man might say whether a certain skin came from the Orinoco jungles, or the Patagonian pampas, or from some cold canyon in the Rockies.

The earliest visitors to this continent mistook the skins they saw in the hands of the Indians for those of true lions, or rather of lionesses, for they missed the mane. Our "mountain lion" is a survival of this, strengthened by the fact that the Spanish-

Copyright, N. Y. Zoölogical Society.   Sanborn, Phot.

THE AMERICAN PUMA, OR MOUNTAIN LION.

speaking people from California to Cape Horn still say *leon.* In New England, however, a worse error took its place, giving it the name panther, or "painter," as Natty Bumppo and his tribe pronounced it. "Puma" is Peruvian, and the best name, because, in addition to its being a native and an easy word, it alone appears to refer to this very animal; for "cougar" is a made word, coined or borrowed by Buffon.

As has been implied, the adult puma has no spots whatever, except that the lips are black, with a patch of white on each side of the muzzle, the outer rim of the ear is black, and sometimes the tip of the tail. Its upper parts may be a uniform pale fox-red, or anything from that to slaty blue. This difference in color has nothing to do with age, sex, season, or locality. The throat, belly, and inside of the legs are white.

As to size, no satisfactory evidence exists of a length greater than eight feet from tip of nose to tip of tail, and the average of "large ones" will fall well below seven feet and a weight of 200 pounds; the amount of individual variation is astonishing.

The comparative fullness of its skull forward gives to the head a rounded solidity not usual in cats, and lends to the face an expression of intelligence quite different from the flat-headed, brutish ferocity of many feline countenances — nor does this wholly belie its nature.

This handsome beast seems never to have been very numerous in the East. Their mating is no doubt temporary save where they are so few that there is little or no choice; but the males travel long distances in their quest for partners, and it is then, if ever, that are heard the fearsome screams which have adorned so many a frontier tale. Females far outnumber males, partly, if Merriam is right, because more of that sex than of males are born, and partly because many young males are killed in their jealous battles with each other. The puma mother selects with **Family Life.** care a secret home for her expected young, choosing some cave or sheltered and inaccessible place among rocks, usually on some ledge attainable by a leap of which no other animal is capable — twenty feet, sometimes; she is justly fearful of danger to the kittens she must often leave unprotected. In a flat country, like our southern states, where there are no caves or rocks, "the lair of the cougar is generally in a very dense thicket, or in a cane brake. It is a rude sort of bed of sticks, weeds, leaves, and grasses or mosses, and where the canes arch over it, as they are evergreen, their long, pointed leaves turn the rain at all seasons of the year."

The young are born as early as February in the Tropics, but in the North considerably later, after a gestation of about ninety-five days. Four or five kittens may come at a birth, but usually fewer, and more than two rarely survive long. At first they are spotted and the tail is ringed, which led some early writers into declaring them half-bred jaguars! But any countryman could have told them their mistake, and that, as in the similar case of lion babies, these markings would mostly disappear in a few months. The cubs do not become well grown before the second summer, and until then associate with the mother and learn to hunt by watching her methods. A very charming picture of puma-kitten life and puma-mother care is drawn by the Sioux author, Dr. Eastman, in his book of stories[130] of the "animal people." In the autumn the family is driven down from the high mountains by snow, and it is then they become most troublesome to the ranchman. Except in some of the wilder parts of the Appalachian and Ozark ranges, or in swamps along the Gulf coast, no pumas are now to be found east of the Great Plains; yet it is hardly more than a century since they inhabited the Highlands of the Hudson.

As to the availability of young pumas as pets likely to remain safe companions for their masters after they begin to get their full size and strength, accounts differ greatly, as no doubt did the specimens tried. The most enlightening discussion of the matter, based upon an actual and most instructive experiment, may be read in J. Hampden Porter's masterly essay [126] on the puma as he knew it in South America. His final word is: "A loose beast of prey is not a fit associate for a nervous man."

Dr. Merriam [48] concludes that in the Adirondacks the puma

breeds only once in two years. If this be true it is a striking example of one of nature's limitations of these destructive beasts, which would seem at first thought to have a clear field for indefinite multiplication. But though their food is ordinarily plentiful, and no active enemies are to be feared, at least outside the Tropics, there are certain insidious foes which they are powerless to resist, in the form of parasites (especially internal), taken into the system from the living animals on which the cat feeds — particularly from hares and other rodents.

"In its essential habits and traits," says Roosevelt,[128] "the big, slinking, nearly unicolored cat seems to be much the same

Hunting. everywhere, whether living in mountain, open plain, or forest, under arctic cold or tropic heat. When the settlements become thick it retires to dense forest, dark swamp, or inaccessible mountain gorge, and moves about only at night. In wilder regions it not infrequently roams during the day, and ventures freely into the open. Deer are its customary prey when they are plentiful, bucks, does, and fawns being killed indifferently. Usually the deer is killed almost instantaneously, but occasionally there is quite a scuffle, in which the cougar may get bruised, though, as far as I know, never seriously. It is also a dreaded enemy of sheep, pigs, calves, and especially colts, and when pressed by hunger a big male cougar will kill a full-grown horse or cow, moose or wapiti. It is the special enemy of mountain sheep. In 1886, while hunting white goats north of Clarke's Fork of the Columbia, I found them preying as freely on the goats as on the deer. It rarely catches antelope, but is quick to seize rabbits, other small beasts, and even porcupines."

The panther was greatly dreaded by the early pioneers of New England and New York, but careful inquirers could find little foundation for their fears. De Kay asserts that he had never met with an instance of their having attacked a man.

Every hunter of his day represented them as always cowardly, and the weight of testimony ever since, and in all parts of the continent, confirms their awe of man and their prudence. The Brazilians dread the puma much less than the jaguar, and the Indians of our continent would rather meet it than a bear, yet both hold it in high respect, and among the Zuñis it stands as chief of the "prey gods."

Some extraordinary stories are told, by otherwise highly credible observers, of the beast's attitude toward man —

Puma and Man. stories which I have recounted and commented on at some length in my "Wild Neighbors." It has happened in hundreds of cases, perhaps, that a puma would dog the trail of a man for days, or lurk about his camping place or shanty,

Brownell, Phot.

PROFILE OF A PUMA.

without harming him; they have been met face to face by hundreds of persons and slunk away after a shout or a thrown stone; yet now and then, as the records prove, one has followed his stalk by the deadly spring, or encountering a child has struck it down, or has attacked a man with tigerish ferocity.

When the experience is almost universal that there is nothing a puma dreads and avoids so much as it does mankind, how shall such a contradiction be accounted for as follows? "In the summer of 1893 a very large puma, in perfect health and vigor, walked one noonday into an extensive logging camp near Davis, West Virginia, traversed one wing of the long building in which the men employed slept, and without making any demonstration of hostility toward those who fled before him entered their dining room and helped himself to the meat on the table, after which he quietly passed out of a side door and was shot from a window." Does this betoken cowardice? Was it the bravado of ignorance? Or was it simply cool daring — admirable courage?

What shall be said of the tales told of the puma on the Argentine pampas by J. R. Spears,[127] W. H. Hudson,[35] and others regarded as competent and honest naturalists? Hudson declares that although the puma there is undoubtedly a bold and courageous animal, yet the account given long ago by Azara, that it will never attack or threaten to hurt either man or child, even when found asleep, is not only true but actually understated. As a matter of fact, he says, it will not even defend itself against a man, though constantly persecuted because of its depredations. Its ravages in some parts of Patagonia are so great that the raising of horses is unprofitable, and Mr. Hudson gives many most extraordinary stories of this friendliness, related to him as facts of personal experience by the plainsmen of his country, whose word otherwise he always trusted. Nor is he alone. Every traveler in Patagonia makes similar assertions; and W. A. Perry,[129] whose excellent account of the animal's habits in Oregon and neighborhood is supplemented by many stories of personal adventure, describes how several cougars there have insisted upon an unpleasantly close but seemingly playful acquaintance with, rather than have made an attack upon, human beings. It is evident, at least, that the animal displays a very different disposition at one time or place than at another.

Cougar hunting is practicable only with the aid of hounds, and success depends upon their skill. A pack will embrace **Hunting** several more or less houndlike dogs whose busi-**the Puma.** ness it is to scent the trail of the puma, and follow it (and nothing else) until the beast is brought to bay, or, as is more likely, takes to the nearest tree. The superstitious antipathy and fear these big cats feel toward a dog is comical in its intensity. A mean little cur, all alone, is often sufficiently terrifying to send a puma in haste to climbing a tree maybe one hundred and fifty feet high. Having treed the cougar the dogs must announce it by barking, and keep it up until the hunter arrives. Good dogs have been known to sustain this noisy vigil for several hours, and to hold the quarry in place even all night. Meanwhile there have been trailing at the heels of the following hunter two or three other and probably heavier dogs, the fighters, whose business it is as soon as they hear the trailers barking "treed" to rush forward and take the brunt of the fighting, if any occurs. Often the cat makes no attempt to get away, but lets himself be shot in the tamest way. Again, he will bolt time after time, retreating from stronghold to stronghold, and fighting dogs and men resolutely.

The chase is likely to be exciting, and many thrilling narratives of it might be chosen from the literature of western sport, but none is so spirited and altogether admirable as that written by President Roosevelt [128] out of his own adventures in Colorado and elsewhere.

The puma is more widely known and familiar to us of the North, but at the head of the list in the South stands the jaguar, — the biggest, handsomest, and most formidable of American cats. Since it exactly takes the place in our tropical forests of the tiger of southern Asia, it is named "el tigre" throughout Spanish America, or "onça" (in Spanish, *onza*) among the Portuguese of Brazil. "Jaguar," "juarite," and the like are derived from Guaranese Indian words explained at length by Azara. But the term "tiger" is as carelessly wrong as is "lion" for the puma, since the jaguar is not striped but spotted, so that it closely resembles a leopard. It is also of about the same size, — 6 to $7\frac{1}{2}$ feet long from nose to tail-tip, and 150 to 175 pounds in weight, but has a bulkier body, bigger head, shorter and more massive limbs, and shorter tail; hence, while less active and supple, it is perhaps more powerful than the leopard, and certainly is stronger than the puma. The ground color varies from the yellowish gray seen in arid Paraguay to almost red in the steaming equatorial swamps, while in the lower Orinoco Valley deep brown and black ones are common; but there is only one species. The coat is everywhere spotted with black, not in the leopard's hollow rosettes,

Copyright, N. Y. Zoölogical Society.

Sanborn, Phot.

ONE OF THE JAGUARS IN THE NEW YORK ZOÖLOGICAL PARK.

but forming variable and irregular groups, each group always inclosing a black central spot.

The jaguar is most at home, perhaps, in the half-flooded forests of the Amazon and Orinoco basins, where it necessarily spends much of its time in trees; but it abounds in the open country south of Brazil, especially along the reedy margins of the rivers. Azara [131] treats the animal with great fullness of information, and says that it was so plentiful in the La Plata Valley when the Spaniards began settling there, that two thousand a year were killed. It ascends the eastern foothills of the Andes, is to be found northward throughout the warmer parts of Central America and Mexico into Texas, and once wandered eastward into the woodlands of Arkansas and Louisiana, but that was long ago. It is hard to see why it did not cross the Mississippi. Black jaguars are reputed to be much more savage than others, but this belief is not supported by facts; and Tschudi remarks that the Indians, at least those of Peru, think every black animal stronger or wickeder than light-colored ones.

All accounts agree that where other food is plentiful men have little reason to dread an unprovoked attack, and that near civilization the jaguar as a rule is shy and **Haunts and** timid. Nevertheless, a jaguar when hungry is not **Habits.** only likely to leap on any human being — who, to his mind, is, of course, only a sort of animal which is rather hard to understand, but is good to eat — falling in his way, but will sometimes haunt a traveling company for days. In this and in other traits, as well as in breeding habits, the jaguar resembles the cougar, which ranges over the same territory. The Indians told Wallace that when one was met on a lonely path, the only safe way was to keep a bold front; if a man turned to run, the jaguar was likely to jump on him. In the Amazonian wilderness these beasts have always been as much of a menace as are leopards in the interior of Africa. Early chronicles tell of places where the Indians made their huts in villages each surrounded by a high palisade as a defense against "tigres"; and Im Thurn [33] relates that even now the forest tribes in the interior of Guiana sleep in hammocks hung high enough above the ground to be out of reach of the jaguar's spring, and build fires around the trees to which the hammock ropes are tied. Innumerable instances of bold attacks on sleeping men, even when in closed huts or boats, occur in the older literature of our Tropics. Mission stations have had to be abandoned to escape inglorious martyrdom by both priests and converts.

The jaguar hunts the largest game of his country, — tapirs, deer, capybaras, and the manatee and cayman of the great water courses. Wherever domestic animals are reared it becomes a destructive pest. For the most part, however, these cats subsist on capybaras and other rodents; and in the North are special enemies of the peccaries, striking down stragglers and then hastening up a tree out of the way of the furious herd of sharp-toothed pigs brought together by the squealing of the first victim. When these have grown tired of besieging the lazy brute overhead, and have gone off, it descends and makes its meal. Rarely found away from water, which seems as necessary to it as to the tiger, and thronging along the great rivers, it is not surprising to find that in such places as the reedy borders of the La Plata fish form its main diet, snatched from the water by the paw. On the Amazon it feeds largely on turtles, which it turns on their backs and scoops out of their shells with a neatness which astonished Humboldt; then it digs up and feasts upon the eggs. It attacks the manatee in its own element, and has been seen "dragging out of the water this bulky animal, weighing as much as an ox." Even the crocodile and cayman are regularly preyed upon. Its fondness for monkeys is also well known, and it is hated and reviled by the monkeys with the same fury as leads the East Indian apes to chase and hurl sticks and bad language at the tiger. If the Brazilians may be believed, the jaguar takes advantage of this by tactics which so excite and infuriate the monkeys that they lose all sense of prudence, and then fall victims to panic; for this, probably, is all there is to the story of "fascination" by cat or snake.

Ordinarily jaguars are hunted with a pack of dogs which follow the trail and drive the animal into a tree, where it is **Hunting Jaguars.** likely to make a better fight than does the puma. Their silence in a battle, or when wounded, has often been remarked, although they are ordinarily rather a noisy animal. Nor when brought to bay do they, according to Porter, whose chapter [126] on these beasts is full of valuable details, "make use of those stratagems that tigers constantly, and lions frequently, adopt for the purpose of intimidating their assailants and causing them to retreat. It would appear that jaguars do not commonly make feigned assaults, but generally charge in earnest, with lightninglike rapidity and desperate determination." In *The Field* (London, Dec. 13, 1879) is described a Paraguayan method of pursuit which must have been very dangerous: —

"The hunter very often chose to go alone rather than with any companion — his dogs excepted; these he would throw into the covert where it was supposed there might be a tiger, while he himself waited in a more open part of the forest, in the direction in which the beast would probably make. His weapons were one or two lances with short, stout blades, a forked stick as thick as one's arm below the elbow, the foot about four to five feet long, and the branches two and a half each, and a large knife. The left arm was thickly wrapped in a poncho. When the tiger was started, the hunter followed him till brought to bay; and then kneeling on the right knee, and resting the end of the forked stick on the ground at his left foot, provoked a charge, which he received on the stick, at the same time stabbing the tiger with the lance in his right hand. I never actually saw a conflict of this sort, but have seen a tiger brought in dead by a man who had gone out a few hours before with no weapons but those described, and there was but one wound in the body, under the shoulder into the heart."

Hudson [35] says that the guachos of northern Argentina capture the jaguar with the lasso, and this strange weapon sometimes paralyzes the animal with perplexity and terror.

Tropical America possesses several small cats of unusual interest and many names. Thus the "tiger cat" of South America, the "manigordo" of Costa Rica, or the "ocelot" of Mexico is known to Texans as "leopard cat." From Oklahoma to southern Brazil it is always found in the woods, and especially in thickets. [167] It takes to the trees

Ocelot.

for safety and for most of its food, in getting which it is extremely active and bloodthirsty. Dr. Woodhouse wrote of it that in Texas it often carried off the game which a hunter shot before he had time to enter the thicket and pick it up. Even the Mexican cactus jungles have no terror for it; for ocelot-skins are sometimes found to be fairly lined with cactus prickles lying flat and apparently causing no annoyance. Dampier, speaking of the Spanish Main, records that: "Here are great numbers of them. . . . But I have wisht them farther off when I have met them in the Woods; be-

THE OCELOT, OR LEOPARD CAT.

cause their Aspect appears so very stately and fierce."

The ocelot is about two and one half feet long in body, stands tall, and has a tail about twelve inches long. The color is grayish, mostly marked with large and small black-edged, fawn-colored spots, tending to run into oval or linear figures; but individuals vary interminably. "As if not content with differing from its fellows," Elliot exclaims, with the impatience of a puzzled classifier, "an ocelot usually succeeds in exhibiting a distinct pattern on each of its sides!" But this irregularity makes the pelt, with its long, soft, pleasingly mottled fur, all the more desirable in the market, and vast numbers are annually collected by both red and white trappers. These cats are to be seen in most menageries, and have been kept in many a household as a family pet, but are of uncertain temper, and rather too fond of rough play; yet some have been thoroughly gentle.

Another beautifully and similarly striped and spotted forest cat is the margay (Guaranese, *mbaracaya*), likewise so variable in color and markings that half a dozen names have been given to its varieties — one is the "cauzel" of Costa Rica. It is rather smaller than the ocelot and seems to be exclusively nocturnal, and to feed mainly on birds, which, judging by the conduct of captives, are stripped of all their feathers before they are eaten. This tiger cat is rarely if ever domesticated. The same region gives us a third cat, Geoffroy's, colored like a leopard, and one of the handsomest of those depicted on Elliot's [134] sumptuous plates. Whether all these, the "ocelotlike" cat of Colombia, the "colocolo" of Guiana, and other American tiger cats, will not finally turn out to be merely varieties of one widespread and surprisingly variable species, remains to be determined. Much information is still needed here.

Margay.

More distinctive is the grass or pampas cat, or "pajero," familiar to the people of the open country between Brazil and the Straits of Magellan. It is rather more robust than a domestic Tom, and its color is predominantly gray, with a tan tinge and white whiskers, but no two are alike. Describing in *The Field* (London, 1897) one in his possession, W. Melville, an English resident near Buenos Ayres, gives the following facts: —

Pampas Cat.

"The tiger spots, just visible through the long fur on the sides, become beautifully mixed with stripes on the belly and legs; the tips of the ears are jet-black, and the tail very short and blunt. Few cats are ungainly walkers, yet the pajero does so with a very awkward roll, due to the phenomenal breadth of chest, causing the elbows to turn outward; the hindquarters have the appearance of being pinched; the fur is almost as long as that of the Persian on the back and sides, the head of the pajero having very much shorter fur, and the tail being less full. Few, indeed, are the animals in a wild state that are unable to make a proper toilet, yet I have frequently killed these cats with the long, fluffy hair matted and soiled on the back, the matted locks being full of dead hair."

As to habits, Azara mentions that it feeds mainly on guinea pigs, but Mr. Melville says that it preys upon the small tinamou, or "pampas partridge," striking a "round" blow; "for" as he explains, "it is one of the distinguishing features of this cat that it can bend its forepaws back almost level with its body, catching thus its prey with a similar action to a round-hand bowler delivering a ball on the cricket field, and does not pounce on its prey as does the tiger cat (margay) and the domestic species." It remains always on the ground. Hudson speaks of it as "inexpressibly savage" in disposition, but Melville's experience is that it is easily domesticated and makes a charming pet with all the manners and graces of Puss, except that it fails to mew, uttering only short, sharp, guttural sounds.

Two notable little cats remain to be mentioned, — the yaguarundi and the eyra. Both are entirely unspotted and have very long tails and round pupils. The yaguarundi, found in forests from Brazil and Peru to northern Mexico, where it is called "leoncillo," is about thirty inches long from snout to tail, while the tail adds twenty-five inches. It is very slender and short-legged, and varies in its uniform blackish gray hue (often reddish) according to the worn condition of the hair, for each hair is ringed alternately with black and gray. Another peculiarity is the pinched appearance of the nose. It lives mostly in trees, and is an expert bird catcher and chicken thief.

The eyra Mivart [135] declares "the most remarkable of all the cats from the extreme length of its body in comparison to that of its limbs — a condition which gives it somewhat the appearance of a large weasel." It inhabits all the American Tropics, northward to Texas, but is nowhere numerous. It is about the size of a house cat, has fur

Eyra.

of a soft chestnut hue with white whiskers and is nimble, quick, and exceedingly graceful both in climbing and when moving on the ground. Some captives have seemed untamable, while others were mild and playful; but none could be trusted with poultry. Azara had one which was fond of curling up on the skirts of any one's garments to sleep or to lie and purr like a happy old tabby. It is a question whether the eyra and yaguarundi are not varieties of the same species.

The Lion in Fact and Fable

Amenemhat I, one of the oldest and grandest of the kings of Egypt, 2000 years before Christ, thought it worth while to record imperishably: "I hunted the lion." That has been a proud boast among men of valor ever since. No animal since the beginning of the world has been so interesting to men generally, nor received more fearsome admiration. Its majestic pose when aroused, its terrifying roar, its power to harm, its apparent supremacy, gave it naturally the rank of king in the minds of a world which saw no reason why the animal tribes should not acknowledge a ruler as well as the tribes of men.

The ancient hunting of the lion must often have been a soul-stirring performance, — a hand-to-hand conflict calling for the best in nerve and muscle a man possessed. David's seizing one, and tearing its jaws asunder by main strength, was a deed matched later by one of his captains, Benaiah (2 Sam. xxiii. 20): "He cut down also and slew a lion in the midst of the pit in the time of snow"; and it won for him promotion to be chief of staff. These incidents can hardly have been great exaggerations of the encounters in which shepherds and hill men, from the Libyan desert to the plains of Persia, defended their flocks and themselves, when all depended on driving home a short pike. What marvels of courage and luck might be written, could the facts of any of a thousand such battles be recovered!

Pausanias tells us of a Greek athlete, Polydamas, who slew a lion at the foot of Mt. Olympus, although he was unarmed.

In the palmy days of the Roman Empire every prominent city had its corps of *bestiarii*, men whose business it was to fight wild beasts in the arena for the amusement of the crowd; but we have no information as to their methods. A Hamran Arab of western Abyssinia does not hesitate even now, when necessary, to face the lion on foot, armed only with a sword and small shield, and in that wonderfully interesting book "Wild Beasts and their Ways,"[147] Sir Samuel Baker describes how on one occasion one of his Arab hunters did precisely that, and saved the lives of both, for as this determined fellow marched slowly forward the lion, instead of rushing to attack, crept like a coward into impenetrable thorns, and was seen no more.

Such incidents give color to the contemptuous view which Livingstone and some others have taken of the lion, which they **Character.** brand as anything but noble — as an arrant coward, in truth. Livingstone writes that nothing he ever learned of the lion could lead him to attribute to this animal either the ferocious or the noble character so often ascribed to it; and tells us how hardly he tried, even with the aid of dogs, to persuade one he had chased into some reeds to come out and show itself — and be shot! The lion's refusal here seems not so much an evidence of poltroonery as of good sense, — that discretion permitted to the most valorous without stain on their reputations. Many a hunter has had an experience like that of R. Gordon Cumming, who, with mounted helpers and a pack of dogs, drove a lion for hours from shelter to shelter, along a river, before he succeeded in shooting it while the harried beast was trying to get away by swimming the broad stream. Cumming assures us, also, it was an animal in the prime of life, with a rank mane and a perfect set of teeth — "a thing which in lions of his age is rather unusual."

All this happened in the daytime, and hundreds of instances might be given of their being out and busily hunting in broad daylight. Among the imaginative absurdities which Buffon wove into what he supposed was a biography of this animal, and which still linger in popular books, was one that the lion's sight is poor, and that he is blinded by sunlight. A man who trusted to this for safety would be as insecure as one who rested upon the "power" of his own eye to outstare the big cat. No animal has its eyes better set for seeing what is going on than this one; and there is every evidence that its vision is both far-sighted and accurate in definition.

One is tempted to think the Lord must have watched over the noble missionary Livingstone, as He did over Daniel, when we read his assertion that he never felt the least alarm as to lions in either daylight or moonlight, for no one since has had such confidence. A. H. Neumann,[136] who had an astonishing hunting career among the game of central Africa in 1894–1895, tells us

BONES OF A LION'S TOE.
Showing the great tendon by which the claw is unsheathed and held down when used.

how he shot two lionesses at the carcasses of some zebras killed the day before. It was a hot sunny midday, and he had dreaded the task of taking off their hides. "But before skinning them," he writes, "I looked across the open plain below us; and there on the far side, skirting just inside the scattered bush, I saw a whole troop of lions, led by a grand old male, the rest either females or immature males, evidently coming from the zebra carcasses. I counted up to ten, and then before I had finished they got mixed up among the bushes; but I am certain there were at the very least (to be quite on the safe side) three more, which, with my two, would make fifteen all together."

This incident, confirmed by a vast experience elsewhere,

disposes of three old errors: First, that this beast always hunts alone, or at most in couples; second, that it does not go **Predatory** abroad by daylight; third, that it is too proud or fas- **Methods.** tidious to eat what it has not itself freshly killed. Incidentally it also implies the truth of the statement, of which direct evidence is difficult to obtain, that the lion is a polyga- mist — may consort with more than one lioness at a time; and it is probable that most troops of lions consist of members of a single family group of various ages. Frequently mates hunt together, having no cubs, or leaving them at home; and two or several males often join for work in concert. Lord Dela- mere met with several such instances in Somaliland.[151] One was a case of three, all with fine manes, leaping on a pony and its native rider. The rider escaped by a flying leap into a thorn bush, whereupon the lions knocked down and calmly ate the pony on the spot, regardless of other hunters near by, showing that the custom of dragging the quarry away and hiding it is by no means invariable. In fact, you never know what a lion will do. In the face of one, a gun is far better than a guidebook to its habits! The other was a case where Lord Delamere arranged to stop the depredations of a lioness which had been prowling near his camp, and would probably come back that night. His men constructed a little fort of thorns, tied a donkey near by as a bait, and Delamere, with a So- mali, lay down in it to watch for the animal. The marauder came but offered no shot, and Delamere presently fell asleep.

"It was a lovely night, but even by the brightest moonlight a lion is not a very easy thing to see. There was an open glade in front of the **Night** donkey, and at last, standing right out in the open, I saw two **Forays.** lions. . . . As I watched they suddenly started and came racing towards us side by side like two enormous dogs. When the lions got up to the donkey they did not seem to stop in their rush, but donkey and lions all went down in a crash together. How they actually knocked him over I did not see, as at the moment I drew back my head involuntarily, because, although we were absolutely safe inside a mass of mimosa thorns, the whole thing felt unpleasantly close. When I looked out again I could easily have touched one of the lions, which was standing with its forepaws on the donkey and its hindquarters within a few inches of our fence. The other lion was standing on the far side looking me straight in the face; but I am sure he could not see me, as the moon was right in his eyes, making them shine as if they were alight."

Brownell, Phot.

HIS MAJESTY, THE LION.

Both these prowlers were killed. Commenting on this and similar experiences, Lord Delamere says: —

" Night-shooting to my mind is a thing to be avoided, except now and then as an experience. It generally means a very disturbed night, especially if there are many hyenas about, and in the morning you are not fit for a hard day's work. Occasionally by bright moonlight it is very interesting, but if circumstances admit of lions being killed by day, it is rather like shooting a boar in a fine pig-sticking country to kill a lion over a bait at night. . . . I have never myself shot more than two lions in one night, but a man whom I met in the country showed me the skins of four he had shot when sitting up over the body of a dead elephant. It was very dark or he might have got any number." [151]

One of the statements often met with is that a lion is incapable of any considerable speed, and never chases prey which escapes his first rush. Baldwin is only one of many who have found that it may put a horse to his best paces to keep a lion who really wants a ride from climbing into the saddle by way of the crupper. Another hunter relates that he once saw a heavy lion which had failed to stalk successfully a black gnu chase it fifteen hundred yards, although it had had a long start, and fairly catch it. So the exceptions go; yet the rule is, that the great cat lies in wait by some drinking place, or rushes from a hiding in a thicket or on a rock whence it may spring far, or creeps through tall grass until near enough for the leap, the felling blow, and the clutch with talons and teeth, which at once drag down and tear apart the stricken quarry. It is at night that the most serious hunting is done. The dusk deepening on the veldt resounds with the roars of ravenous lions setting forth upon their forays, careless whether the game hear and take warning; and no ox or antelope, stately giraffe or timid gazelle, approaches its drinking place — especially when this is only some spring-fed basin in the plain — without a shrinking dread which nothing but thirst could overcome, for in every wind-stirred grass tuft he thinks he sees a lion's gathering spring, and each shadow takes the shape of this deadly terror of the night.

Another tradition is that a lion having chosen a mate keeps her as long as one or the other survives. How nearly true **Mating.** this is we do not know. In the first place, the choice seems to lie with the female rather than on the part of the male; and the continuance of the union appears to depend upon the power of the lion to hold his fickle spouse to her allegiance. At the mating season of the year the lioness is ready to flirt with every new male she sees — in truth does her best to attract attention. Should a wandering knight answer her roaring, and appear on the edge of the moonlit glade which serves as her boudoir, the lioness, purring a wanton welcome, creeps forward to meet him. But her mate, with burning eyes and lifted mane and lashing tail, bounds before her, and the air quakes with his indignant challenge. It may

After an etching by van Muyden.

LIONESS AND CUBS.

be sufficient, and the abashed intruder slink away; but if he does not, the forest soon trembles with the shock of such a duel as it would tax the epic pen of a Homer to depict: and the lithely crouching lioness watches the struggle in tense excitement, ready to glory in her lord if he win, or to fawn upon the stranger should he become conqueror.

To the frequency of such battles, in which young, weak or unfortunate males must often be killed, is supposed to be due the fact that in Africa, at least, females far outnumber the males. This is nature's merciless method of weeding out the worst and discovering and saving the best to become sires of a race which shall inherit, with each new generation, the qualities of the best of its kind. To this custom of courtship by battle is attributed, also, the growth of the protective mane which no doubt saves many a life in these combats, wherein nature must not permit *too* high a death rate. Any such inequality of numbers between the sexes as certainly exists, would naturally result in the polygamy alluded to, some lions, it has been stated, having as many as five wives. Much remains to be learned, however, in this direction; and it will probably be found, if it be possible to discover the truth at this late day, that polygamy is rather exceptional.

Leo's family home is in some dense thorn thicket, reed bed, or cavern, where in the spring from two to six whelps are born — usually four. He is reputed to be good to his family, bringing his mate food while she is kept at home in nursing her newly arrived babies, and defending his household from danger. Pleasant stories are related also of the mother's care for her mottled cubs; and when they get large enough to go abroad with her she guides and controls them. Thus she has been seen to compel them to stay back and keep quiet when she sights prey and wishes to stalk it; and so they see how the work is done. More often than in the case of other cats, apparently, the father lion leads the family hunt and strikes down the victim, his mate waiting near ready to lend a hand. Here, in the old books, would follow tales of "magnanimity," with moral reflections whose only defect lay in having no foundation in fact. Instead of standing back and politely allowing his "beloved" family to satisfy their hunger (and incidentally consume the tidbits) before him, an old lion will far more likely, as in the lionine family meal watched by Drummond,[144] crossly keep them away until he has eaten all he wants. Only then may the others approach to get what they can, leaving the bones to be cracked by hyenas and scraped by jackals — both of which are liable to be pounced on and devoured themselves. None sits at the first table in a lion's house unless he is as strong as the host.

The lion feeds on anything he can get. He has been starved out rather than killed out of Asia, and survives in Mesopotamia and eastern Persia mainly on the half-wild pigs and goats of the peasantry. In prehistoric days there were wild horses, asses, and camels to sustain him on the Asian steppes, as well as saigaks and similar game; and afterward he naturally became a scourge of the caravan roads. Increasing by their high birth rate more rapidly than any other beast of prey, only persistent resistance could keep down these ravagers; thus, when the Jews came back from their long captivity in Babylon they found Judea overrun with lions. Later, when Xerxes' hordes were moving through the mountainous country northwest of the Ægean Sea, on their way to overwhelm Greece, serious hindrance was caused by the attacks of lions on their camel trains. Buffon's assertion that in the Sahara a single lion would attack a whole caravan is not true, as a rule, if it ever happened — *there*. Lions are practically absent from the real desert, where there is little chance for food; and this is a point to be noticed in respect to the hasty conclusion that their dust-colored hide is a protective coloration with reference to a background of sand. Densely forested regions, such as certain areas of West Africa, are likewise without lions, which also in India have left the jungles to the tiger.

The grazers have everywhere been the lion's principal resource, but no wart hog, daman, or other small animal is refused when it comes handy; and any lion, apparently, will gorge carrion, even if full of maggots, or even when it is the carcass of another lion. Laziness is one of this beast's most prominent traits, and to this may be due his willingness to eat carrion, and also the fact that he rarely kills except for food, not manifesting that Berserker-like blood thirst which leads a puma, leopard, or weasel to slay uselessly when opportunity occurs. His apparent cowardice may often be really indolence.

The elephant, rhinoceros, and hippo are ordinarily safe from attack, more probably because of the difficulty and danger of overcoming them rather than from any sense of fear.

Courage.

Porter [126] quotes a narrative of a remarkable struggle with an Indian lion some fifty years ago, by two British sportsmen mounted on elephants, and aided by an army of beaters. The arrangements, in short, were the same as for a tiger hunt, and the lion carried out his part of the programme perfectly, charging again and again though badly wounded, repeatedly leaping upon the elephants and tearing them until they became nearly uncontrollable, killing a beater or two and endangering everybody, and making a splendid display of courage and endurance against fearful odds until the last. Here the fear was on the part of the elephants, which the lion attacked (as though his real enemies) without an instant's hesitation.

An African buffalo is more nearly a true match for a lion, as many a pair of skeletons mingled in the grass has attested — none more remarkably than in one case described by Cameron [145] near Lake Tanganyika: —

"During my rambles," he notes, "I noticed the remains of a lion, buffalo and crocodile, lying together in a heap, and was told . . . that when the buffalo came to drink the lion sprang upon him, and, both rolling into the water together, they were seized by a crocodile. He in his turn was dragged about twenty yards from the bank by the struggles of the two beasts, and then the trio perished in inextricable entanglement."

A single lion, indeed, will rarely attack a buffalo; and two or three together are sometimes beaten off. Nevertheless this great animal is so constantly assailed, that on every occasion when Drummond [144] saw lions hunting by daylight they were in pursuit of this game. This judicious observer considered the zebra the lion's favorite food, on account of the succulent fat in its body; but these wild horses are extremely cautious. Another reason for the preference is their small ability to defend themselves when caught, whereas several of the large antelopes

A STRUGGLE BETWEEN LIONS AND AN AFRICAN BUFFALO.

can fight off a lion or leopard as well as the buffalo, doing it, however, more after the manner of a swordsman. Schulz, whose book [152] is a storehouse of facts for the student of African zoölogy, notes that a lion does not dare attack such antelopes as the sable or roan in the usual manner, *i.e.* from behind, for with their backward-sweeping, scimiterlike horns they would transfix him the instant he alighted on their haunches. But even seizing by the nose becomes perilous in the case of so well armed a species as the gemsbok, or any oryx, which, Schulz asserts, with its straight horns capable of acting both behind and before, coupled to its heroic spirit, is the most formidable animal the lion can attack.

How do the human tenants of his realm get on with this terrible neighbor? The beast everywhere disappears before

Lion and Man. determined and well-armed opposition, but otherwise humanity simply becomes a part of its food resources. When in the flourishing period of Rome the colonists in North Africa were forbidden to kill lions because hundreds must be captured alive annually for the Imperial circus games, they became at last such an unendurable scourge to agriculture and travel that the Emperor Honorius was obliged to choose between his playthings and the lives of his taxpayers, and allow the former to be killed off. Were the African negroes the pusillanimous creatures that many East Indians are, their continent would be practically uninhabitable, but most Africans are brave folk, and are little hindered by a craven beast worship, such as shields the tiger in many parts of India. The nearest approach to that is hinted at in a remarkable yarn told to Cameron [145] by one of his men in Kasongaland, southwest of Lake Tanganyika.

"In the village next to that in which he [Cameron's informant] lived the people were on most friendly terms with the lions, which used to walk in and about the village, without attempting to injure any one. On great occasions they were treated to honey, goats, sheep, and ugali, and sometimes at these afternoon drums as many as two hundred lions assembled. Each lion was known to the people by name, and to these they responded when called. And when one died the inhabitants of the village mourned for him as for one of themselves."

Many apparently honest natives vouched for the truth of this as eyewitnesses, but Cameron tells us to judge of it for ourselves. At any rate, such a sentiment is not widespread. As a rule the negroes fear lions little in the daytime, but where they are numerous guard their encampments carefully at night against them and the equally dreaded leopards. While some tribes will suffer long-continued raids upon their cattle, or even repeated losses of women and children, others instantly proceed against the marauder, for they know when one of these great cats has learned that it is easy to seize a man or a bullock it will continue to do so, and that it is quite as likely to be young and vigorous as aged and decrepit. The Buffonian fallacy that the nobility of the lion forbids him to attack anything but wild big game, "worthy of his steel," was long ago discredited by awful experience.

Even before the days of guns, a party of bold hunters would track him to his lair, and kill him with arrows and assegais, or would catch him in a pitfall and smother him to Savage death with smoke. Andersson describes how non- Lion Hunts. chalantly half a dozen Damaras near Walfisch Bay hastened into the brush at midnight to drive a lion from a zebra he had been heard to strike down, and stayed to cut it up and carry it away, although the angry beast was marching up and down so near that they hurled firebrands at him now and then to warn him off. Andersson adds that he knew of bands which subsisted largely by watching beside water-holes where lions came nightly to feed, and then driving the lions away from their well-earned quarry.

In some tribes, as the Zulus, an army would be ordered out by a chief to surround a man-eater as soon as he became troublesome; and then would be seen a grand display of savage war-fare, in which the enemy's magnificence of rage and power against overwhelming odds would surpass anything imagined of him. Drummond draws a thrilling picture of such a com-bat, and Freeman, Baker, and others confirm its truth.

Some of these animals show amazing boldness in their noctur-nal forays. The story of the lion which leaped upon Gordon Cumming's [142] party, and seized one of two men sleeping under the same blanket beside the fire, is familiar to all readers of adventure tales. The history of frontier Africa abounds in similar bloody incidents, and makes it plain that at times noth-

THE KING RESTS.

ing daunts the great beast. Gibbons, for example, says that a lion gnawed through a palisade of stakes of the thickness of a man's arm to get at cattle and human beings in a kraal he visited. Nevertheless the strength, though astonishing, has been overstated. One is certainly able to drag away into the bushes the carcass of a big buffalo; but Baker, one of the sanest and best-informed of men, refuses assent to the stories of lions leaping high fences with buffaloes in their jaws; or that they could even carry anything approach-ing its weight. The Tsavo lions, described below, jumped no fences with their victims, but dragged them through the hedges; but one was known to take away three full-grown goats and a two-hundred-and-fifty-pound iron rail to which they were tied.

Man-eaters have never been so numerous in Africa as in the

East, yet every district has tales of such pests. The most striking is that of the two lions which for three weeks, as the culmination of a long period of terror, "held up" the Uganda railway, then (1898) building across the valley of the Athi River in British East Africa. Encamped at a point named Tsavo was a construction force of several hundred East Indian coolies and workmen, besides many negro helpers and camp followers, superintended by an English engineer and army officer, Colonel J. H. Patterson and some assistants — the former a man of heroic mold, as so many of his countrymen in similar positions have proved themselves to be!

The very first night of the encampment "one or two coolies disappeared," no one knew exactly how; but soon after a powerful Sikh foreman was dragged from his tent in the midst of the camp by a **Tsavo** lion, taken into the bush and eaten. That night Colonel Patter- **Lions.** son sat up in a tree near the jemadar's tent and listened to the screams which told that another man had been snatched from sleep and life in a more distant part of the scattered camp. To hunt the animals by day in the jungle was utterly futile. . . . Colonel Patterson and the station doctor built a thorn fence around their tent, but had little confidence in it; and, as the former remarks in a detailed account of the affair in *The Field* (London, Feb. 17 and 24, 1900), "it was jumpy work to sit reading or writing there after dark, as we never knew but that a lion might spring over the boma and be on us."

In spite of concentrating the camps, keeping fires and watchers, every second or third night a man was taken, several times from the hospital. Continual efforts to see and shoot the man-eaters met with failure, and proved exceedingly dangerous. One night the Colonel and another man placed themselves inside a freight car standing on the track and waited, only to be surprised by a lion leaping at the door and falling back from the blaze of guns in his face after he had alighted on the floor of the car. Other sportsmen came to camp and sat up with guns at various likely places over night, laid traps and tracked the brutes by daylight, but got neither of them, for it was now well ascertained that there were two working in company; and the murders continued.

Then came an unaccountable quiet, and after six months of peace every one believed the danger passed, when suddenly the man-eaters reappeared, and night after night the former dreadful scenes were reënacted. The lions grew so bold as to be indifferent to shots, firebrands, or noise, sometimes calmly devouring their victims almost on the spot where they were seized. "I have," says Colonel Patterson, "a vivid recollection of one particular night when they took a man from the railway station and brought him close to my camp to eat. I could distinctly hear them crunching the bones and purring like cats over the meal. . . . I have experienced nothing more nerve-shaking than to listen, after darkness had closed in, to the deep roars of these monsters growing gradually nearer and nearer, and to know that one or the other of us had to be their victim before the morning dawned." The men took to sleeping on top of buildings, water tanks, trees, and in like places, yet some one was taken nightly; many ran away, even seizing trains by which to escape; all construction of the railroad ceased, and the great Lord Salisbury informed Parliament (in effect) that the British lion was no match for two African ones. This state of siege continued for weeks, but at last the persistent and plucky efforts of the superintendent were rewarded.

"My continued ill luck was most exasperating. The Indians were, of course, further confirmed in their belief about a devil, and, indeed, the lions seemed to bear a charmed life. . . . I tried to track the beast I felt sure I had wounded, but could not keep on the trail; there was no blood on the rocks to give a clew which way he had gone. I returned to look at the dead donkey, which I found slightly eaten at the quarters. Lions always begin at the tail of an animal and eat up toward the head. It was practically certain that one or other of the lions would return at night to finish the meal. There was no tree of any size near, so within ten yards of the dead donkey I made a staging about twelve feet high of four poles, with their ends fixed in the ground. They inclined toward each other at the top, where a plank was lashed for me to sit on.

"At sundown I got on the machan. Much to the disgust of my gun-bearer I went alone. I would have taken him, only he had a cough, and I feared lest any noise or movement should spoil all. Darkness fell almost immediately. The silence of an African jungle about this time is most impressive, especially when one is alone and isolated from his kind, for man has retired, and the wild denizens of the woods have not yet raised their cry. I was startled out of the reverie I had fallen into by the snapping of a twig, and, straining my ears, I heard the rustling as of a large body forcing his way through the bushes. 'The lions,' I whispered to myself, and my heart gave a great bound. 'Surely, to-night my luck will change, and I shall bag one of the monsters.' Such were my thoughts during the stillness that had again fallen. I sat like a statue and waited. Soon all doubt as to the presence of the lions was dispelled. A deep, long-drawn sigh (sure sign of hunger in a lion) came up from the bushes, and again the rustling commenced as they advanced. A sudden stop, followed by an angry growl, told that one of them had spied me, and I began to think disappointment awaited me once more. However, matters took another turn, and the lions began to stalk me. For about two hours they horrified me by slowly creeping round and round my machan, gradually drawing closer. I feared they would rush it, and if one of the rather flimsy poles broke, or if they could spring twelve feet — ugh! the thought was not a pleasant one. I began to feel distinctly creepy, and heartily cursed my folly for placing myself in such a position.

"I kept perfectly still, hardly daring even to blink my eyes. Down below I could but faintly make out the body of the donkey. Imagine what I felt like when, after a continued strain like this, something came flop and hit me on the back of the head. I was thoroughly terrified for a moment, and almost fell off the plank. I thought it was one of the lions that had sprung at me from behind. A moment afterward I knew I had been struck by an owl, which, no doubt, had taken me for a branch of a tree — not a very alarming thing to happen, I admit, but, coming at the time it did, it almost paralyzed me. I was not kept long in suspense after this. One of the lions crept up to the donkey; I could just make out his form as he crouched among the whitish yellow undergrowth; still, I saw enough. I took careful aim as near as I could in the direction of his heart, and as he wrenched off his first mouthful I fired. A bound and a roar told me he was hit. His bound had taken him out of sight, but he was evidently badly wounded, as he did not go far, and I emptied my magazine in the direction from which his dying roars came. In a few moments his last groan had rattled in his throat, and I knew that one of the 'devils' was dead."

It was not until some weeks later, however, that the second man-eater succumbed, after giving Mr. Patterson an even more thrilling experience, and work could be safely resumed. It would be difficult to find a more exciting episode in all the romantic history of railway building.

The lion, like the other great cats, is a relic of a diminishing race and dominion. In the early Stone Age the "cave" lion roamed throughout the southern half of Europe; and it is believed that along the Mediterranean, at least, its extinction was due to prehistoric man. The battle has gone on ever since. Long ago lions were exterminated from Afghanistan, Beluchistan, and northern Persia. A century ago they were more **Indian Lions.** or less prevalent in northwestern India, but now none remain save a few in the Gheer, a wooded hilly tract of Kattiawar, where they are "to some extent preserved by the Nawabs of Joonaghoor." [214] In Persia they survive only in Farsistan, where the marshes about Niris Lake afford shelter, and the hosts of pigs feeding on the acorns of the oak forests furnish subsistence. Similar conditions enable a few lions to maintain themselves along the lower Euphrates and Tigris; but they were long ago exterminated from all Asia Minor, Syria, Arabia, Egypt, and Algeria. From Abyssinia, and the southern Sahara southward to the Orange River, lions still exist except in the most populous districts, and in some places are very numerous. Very few skins now reach the London fur-market, where good specimens, suitable for rugs, brought in 1905 from $500 to $1000.

There seems never to have been more than one species, nor, in spite of the former belief in the "maneless lions of Guzerat" and the "black-maned" ones of other places, is any variety well localized. Lions with full manes have been shot in India, as well as those with hardly any; and "out of fifty male lion-skins scarcely two will be found alike in color and length of mane." So says Selous, in whose books [150] will be found more that is worth reading about this beast than anywhere else.

A lion of large size measures about nine and a half feet from the nose to the tip of the tail, which is about three feet long; stands three and a half feet high at the shoulders; and weighs about five hundred pounds. Most specimens, however, fall far short of these figures; and the largest examples have come from South Africa. The uniform pale tawny or yellowish gray of its coat is both adaptive to the animal's customary surroundings and a mark of the antiquity of its race, for the spots which reappear in each young kitten are regarded as outgrown markings, as in the case of the puma and other concolorous cats. A completely black lion has not, so far as I know, been recorded; but now and then very dark ones are seen, from perhaps the same litter with almost silver-white ones; and more frequently the mane is darker than the coat, or is diversified with blackish patches. The lioness is somewhat smaller than her mate and has no mane, nor have the young males. It is recorded that hybrids were produced between a lion and a tiger in England in 1827, and the skin of what is believed to be one of this mongrel litter is preserved in Salisbury museum, and resembles a leopard inclined to be striped. Similar crosses have taken place recently in the Hagenbeck menagerie near Hamburg.[248]

Tiger and Leopard and Leopard Cats

Though so different in outward appearance, the gaudily uniformed tiger and khaki-dressed lion have many points in common. It would require an expert to tell their skeletons apart, except by comparison of skulls. The size and weight of average examples are about the same, only the very largest males exceeding six and a half feet in length, measured from the nose to the root of the tail in a straight line; the tail, which tapers to a point, adding about three feet. Females are always twelve or fifteen inches shorter than males.

The present distribution of the species is curiously broken. It is to be found in the mountains and swamps around the southern end of the Caspian Sea, but not in Persia generally, nor in central Asia, nor the lower Indus Valley; but it inhabits the Elburz range of northern Persia, and thence ranges eastward throughout southern Siberia, Mongolia, northern Manchuria, Sakhalin, and Yesso; and formerly, as is shown by fossil remains, the species ranged northward of the Arctic Circle. From Mongolia the tiger range extends southward through China and the Siamese and Malay Peninsula to Java, but not to Borneo. Westwardly it passes around the Bay of Bengal, and extends over all India except the barren northwest; but the tiger has never crossed to Ceylon, though quite able to pass along a train of connecting islands. This circumstance, and its absence from Borneo, lend force to Blanford's theory that this animal is a comparatively recent immigrant from the north into southern India and the Malay islands. This distribution also shows that the tiger is a creature of the mountains and forests rather than of open plains, and is used to a cold climate; in fact, it is far more worried by heat than is its African brother, and loves to wallow in cool, shallow water.

Copyright, N. Y. Zoölogical Society.   Sanborn, Phot.

A RAJAH OF THE JUNGLES.

The habits of the tiger — its nocturnal hunting, its prey, its family life, its behavior when attacked and relation to mankind **Haunts and Habits.** — are practically those of the lion. Both cats are accustomed to their own narrow, almost undisputed way, are moved to exertion mainly by hunger and jealousy, are suspicious of everything strange and inclined to fear whatever they do not understand, are capable of terrific force, yet are dull save in the line of their predatory instincts, and change from timidity to reckless bravado with season, mood, and in-dividual temperament. The tigers of India and the Malayan countries, at least, have furnished material for a large library of books written by men who have studied their subject with close observation along the ridge of a rifle barrel, as well as by more scientific persons. Sir Joseph Fayrer devoted a whole volume [154] to this animal; the general writers, Jerdon, Sterndale, Blanford, Lydekker, and other Asiatic specialists, give it much space in their faunal zoölogies; and it is the star subject in those many admirable books by Anglo-Indian sportsmen which form so valuable a part of the literature of natural history. Fore-most among these men are Cumming, Campbell, Bevan, Shakspear, Baker, Inglis, Pollok, Rice, Leveson, Brown, Kinloch, Sanderson, Macintyre, Barras, Forsyth, and Whitney, all of whom must be read if one is to become really ac-quainted with the large animals of the East. This mass of material compasses a circle of information as to tigers equaled in the case of few other animals; and it would be hard to find in it a statement by one man that the tiger "never is" or "never does" thus and so, which is not met by a positive statement by another equally credible witness that he has *seen* the animal doing that very thing. We must conclude, then, as we did with regard to the lion, that it is unsafe to predict anything precisely as to its behavior; and that tigers differ in characteristics and qualities, quickly adapting their tactics to circumstances.

The relation between the people of the Orient and the tiger is very different from that between the Africans and their lions. In the first place, the former is a far more formidable and dangerous animal, take him "by and large," than the lion, — more quick, powerful, sly, subtle, and cunning. It is the opinion of the most experienced hunters that no man, however well trained and modernly armed, is a match for a tiger on foot. Certain bold hill tribes used, it is true, to surround a trouble-some tiger with strong nets, and then spear him to death through their meshes; but no such feats of single-handed conquering as abound in the history of the lion can be undertaken here. The nearest to it that is known to me is Basil Hall's [168] description of an arena show at an Indian Rajah's court, in which a Hindoo armed only with a Goorkha's knife met a tiger, cleverly avoided its spring, hamstrung it as it passed, and then delivered a second stroke quickly enough to cut through the animal's spinal cord and kill it. The Goorkhas do sometimes kill wild tigers with their celebrated knives, — or used to; but they are hardy fellows of the mountains. Most of the Hindoos and Malays meekly accept the tiger as an evil to be endured, and in this mood have lifted it, with superstitious terror and reverence, into a sort of malignant deity, which must and may be pacified. "You can be shown to-day," remarks J. L. Kipling, "forest shrines and saintly tombs where the tiger comes nightly to keep pious guard, and you may hear in any Hindoo village of jogis to whom the cruel beasts are as lapdogs." One of the difficulties which British officers have encountered in certain parts of India, in their attempts to kill off the cattle-lifting or man-eating tigers of some dangerously infested neighborhood, or to have sport with them, is the opposition of the people to their destruction. A comical illustration of this is given in the century-old, but ever interesting, book of the "Old Forest Ranger" (Colonel R. Baigrie), the scene of the incident being not far from Bombay: —

Supersti-tions.

"While sitting at breakfast we were alarmed by hearing cries of distress proceeding from the jagheerdar's hut, and on running out to ascertain the cause, we found old Kamah in a furious state of excitement, his left hand firmly fixed in the woolly pate of the hopeful scion of the house, and belaboring him stoutly with a stout bamboo. We inquired what crime young Moideen had been guilty of to bring upon him such a storm of parental indignation, and learned to our astonishment that it was all owing to his having killed a tiger! One of his father's tame buffaloes having been killed by a tiger on the previous day, the young savage had watched for him during the night, and shot him from a tree when he returned to feed upon the carcass. This most people would have considered a very gallant and meritorious exploit on the part of a lad of fifteen, but the old forester was of a different opinion.

"'It was all very well,' he said, 'for us who lived in the open country to wage war with tigers, but with him, who lived on sociable terms with them, in the jungle, the case was different. I have no quarrel with tigers! I never injured one of them, they never injured me; and while there was peace between us, I went among them without fear of danger. But now that this young rascal has picked a quarrel, and commenced hostilities, there is no saying where the thing will end!'"

Perhaps, after all, the most typical of all the Felidæ, as it is the most widely distributed, is the beautiful leopard or panther — an "all-round cat." Anciently it was to be found all over Africa and Arabia, eastward to Japan,

Leopard.

and southward as far as Ceylon, Java, and Borneo; but, unless we regard the ounce as a mere variety, the species does not range north of the Sahara, Turkestan, or the Himalayan foot-hills except in northern China. Bones indistinguishable from those of the modern leopard are exhumed, however, from the caves and superficial deposits of southern Europe, even as far west as England. In such a vast range highly diverse climates and conditions must be met, and we should expect to find as we do, much variety within the species.

In size, the differences are so great, that "while in the smallest examples the total length of the head, body, and tail does not exceed five feet, in the largest it reaches to as much as eight feet." The biggest known have come from eastern Siberia. The tail is usually about as long as the body, but varies greatly in relative length. The ground color in general is yellowish-fawn, deepening in some examples to red or to a rich nut-brown, and light-ening into pure white on the throat and abdomen, profusely spotted. The spots take the form of rosettes or incomplete rings of black, inclosing an area without any central spot, which may or may not be darker than the ground tint; on the flanks, lower legs, and tail, the spots are smaller and mainly solid, and toward the end of the tail they become rings. Local influences vary this typical pattern. Thus the skins of African leopards may always be distinguished from Asiatic skins by their smaller and more solid spots; further, the leopards from peninsular India are less richly colored than are those inhabiting the damp forests about the Bay of Bengal. Albinos are almost unknown, but black leopards are common in the tropical East, and one or two may be born in a litter otherwise normal. These are reputed to be extremely savage — a reputation justified by their behavior in menageries; and this disposition may be due to a sense that they are more conspicuous than they should be. No black leopards have been found in Africa, but a dark local race frequents certain hills near the Cape.

The leopard is a far lighter, more active and agile animal than either the lion or the tiger, and is sly and cautious withal, **Reputation.** so that it is doubtless responsible for a large part of the wickedness laid at the doors of its bigger brethren. Hundreds of wild adventures with leopards may be read in the books of the sportsmen already referred to; and Sanderson has full support for his assertion that "although its powers of offense are inferior to those of the tiger, it is in some respects a more dangerous animal as it is roused by less provocation, and is more courageous in attacking those who disturb its repose. The favorite haunts of leopards are rocky, brushy hills with holes suitable for a den, where they may watch the surrounding country, and at sunset descend with astonishing celerity and stealth to cut off any straggling animal returning to the village at nightfall. They prey boldly on the small Hindoo cattle and ponies, but more habitually on the sheep, goats, and dogs, and now and then (but rarely) turn man-eaters. Forsyth sketches at length a famous leopard in northern India which killed nearly one hundred persons before he was got rid of, and similar African cases are on record.

The leopard cannot overcome, ordinarily, animals as large as the lion and tiger slay, but everything of lesser size is acceptable, down to robbing birds' nests and clawing grubs out of rotten wood. Carrion is eaten, and this makes even a scratch from a leopard's teeth or claws very dangerous. Birds, both in trees and on the ground, are struck down, and peafowl, crows, and the like break into noisy clamor the instant the enemy is caught sight of; there is nothing monkeys justly hate and fear so much, and swear at so volubly. Of the smaller animals the forest pigs probably contribute most to "spot's" bill of fare. The old boars alone feel safe, for even a hungry tiger hesitates to tackle *them;* and in one case of such an attempt, witnessed by Gen. Douglas Hamilton, he came off rather the worse. Usually the leopard's "harsh, measured, coughing" roar is heard in the early evening, when it sets out upon its foray after lying asleep at home all day; but such habits are by no means the same everywhere, nor invariable in any individual.

Copyright, N. Y. Zoölogical Society.   Sanborn, Phot.

AN INDIAN LEOPARD.

The notorious fondness of the leopard for dogs is one of its specialties, and, like many other points in its character, reminds one of the jaguar, which, in fact, is probably descended from the same stock. It is not uncommon in India for dogs to be carried off from public places, sometimes where the presence of a beast of prey is unsuspected.

So closely allied to the leopard that one suspects it must be substantially the same animal, which has adapted itself to life in a very cold country, is the snow leopard, or "ounce," long known from the beautiful skins brought to market

from the high interior of central Asia. It inhabits the
plateaus and mountains of Tibet and Mongolia, keeping
Ounce. near the snow, whose retreat it follows in summer to
the height of eighteen thousand feet or more in pursuit of the game, so that it is not surprising to find it clothed
in a long, dense, woolly coat very light gray in color above and
pure white on the under parts.

The markings are leopardlike blackish rosettes, most of them filled
with a dusky tint and becoming black circles on the long heavy tail. The

Copyright, N. Y. Zoölogical Society. Sanborn, Phot.

THE SNOW LEOPARD, OR OUNCE.

result is a pelt of peculiar beauty and market value. The legs are short,
and the fore ones have the massive strength needed by such a climber and
hunter of powerful game. The ounce is rarely seen, though numerous, at
least in the northwestern Himalaya, for it goes abroad mainly at night, and
is timid. It preys upon wild sheep and goats, musk deer and mountain
marmots; and in winter seizes the smaller domestic animals of the villagers,
but avoids man. Of the few brought to Europe, one lived for a few
months in 1894 in the London "Zoo," and was perfectly gentle. The
example photographed above was captured in northern Thibet; and received at the New York Zoölogical Park in October, 1903.

Captain Baldwin, in his book on the large game of Bengal, has a most interesting chapter on the ounce, and relates how a fine old snow leopard, believed to be the mother of a cub which he captured but did not succeed in saving, was killed by one of the party of Tibetans in a curious and unexpected way. It was seen at a little distance, basking on a ledge of rock at the mouth of its den, and apparently asleep, when the Tibetan, looking over upon it from above, dropped a large stone with such precision that it struck the sleeping animal in the middle of the back and broke its spine.[140]

Still farther from the true leopard in markings, though approaching it in size, is the clouded leopard, or "tree tiger" of the Malays, found from Bhutan down through Assam, Burma, and the Malay Peninsula to Borneo and Formosa. It is nowhere numerous, and passes the whole of its **Clouded** time in trees, sleeping there by hanging across a thick **Leopard.** crotch, and catching birds, monkeys, and other small animals for food. It lingers about villages and raids the native poultry, but otherwise is regarded as harmless, despite the fact that its canines are longer and sharper than those of any other cat. Captive specimens are usually gentle and playful, twisting and turning somersaults about their cages like huge squirrels. Its beautiful buffy coat is thickly spotted and streaked with black, often running into long, irregular, winding patches. Almost exact miniatures of it are the marbled cat of the same region and the Tibetan cat; and here, too, should be mentioned the golden cat, the fishing cat, and the leopard cat.

The first-named is probably the handsomest cat in existence — a pale, golden chestnut in color, becoming bay along the back; the throat and under parts are white, while the face is strikingly ornamented **Golden** with stripes of black, white, and orange. It is known in all **Cat.** the eastern Himalaya, and thence down the mountain ranges of the Malay Peninsula; and it is believed that from it has been derived that most extraordinary of domestic cats, — the Siamese, formerly reserved for royal laps and cushions alone, and still uncommon and precious. It is uniformly tawny in color, with dark muzzle, under parts and limbs, and has short legs and blue eyes. The flat-headed cat (*Felis planiceps*) is another Malayan species of uniform coloration, which may have had a share in the ancestry of these favored pets.

The fishing or viverrine cat is a long-bodied, short-limbed, rather large species, striped and spotted in lines somewhat like a civet, which occurs wherever there are watery swamps from Nepal to China, and in Ceylon, but not in the Malayan **Fishing** islands. It is said to feed on fish, and on the **Cat.** snails and fresh-water mussels, but no one knows just how the fish are obtained. It also catches birds, lizards, and snakes, and comes out of its jungle now and then to terrorize the neighborhood by carrying off not only sheep, calves, and dogs, but pickaninnies that have been left unguarded — even breaking into huts to do so. Everybody credits it with willingness and ability to whip its weight (and more) in any sort of wild-cats you can bring. It will attack a man on sight if he is in its road to liberty, or if it happens to feel like it; and one which Blyth tried to keep broke through a partition the very first night and killed a leopard double its size in the next room. One hesitates to believe that a cat which makes its part of the jungle as interesting for its enemies as that one takes any large part of its daily bread in the form of fishes and snails.

The leopard cat, or Bengal cat, is a much smaller species, which avoids the swamps and keeps to the forested hills, and **Bengal** is to be met with as far east as the Philippines. It **Cat.** is only about two feet long, with another foot of tail length; and is so precisely like a little leopard in appearance that it is frequently mistaken for a young one. It, also, is noted for boldness and savagery, and though often trapped can rarely be brought, even as a kitten, into friendly relations with its keeper. Finally, India and Ceylon have the little "rusty" cat, — smallest of its tribe, — which is usually yellowish red but often gray, with stripes on the face and black spots elsewhere, except on the tail. It lurks mainly in **Rusty Cat.** tall grass and thickets, and is one of the quickest creatures on earth. Dr. Jerdon [187] relates an incident illustrating its instinctive recognition of prey and intuitive knowledge of what to do — and lose no time about it.

"I had a kitten brought to me very young . . . and it became quite tame and was the admiration of all who saw it. Its activity was quite marvelous and it was very playful and elegant in its motions. When it was about eight months old I introduced it into a room where there was a small fawn of the gazelle, and the little creature flew at it the moment it saw it, seized it by the nape, and was with difficulty taken off. . . . It would occasionally find its way to the rafters of bungalows and hunt for squirrels. Sir W. Elliot notices that he has seen several undoubted hybrids between this and the domestic cat, and I have also observed the same."

Leaving Asia for the present, let us turn to Africa and speak first of the big serval, which is met with throughout that continent, yet whose habits are little known. Its body may measure thirty-eight inches, and the tail add sixteen inches more; and it stands on long legs and wears a black-spotted coat of no particular color or value. Nevertheless, as the fur is long and soft it is a good deal used by furriers, and wholly black skins frequently come to market, as is the case with most cats. Africa has some other cats of her own of which we know little, and a few which she shares with Asia or Europe, and these last form a connected group of historical interest.

Puss and her Ancestors

If you were to go into that magnificent storehouse of Egyptian antiquities at Boulak, near Cairo, you would see rows of skillfully wrapped mummies of cats and of the richly adorned cases in which many of them had been laid to rest with pious care. One may imagine the pain and dismay with which any of their former mistresses would view them here, **Veneration for Cats.** set up as "objects of interest" for idle and irreverent eyes, for these were beloved companions or revered pensioners of the days of the early Pharaohs. Read Miss Agnes Repplier's [138] account of them: —

"However mysterious and informal may have been her birth, Pussy's first appearance in veracious history is a splendid one. More than three thousand years ago she dwelt serenely by the Nile, and the great nation of antiquity paid her respectful homage. Sleek and beautiful, she drowsed in the shadow of mighty temples, or sat blinking and washing her face with contemptuous disregard alike of priest and people. There is no mention of her in Holy Writ; but when Moses led the Children of Israel into the desert, she watched him go —

'With somber sea-green gaze inscrutable.'

Deserts, indeed, offered scant allurement to her. No wandering people have ever enjoyed her sweet companionship. The Arabs loved and valued her; but could do no more than carry her across the trackless sands for the enrichment of softer homes than their black tents could offer.

'And the bubbling camels beside the load
Sprawled for a furlong adown the road;
And the Persian pussy cats, brought for sale,
Spat at the dogs from the camel-bale.'

"Egypt, as the granary of the ancient world, had especial need for Pussy's services, and the Egyptian cat was a mighty hunter,

A CAT MUMMY AND ITS CASE.

" I was a little Egyptian cat,
    Meouw, Meouw, Meouw !
I lived in King Pharaoh's palace, I did.
The rats and the mice, I would chase with delight;
I often caught birds, which I know wasn't right;
And, instead of a fence, I would sit up all night
And *meouw* on the top of the Pyramid.

" But one day I was greedy and ate seven mice,
    Meouw, Meouw, Meouw !
So I had a bad fit, and I died, I did!
Then they hurried and made me this beautiful case,
It covers me all, just excepting my face,
And they put me away in a nice quiet place,
On a shelf right inside of the Pyramid.

" And there have I been for these thousands of years,
    Meouw, Meouw, Meouw !
And I hoped to lie hidden forever, I did.
But they hunted me out and they brought me away, —
Oh, isn't it horrid that I have to stay
In a dusty museum here day after day,
When I want to go back to my Pyramid !
    Meouw, Meouw, Meouw !"

not only of rats and mice, — ancestral prey, — but of wildfowl caught in reedy marshes, and in shallow waters where she could swim with ease. Her sacred character was in no wise impaired by her usefulness. She was the favorite of Pasht, who, in smiling mood, had given her to the world; and the deep veneration in which she was held provoked biting jests from travelers, who then, as now, lacked sympathy for strange customs and strange gods. . . .

"The exact era of Pussy's domestication in Egypt is lost in the dawn of history. It was so very long ago that our minds grow dizzy contemplating the vast stretch of centuries. A tablet in the Berlin Museum, which has on it a representation of a cat, dates from 1600 B.C.; and another, two hundred years older, bears an inscription containing the word *maū*, or 'cat.' The temples of Bubastis, of Beni Hasan, and of Heliopolis were the most sacred haunts of this most sacred animal. There, petted, pampered, wrapped in silken ease, and, above all, treated with that delicate reverence she is so quick to understand and appreciate, she lived her allotted lives; and there, when all nine were well spent, her little corpse was lovingly embalmed, and buried in a gilded mummy case with dignified and appropriate ceremonial. . . .

"The great burying grounds of favored Egyptian cats were the thrice-blessed fields of Speos Artemidos near the tombs of Beni Hasan, where thousands of little mummies reposed for centuries. It was reserved for our rude age to desecrate their graves, to fling their ashes to the four winds of heaven, or, with base utilitarianism, to sell the poor little swathed and withered bodies — once so beautiful and gently tended — for any trifling sum they would bring from ribald tourists who infest the land. Many were used even as fertilizers of the ancient soil — a more honorable fate, and one which consigned them gently to oblivion."

Now who or what was this little Egyptian cat, so respected and loved and made immortal? History does not record its paternity, nor legend throw light upon its origin and kindred. But the mummy has revealed the secret. When, moved by curious interest, you ascend the Nile to Beni Hasan, and bend your steps to the pit tombs of the sacred cats behind the ruins of the great temple of Bubastis, you may perchance catch sight of a living and elegant wildcat watching you from some rocky knoll, or, oblivious of your noiseless approach, furtively creeping toward a trochilus by the riverside or stiffening its muscles for a leap upon some toothsome hare or jerboa. In that lithe and eager beast,

Egyptian Wildcat.

which seems so familiar, although you have never seen it before, stands the parent of our "fireside sphinx." It is the Egyptian, or Caffre, or Libyan, or gloved cat — for by so many names does *Felis libyca* go into our books and museums.

"The caffre cat," as described by Lydekker, "is about the size of a large domestic cat, and is generally of a yellowish color (becoming more or less gray in some specimens), darker on the back, and paler on the under parts. The body is marked with faint pale stripes, which assume, however, on the limbs, the form of distinct dark horizontal bands; and the tail, which is relatively long, is also more or less distinctly ringed towards its tip, which is completely black. The sides of the face are marked by two horizontal streaks. Very generally the soles of the hind feet are black."

Its habits are simple. It hunts largely by night, yet is often seen abroad by day, catching the various birds and small mammals of the desert. Anderson, whose magnificent work on Egyptian zoölogy contains a portrait from which our plate has been drawn, informs us that it "inhabits dry situations in rocks or wooded districts . . . and lives in deep holes which extend underground for a considerable distance" — holes dug by other animals. The cat is known all over the more open parts of Africa, and is so variable that formerly several specific names were given to its different phases. Everywhere it seems to cross freely with domestic cats; and Anderson was told by Stanley Flower that he had seen house cats near Suez which could scarcely be told from *Felis libyca*.

That this cat was domesticated by the people of ancient Egypt is evident not only by the identity with it of the mummy skeletons, but is demonstrated by an old Egyptian wall painting preserved in the British Museum, representing a family hunting expedition into the reed beds along the Nile where waterfowl abounded. A prominent figure is a cat, unmistakably the *libyca*, whose business evidently is to retrieve if not to catch the birds slain by arrows or throwing-sticks. She has just caught one in her mouth, while she holds another with her forepaws and a third between her hind-paws! Truly, a useful cat.

So much for the tamed cats of Egypt; but what have they to do with our own Puss? Everything, for it now seems certain that she has come down to us from these same "little Egyptian cats," and even owes to them her pet name. A century ago it was generally believed that all the house cats of the world were derived from Europe, and came from tamed wildcats — the common wildcat (*Felis catus*), still numerous in the forested central parts of that continent, though nearly extinct in Great Britain. It is the only one of the smaller cats to have the honor of a descriptive book [132] all to itself, while its career in Great Britain, where it has been the **Eastern Wildcats.** subject of much curious hunting history, furnishes entertaining chapters to Bell,[93] Harting,[109] and other British writers, not to speak of continental authorities. So we know this animal better, perhaps, than almost any other of its kind.

Eastward of the Caspian Sea its place is taken by Pallas's cat, or the "manul," which is rather smaller, "is pale whitish gray, with some narrow dark markings on the chest, loins, and limbs, the tail being short and ringed . . . and differs from all other Old World members of its genus by the great length and softness of its fur." The Russian naturalist Pallas suggested that this cat was the original of the long-haired Persian or Angora breed, and this is probably so, since, "with the exception of the shortness of the tail and its dark rings, all the characters of this species are just those which might be expected in the ancestor of the Persian breed"; and Lydekker thinks that the points mentioned may have been eliminated by careful selection or crossing.

In the same wild, dry uplands of central Asia lives also the steppe cat, especially numerous in Bokhara, which is yellowish and thickly speckled with small, irregular brown spots that arrange themselves into lines or even streaks on the fore shoulders and the thighs. A near ally to it is the desert cat, smaller, more whitey brown, and prevalent on the arid plains of northwestern India. Its habitat is shared by the Indian wildcat, which resembles the European one but is smaller and more reddish; and by the more familiar, short-tailed jungle cat, or "chaus," which is sand color, more or less dark and unspotted, all markings being very obscure and variable and most evident in the young. This chaus ranges all over India and Ceylon, and thence westward through Persia and Asia Minor to the Delta of the Nile, where, as elsewhere, it is partial to low, marshy ground, sugar-cane fields, and similar thick cover where it preys largely on game birds.

Special attention has been paid to this group of Oriental wildcats, because they and some others there less noticeable **Kinship.** seem very closely akin; and also because to them we must look for the parentage of the Indian domestic breeds. Most if not all of these wildcats will interbreed and will cross with domesticated breeds, producing fertile offspring. This reproductive faculty extends to both the European and Egyptian wildcats, which Hamilton [132] long ago suggested were derived from a common ancestor. Professor G. Martorelli, of Milan, took up the subject more lately, and having studied not only the present structure and the mummy skeletons, but also fossil remains, came to the conclusion that all of the foregoing species are offshoots of a stock now nearly represented by the Egyptian cat. Dr. Lydekker has summarized his results thus: —

"If the views of Professor Martorelli be found substantially correct, the following will be the lines of evolution: Firstly, we have the ancestral types of the Egyptian cat (*F. libyca*), inhabiting northeastern Africa and a considerable part of Europe during the Pleistocene, and perhaps a part of the Pliocene, period. From this original species originated in the Eastern side of the world the Mediterranean cat (*F. mediterranea*) and the wild-cat (*F. catus*). When man became dominant, he produced the European domesticated breed, either from the typical Egyptian cat or from its variety, the Mediterranean cat, and this original domestic breed soon became crossed with its immediate cousin, the wildcat. On the other hand, in the East, the original Egyptian cat gave rise to the jungle cat (*F. chaus*), the steppe cat (*F. caudata*), and presumably, therefore, that near ally of the latter, the Indian desert cat (*F. ornata*). From the latter are derived the spotted Indian domesticated cats, while the fulvous domesticated breed of the same country has been produced by a cross with the jungle cat. Both these are now largely crossed with their somewhat remote cousin, the striped domesticated cat of Europe. The Persian cat . . . may probably be derived from Pallas's cat, which has no sort of connection with the Egyptian cat; and the cross between the Persian and European 'tabby,' now so common, is consequently a very mixed breed indeed."

This brings us naturally to the pedigree of our household mousers. The old, thoughtless notion as has been said, was that they were simply tamed (European) wildcats. People read in their translations of the classics of the "cats" of ancient Greece, and said that these had been domesticated before written history began, and had become changed during the long centuries since they began to catch mice in the halls of Mykænæ or between decks on the ships of Tarshish.

But careful students began to foresee that this simple explanation would not suffice. Faith in it was disturbed in the first place by the criticism [184] that the Greek word *ailuros* had been improperly translated as "cat." Really it meant the white-breasted marten (*Martes foina*) which the early Greeks kept as a ratter, much as we now employ its relative, the ferret; and they did not have any true cat at all. Next, the anatomists found that there were essential and constant differences as to certain bones and in points of color between the wildcats and the house cats of Europe, which could not be reconciled. Then archæologists began to collect mummied cats in Egypt, whose bones, the anatomists told them, precisely agreed with those of the Egyptian wildcat (*Felis libyca*); and pictured evidence appeared that such cats were domesticated anciently along the Nile. At that time all Europe was a savage wilderness, except, perhaps, some beginnings of civilization in Greece and southern Italy. Pres-

Pedigree of Domestic Cat.

ently fossil remains turned up in England and in Belgium, which bore closer resemblance to the Egyptian than to the European wildcats, and examination revealed that the living wildcats of Sardinia and Tuscan Italy were not of the European type, but were (and are) a Mediterranean variety of the Egyptian cat.

Lastly, research in another direction, namely, of the relics from the graves of the early inhabitants of northern Italy, 300 or 400 years before Christ, and of the earliest remains of Roman colonization in Britain, proved that those peoples had domestic cats. Now both these places traded with the Phœnicians, who were the carriers of Egyptian trade as well as of their own; and it is fair to infer that they introduced cats from the Levant. Thus all the evidence points to the Egyptian cat as at any rate the principal source of the house cat of Europe, and hence of America and the western world generally. Our very word "Puss" is only a domestication, so to speak, of the name of the Egyptian moon goddess Pasht.

But this is not the end of the matter. In all parts of the world one or another of the smaller wildcats of the country have been kept as pets in native houses; and wherever the people have been far enough advanced to raise and store grain, they have cultivated a cat or some other animal to free their granaries from thieving mice. It was for this purpose, no doubt, that the cats of Egypt were first tamed; and then, to make the people prudently keep them and care for them, the priests got up a religious story, and invented a beneficient and cheerful cat goddess, who, naturally, was said to walk abroad mostly by moonlight. It is believed that the early agriculturists of Europe subjugated their wildcat to the same end. If so, when the Egyptian cats reached Europe they would certainly soon meet and interbreed with the native stock, since, if Martorelli is right, the two were only distant cousins; and to such crossing is probably due the prevalence of banded or "tabby" cats there; in fact, until Eastern breeds began to be imported, comparatively recently, there was no other style. On the other hand, brindled cats were unknown in eastern Asia, whose spotted or foxy domestic cats were derived, as we have seen, from other and local sources; yet are so closely akin that they readily produce fertile offspring when crossed with western breeds.

Lynxes, Bobcats, and Cheetas

All the cats thus far have had long tails and rounded ears; but toward the end of the list the ears grew sharper and a little tufted, and the tails much abbreviated, especially noticeable in the jungle cats. This tendency leads toward a group of short-tailed, tufted-eared cats, the lynxes, or "bobcats," of special interest to us, because among them are our North American wildcats. "There are a number of species," said Coues, "inhabiting Europe, Asia, Africa, and North America.

They are of moderate size among the Felidæ, but considerably larger than any house cat, with a short body, a very short tail, large and long limbs, usually bearded cheeks and tufted ears, and spotted, marbled, or clouded coloration. Some have been known from time

Copyright, N. Y. Zoölogical Society.   Sanborn, Phot.
THE CANADA LYNX.

immemorial, and famed for their supposed sharp-sightedness, which probably is no greater than that of any other cats."

These characteristics, and their lack of the usual upper pre-molar, have led many zoölogists to put them into a separate genus (Lynx). They are northern animals, but one species ranges throughout Africa.

The typical and original lynx is that of the far North, — Scandinavia, northern Russia, Siberia, Alaska, and Canada, — and known to us as the Canada lynx, "catamount," or "lucivee"; the last is a shortening of the French *loup cer-*

Canada Lynx. *vier*, or "deer wolf" — a term of obscure meaning perhaps arising from some weird superstition of the Middle Ages. In the arctic borders it reaches a great size, old males there, it has been said, being sometimes fifty inches long, but southerly specimens rarely exceed forty inches, such standing about eighteen inches high, with a tail adding about five inches. The males differ widely in the length of the peculiar neck ruff, and of the black pencils on the ears. In color they are grizzled, with a varying tinge of reddish or brown-ish showing through from the base of the hairs; this tinge is stronger in summer than in winter, and some specimens are indistinctly spotted, especially when young. Those of high and dry Tibet are noticeably pale, while those of damp and cloudy Newfoundland show an excess of dark color, and have even been regarded as an isolated species. A kind of lynx inhabiting the northern shores and islands of the Mediterranean is redder and more spotted than those of the North (as happens in America with southern varieties) and is deemed a separate species called the pardine lynx.

The lynx is undoubtedly the most dangerous and destructive beast of prey left in Europe. One who reads the admirable biographies of Tschudi or Brehm sees that he lives by stratagem. He has not a particularly fine sense of smell, nor is his pace rapid. It is his patience, and the skill with which he creeps noiselessly up to his victim, that brings him a reward. "More patient than the fox, he is less cunning; less hardy than the wolf, he leaps better and can resist famine longer. He is not so strong as the bear, but keeps a better lookout, and has sharper sight. . . . Every animal he can reach with one of his bounds is lost and devoured; if he misses he allows the animal to escape, and returns to crouch in his post of observation, without showing his disappointment. He is not voracious, but he loves warm blood, and this habit makes him imprudent. . . . If he comes

upon a flock of goats or sheep, he approaches, dragging his belly along the ground like a snake, then raises himself with a bound, falls on the back of his victim, breaks its neck, or cuts its carotids with his teeth, and kills it instantly." In view of these traits, which are manifested by American examples whenever they are in the neighborhood of settlements, it is not surprising that their extirpation is one of the first duties of pioneers.

Our Canada lynx is now rarely seen south of Lake Superior except in eastern Quebec and the adjoining forests of Maine and New Brunswick; but their skins, obtained easily by trapping in winter, form one of the most profitable items in the season's catch of furs by the Indians of Quebec and the Hudson Bay country.

On the Pacific side the animal comes well south in the high mountains. Nowhere is it numerous, and it varies in abundance from year to year according to the local plenty or scarcity of food—especially of hares. "To the lone hunter who camps in the dark and gloomy forests it

BOBCAT AND CANADA LYNX.

Illustrating varietal difference.

seems a very dangerous animal, but in reality it is not so." Nevertheless long-continued hunger will give them extreme boldness; and, like their southern cousins, they will at such times recklessly pounce even upon the porcupine, get their paws and face full of quills, and finally die of them as the barbs work their way into the flesh, inflaming the mouth and throat until feeding is impossible, and perhaps reaching the eyes and so producing blindness and starvation.

"The lynx," say the authors of "American Animals," "appears to have its summer home in tangled thickets and snarls of young growth, where the interlocking branches of fallen trees afford protection. Here the ill-natured kittens are raised and taught to hunt, so that when the bitter struggle of winter is forced upon them they may, if possible, hold their own and prolong their lives at the expense of others in order that their race may live and hold on to life grimly through long, cold nights in the dark northern forests, believing somehow that at last spring will be in the woods again, bringing flight birds from the South, and awakening the small creatures that sleep all winter down deep in frozen earth where the most desperate lynx can never reach them. Until then the lynxes must hunt as best they can, tireless and in splendid health and quite unconscious of the cold, but oh, so hungry!

"One of the most astonishing facts in nature is the length of time that most flesh-eating animals can go without food, on long hunts through deep snow, night after night, breathing frozen air that drives a man hungry soon after the heartiest meal, yet still holding their strength ready for a desperate struggle when at last the long pursuit draws to a successful end."

This may be true of New England, but in Canada food (big hares) is in winter most abundant and easily obtained.

More familiar is that smaller, more spotted, less splay-footed but equally unregenerate southern lynx, — the bobcat. It **Bobcat.** differs, however, from the Canada lynx in so small particulars as to make its specific distinction as *Felis rufa* more a matter of convenience than of necessity. As it has little use for snowshoes, its feet are not big and furry; the ears make less show of tassels than in the other species; the coat is not so long and shaggy, and the fur is more decidedly tinted (especially with yellow and red), and is spotted. As to size, average specimens are much the same (about thirty-five inches long) when taken on the meeting ground along the Canada border. As the lucivees increase in bulk toward the north, — apparently the proper habitat of the group, — so the bobcats grow smaller toward the southern limits of their range, those of the deserts on the border of Mexico, for example, being not more than two thirds the bigness of Alaskan ones. Similarly these wildcats vary in warmth of color and degree of spottedness according to region, in conformity with the law of climatic effect observable generally, that southern animals are brighter and more plentifully marked than northern ones of the same kind; and that those of a moist region are more highly colored than those of an arid country. It is not surprising, then, to find that the early naturalists, getting isolated specimens from remotely separated localities, and not seeing the inter-grading forms living between, should have regarded them as separate species; and ten or a dozen varieties of the bobcat are still named by the systemists, whose eyes are much more keen for distinctions than for resemblances.

These bobcats yet linger all over the country wherever mountains and woodlands, swamps or deserts, give them a refuge, and their habits are much the same as those of wildcats elsewhere; but they are steadily diminishing before the persecution of farmers and ranchmen, of trappers who covet their pelts, and of sportsmen who enjoy outwitting their stratagems and witnessing the futile rage when at last, in the face of dogs and rifles, the furious little beast fights gamely to the end without a chance for life. The literature of sport and pioneering is filled with stories of wildcat hunting — none more interesting than those related by Audubon as he saw it in the South during the second third of the nineteenth century; but at present if one wants to enjoy that sort of thing he must go into the far West. No better guide can be found than Theodore Roosevelt, who has vividly pictured the incidents of such a chase, the method of which is much the same as that of puma hunting with dogs.[128]

One more foreign species requires mention, — the caracal,

a small, slender, active animal of the open country of eastern Africa and southwestern Asia; it is uniformly bright red-dish fawn in color, and has no ruff, but the long ears are sharply penciled with black, and the rather long tail has a black tip. It climbs trees, of course, and its power of long leaping and activity are marvelous. It has been known to steal up to a covey of francolins (a kind of quail) and, at the instant of their rising, to spring into the air and knock down one with each paw. It is also said to hunt rabbits, etc., on the ground by chasing them in packs after the manner of wolves, and, like the jackal, to follow its betters for the "crumbs that fall from the master's table"; but why, on that account, should it be called "lion's provider," as the books allege? No soft influences have ever brought this fierce lynx into domestica-tion, but for centuries Eastern princes have subdued it (by the hands of their shikaris) into a hunting servant resembling a hawk in the nature of its work.

Caracal.

The foremost cat trained for sport, however, is the cheeta, or hunting leopard, which closes the list of the family, and stands separated in the genus Cynælurus in an intermediate position between the cats and the dogs. Its claws are only partly retractile into sheaths; there are many doglike features in its dentition and muscles, and its habits and dis-position are a curious mixture of feline and canine. The cheeta has a tall, wolflike figure, except in its small, round head, very slender limbs, and thin, "tucked-up" hindquarters; the neck and shoulders are surmounted by a mass of lengthened hair; and the tail is as long as the body, and grows thicker to the end. "General color, fulvescent cream or bright nankeen, more or less deep and dotted over with numerous round black spots," the face having a conspicuous black streak passing down from the corner of each eye, the pupils of which contract circularly.

Cheeta.

This animal inhabits all the more open parts of Africa, Arabia,

CHEETA STALKING ANTELOPES.

and thence eastward to central India. In general manner of life it is a leopard, except that it is little fond of the forest, living mainly among rocky, barren hills, and attacking deer, antelopes, and the herdsman's flocks. Occasionally one settles down to a raiding life until killed as a public nuisance. It does not attack men. Blanford [19] declares that its speed in pursuit of quarry exceeds that of any other beast of prey, or even that of a greyhound. One has been seen to catch within four hundred yards a blackbuck that had a fair start.

The cheeta is principally interesting, however, because for ages it has been trained in India to capture game for its masters, — it will not do to say it "hunts" for them, since it does nothing of the sort. This use of the large cats is of great antiquity.

When Ælian wrote, in the third century of our era, the natives of India knew how to train the black-maned lion of that country for the chase, leading it in a slip. Marco Polo mentions that the Great Khan **Antiquity of Sport with Cheeta.** of Tartary had not only leopards and lynxes trained to hunt, but tigers, which were taken to the field on cages drawn in carts, and chased wild boars, wild cattle, deer, roebucks, and other beasts. In the *Revue Britannique* for October, 1885, will be found a very interesting article on hunting with the cheeta, written by Baron Dunoyer de Noirment, high authority on the history of the chase. He traces the progress of this sport from the earliest times. The cheeta is figured on Assyrian bas-reliefs in the act of seizing an antelope, and is represented on Egyptian monuments, 1700 B.C., as led in a slip with a very ornamental collar. The Crusaders found this kind of sport much in vogue with the Mussulman princes of Syria; and a celebrated Arabic writer on hunting and hawking, Sidi Mohamed el Mangali,[148] enters in great detail upon the mode of taming and training caracals and the cheeta (deprivation of food and sleep being the chief means of subjection) as practiced in his day, about 1348 A.D. He declares that Persians knew the art best; mentions various local varieties, including a black one from South Arabia; and says that a leopard trained to hunt in concert with a falcon was of inestimable value.

Tippoo Sahib, the last Sultan of Mysore, was, like most Eastern potentates, an enthusiastic sportsman, and kept no less than sixteen cheetas. When Tippoo was killed at the taking of Seringapatam in 1799, two of these were sent to England and were kept at Windsor until they died, and it was with one of them that an attempt was made to give an exhibition of the sport in Windsor Park, resulting in a short stampede among the noble spectators and a long laugh for all England.

The Italians, who had close trade relations with the Saracens, introduced the first trained leopards into Europe. When, in 1459, a French ambassador, sent by the Duke of Burgundy to Pope Pius II, stopped on his way at Milan, and hunted with Francis Sforza, first Duke of Milan, he was astonished to see leopards carried on horseback (on a pillion behind their owners) and slipped at hares, which they coursed and killed. An illustrated account of such hunting may be read in La Croix's work.[141]

Both Charles VIII and Louis XII of France kept trained animals of this kind with which they killed hares and roedeer. After a kill, the cheeta, on being shown a little blood in a tin bowl, would leave its prey and jump on the horse's crupper behind its master. "One would imagine," as J. E. Harting remarks, "that the horse would require almost as much training as the cheeta to stand quiet under such circumstances." This sport continued among the French nobles until the time of Henry IV, and was revived in Germany by Leopold I, who died in 1705, but it was never followed in Great Britain.

In India the sport is still popular, especially among the native princes, and is conducted much as of old. Of the many descriptions of it I prefer that of the senior Kipling,[11] who places the picturesqueness of it, as it seems to me, where it belongs: —

"The Rev. J. G. Wood descants on the great powers of the Orientals in training the cheeta or hunting leopard. In this instance the only point where real skill comes into play is in the first capture of the adult animal, when it has already learned the swift bounding onset, — its one accomplishment. The young cheeta is not worth catching, for it has not learned its trade, nor can it be taught in captivity. . . . There are certain trees where these great dog cats come to play and whet their claws. The hunters find such a tree, arrange deer-sinew nooses around it, and await the event. The animal comes and is caught by a leg, and it is at this point the trouble begins. It is no small achievement for two naked, ill-fed men to secure so fierce a captive and carry him home on a cart. Then his training commences. He is tied in all directions, principally from a thick grummet of rope round his loins, while a hood fitted over his head effectually blinds him. He is fastened on a strong cot bedstead, and the keepers and their wives and families reduce him to submission by starv-

Training.

ing him and keeping him awake. His head is made to face the village street, and for an hour at a time, several times a day, his keepers make pretended rushes at him and wave cloths, staves, and other articles in his face. He is talked to continually, and women's tongues are believed to be the most effective antisoporifics. No created being could resist the effects of hunger, want of sleep, and feminine scolding, and the poor cheeta becomes piteously, abjectly tame. . . . Of actual training in the field there is little or none. So it is not wonderful that the cheeta loses its natural dash and is often left behind by the antelope. At the wedding festivities of a Punjab chief the other day, the guests were shown this sport, and the cheeta caught and killed a blackbuck; but it was found the Raja's servants, by way of making quite sure, had first hamstrung the poor antelope.

"The ordained procedure is that the hooded leopard is first taken afield on a cart driven near a herd of blackbuck, shown the game, and slipped. In a few bounds he reaches and seizes it, is rewarded with a draught of blood, or a morsel of liver in a wooden spoon, and put on his cart again; but there is a large proportion of failures. And the creature is not practicing a feat he has been taught, but is merely let loose to perform an act he learned in his wild state which his keepers cannot teach, and for which, in fact, their teaching seems to unfit him."

Civet Cats, Mungooses, and Meerkats

Among the earliest carnivorous mammals "viverrine" characteristics of structure prevailed, — that is, such features as now mark the small, flesh-eating animals which we know as civet cats, and place in the family Viverridæ. As early as the Oligocene period these characteristics became distinctly developed in certain forms, and even the typical genus, Viverra, may be traced back to that era. One of the most ancient of the viverrine lines survives in the foussa, which stands intermediate between the cats and the civets, having thirty-six teeth, of which the hinder ones are very catlike, retractile sheathed claws, and other feline peculiarities. It is confined to Madagascar, where it is the largest beast of prey, not common, and very imperfectly known except as a scourge to herds of goats and kids. Large specimens nearly equal our puma in size, but the form is slender with high haunches, the color is uniform pale brown, and the whole animal more resembles a large eyra.

Barring this remarkable beast, the family Viverridæ falls into two divisions: (1) the true civets (viverrines); (2) the mungooses (herpestines). Both divisions are now limited to Africa and southwestern Asia, but in Tertiary times they occupied Europe; none now belong to either America. All are small animals, none much larger than a house cat, with flattened bodies, long,

THE FOUSSA OF MADAGASCAR.

pointed heads, the jaws having normally forty teeth, of which the rear ones are doglike; short limbs, with the claws retractile in some, in others not so; long tails and thick coats of fur, usually handsomely marked. All are nocturnal, solitary, predatory, and fierce. The species number about forty-five.

The civets proper (viverrines) have elongated bodies, terrier-like heads, small, round five-toed feet with hairy soles and sheathed claws, long and often bushy tails, coats **Civets.** of rough hair sometimes rising into a crest along the spine, and marked on a dark gray ground with black stripes and bars, and with lengthwise lines of squarish blotches very distinctive of the tribe. The fur has some value, particularly in China. The habits of these animals are much like those of foxes, as they are wholly terrestrial, live in holes in the ground, and subsist mainly on birds and small mammals, but some also like fish, frogs, snakes, crabs, insects, earthworms, eggs, etc., and frequently steal poultry.

The distinctive peculiarity of the true civet cats is the possession of a pair of open pouches beneath the root of the tail, in which (in the male) is

THE AFRICAN PERFUME-YIELDING CIVET CAT.

secreted an oily substance having an intense musky odor and known as "civet." This is present in the five Oriental species, but is most copious in the civet cat of northern Africa. Although overpoweringly disgusting to our nostrils in its raw state, it is not so to some barbarians, so that it has always been used as a perfume in the East, and in Shakespeare's time was fashionable in Europe. In parts of Egypt, in Abyssinia, and especially in Java, one or another species is kept in captivity for the sake of this secretion, which is scraped from its pouches every few days and sold to perfumers; as its secretion and flow are increased by irritating the animal, it is forced into a long, narrow cage, which has the double effect of infuriating the subject and making the use of the spoonlike instrument safe. Civet finds a steady market, London alone importing some twenty thousand ounces annually. One of the most widespread of Oriental species is the rasse, which has no dorsal crest and is a good tree climber; it is easily tamed, and in China and Formosa is eaten, despite its strong musky taint.

A Madagascan species, the fossane, closely resembles it externally, but has no scent pouch.

The genets are similar animals, but like weasels in their slenderness and activity, prettily marked, and producing hardly any musk. They inhabit Africa, with one species along the north shore of the Mediterranean and in Asia Minor. When a genet is stealing cautiously through the grass it looks more like a snake than a mammal.

Handsomest of the family are the East-Indian linsangs, for they are graceful and wear a velvety fur of reddish fawn color, marked with lines of large black blotches, **Genets and** becoming rings on the tail. They seek their food, **Linsangs.** mainly birds, both on the ground and in trees, and make their homes in hollows of trees, where two litters a year are produced.

There is a West-African species (Poiana), whose behavior is more like that of a genet. West Africa also possesses a single isolated form (Nandinia) of another

A PARADOXURE.

large and more familiar Asiatic group known as palm civets, or "tree cats," because they spend their lives mainly in the palms and mangoes, where they sleep by day and prowl by night, often several in company. There are about a dozen species, ranging from Ceylon around to China and Formosa, and along the Malay Archipelago to the Philippines; all have a grayish or brownish fur, with the usual dark markings. The only one at all well known is the Indian "toddy cat," so called because of its fondness for drinking the sweet, intoxicating juice of the toddy palm, from the buckets in which the people of southern India collect this sap from the tapped trees. This pretty animal is fond of making its residence in thatched roofs, and becomes an interesting house mate.

Two other Malayan palm civets, called "small-toothed"; the two hemigales of Borneo, remarkable for the broad, dark bands lying across the back; the web-footed, fish-catching, and otterlike cynogale; and the black binturong, or "bear cat," the only animal of the Old World not a marsupial which has a prehensile tail, complete the catalogue of the viverrines.

Turning now to the second division, the Herpestines, it must be noted first that they differ from the viverrines by anatomical features; by the fact that their claws are not retractile; by the absence of scent pouches; and by being unspotted. Sixteen of the most typical species form the genus Herpestes, leaving a few more for other genera. The smallest are no larger than a weasel, while the largest rival a house cat. They are active, bold, and predaceous, and live on small mammals, birds and
Ichneu-   reptiles, insects and eggs, and occasionally eat
mons.   fruit. They live in holes in the ground and similar places. When angry or excited they erect their long hairs, especially those of the tail; and are deadly enemies to snakes.

Popular interest in these animals centers upon the ability to kill dangerous reptiles shown conspicuously by two species,— one common all along the south shore of the Mediterranean, in Egypt, Asia Minor, and Spain, and the other in India. The former is a sleek, mink-shaped but more robust creature, of rather large size, the head and body measuring about twenty inches, and the tail, which is thick and tapering, about fifteen inches more; the color is a uniform brownish grizzle with a stripe on the nape and the top of the tail black.

This animal has always been numerous in the Nile Valley, where the Egyptians call it Pharaoh's rat, and the Greek colonists, long before the Christian era began, named it *ichneumon*, that is, "tracker," because it was believed to smell out the trails of the crocodiles to and from their nests, and then to dig up and eat their eggs. At any rate, it will eat these eggs when it comes across them; and Diodorus Siculus remarks that there would have been no safety in sailing upon the Nile but for it. This belief was sufficient to cause the Middle Egyptians to protect the ichneumon until it became one of their sacred animals, and its cult arose at Heracleopolis, as is shown by wall paintings, mummies, etc. Anderson [55] thinks, however, that more probably the animal was cherished for its willingness to fight asps. Even now it is frequently tamed and kept in Egyptian houses to protect them from snakes, rats, and mice. The old term ichneumon is now little used, the whole group going by the native name, "mungoos," of the more familiar Asiatic species.

The East Indian mungoos is considerably smaller than the Egyptian one, is more rufous in hue, and has no black markings; it occurs throughout peninsular India and Ceylon, but not east of the Bay of Bengal. It inhabits thickets, broken, bushy ground, and village fields rather than dense forests, and makes its home in holes among rocks or in the earth. Its multiplication is rapid. Snakes and lizards, small birds and rodents, are the items oftenest on its bill of fare, and it is an arrant poultry thief. "I have often seen it," Jerdon writes, "make a dash into a veranda where some cages of mynas, parrakeets, etc., were daily placed, and endeavor to tear the birds from their cages." In spite of this weasel-like fierceness, it is easily tamed, not only as a useful mouser (for which thousands are kept in the East) but because it makes a gentle and affectionate pet, often seen in the company of wandering Hindoo snake charmers and showmen. These virtues led to the introduction of the mungoos into Jamaica in 1872, to destroy the rats which beset the plantations of sugar cane and seemed unconquerable. The surprising results of the experiment have been related in a book by D. Morris,[170] and in many newspaper articles. The general effect I have summed up elsewhere as follows: —

Mungoos.

"At first they were highly beneficial, reducing the stated annual loss from rats from $500,000 to one half that, but in less than twenty years the island was almost overrun with them. Not only did they kill rats and mice, however, but snakes, lizards, ground birds, and even poultry. At one time snakes had become so rare that they were regarded as practically exterminated, but since 1896 they are apparently on the increase. The ground doves and other terrestrial birds, partly, at least, by change of habit, are also adapting themselves to this new enemy, and their extermination is no longer to be feared. At the present time the mungoos is common and very tame in most parts of the island, and in many other islands, and is generally looked on with favor." A similar experience was had in Porto Rico and Hawaii, and the laws of the United States now prohibit the importation of a single one of these animals.

As a skillful conqueror of venomous serpents the mungoos has attracted attention since ancient times. Aristotle and Pliny declared that the Egyptian mungoos first coated its body with mud, and in that armor could defy the serpent. Old Topsell [171] informs us that the ichneumon burrows in the sand, and "when the aspe espyeth her threatening rage, presently turning about her taile, provoketh the ichneumon to combate, and with an open mouth and lofty head doth enter the list, to her owne perdition. For the ichneumon being nothing afraid of this great bravado, receiveth the encounter, and taking the head of the aspe in his mouth biteth that off to prevent the casting out of her poison."

It is a widespread belief in India that a certain herb is eaten by the mungoos when wounded in a bout with a cobra, and this notion has been carried to the West Indies, where the little creature attacks the fer-de-lance; but it has no foundation in fact. The mungoos is not always eager for the fight, nor invariably successful, being sometimes killed and swallowed by the snake; but ordinarily it is victorious through its amazing activity and skill, aided by the thick fur which stands straight out when it is enraged, so that the serpent's fangs rarely hit the small body at the center of the restless, hairy mass in front of him. The mungoos waits, alert and tense, until the snake strikes, then dodges, and before the reptile can recover pounces upon it and crushes the head, which it then eats, poison and all.

The other ichneumons of both Africa and Asia differ from these two only in minor particulars, mainly of color. An Abyssinian one sports an extraordinary pure white tail, shaped like that of a horse! One East Indian species distinguishes itself by a diet of frogs. Certain more different ones live on the West Coast of Africa, and a curiously distinct group is native to Madagascar. An aberrant species, the suricate, or "meerkat," of South Africa, is a pet on almost every Boer farm, — and it is no wonder, after reading Mrs. Martin's account of it: —

WHITE-TAILED ICHNEUMON.

"In their wild state the meerkats live in colonies or warrens, burrowing deep holes in the sandy soil, and feeding chiefly on succulent bulbs, which they scratch up with their long, curved black claws. They **Meerkats.** are devoted sun worshipers, and in the early morning, before it is daylight, they emerge from their burrows, and wait in rows until their divinity appears, when they bask joyfully in his beams. They are very numerous on the Karoo, and, as you ride or drive along through the veldt, you often come upon little colonies of them sitting up sunning themselves, and looking in their quaint and pretty favorite attitude like tiny dogs begging. . . . The quaint, old-fashioned little fellow is as neatly made as a small bird; his coat, of the softest fur, with markings not unlike those of a tabby cat, is always well made and spotlessly clean; his tiny feet, ears, and nose are all most daintily and delicately finished off; and his broad circle of black, bordering his large dark eye, serves like the antimony of

an Egyptian beauty, to enhance the size and brilliancy of the orbs. . . .
His bright, pretty little face is capable of assuming the greatest variety of
expressions, that which it most frequently wears when in repose being a
contented, self-satisfied smirk, impudence and independence displaying
themselves at every line of his plump little figure. . . . He is absolutely
without fear, and with consummate coolness and audacity will walk up to
the largest and most forbidding-looking dog, although a perfect stranger
to him, and, carefully investigating the stranger on all sides with great
curiosity, express disgust and defiance in a succession of little short, sharp,
barks." [172]

There lives in the unforested parts of Africa a strange and
rather rare animal called aard-wolf (*i.e.* "earth wolf") by the
Boers, and deeb among the Arabs of Upper Egypt, which
Aard-wolf. somewhat resembles a large, thin-bodied, striped
hyena, but has longer ears and a more pointed muzzle. The tail is long and bushy, the reddish, black-striped coat
is coarse and long, and rises in anger along the ridge of the neck
and back into a bristling crest. It has five toes in front and
four behind, and its skull and teeth are somewhat like those
of a mungoos, the latter being small and weak and only thirty
or thirty-two in number. Consequently, although it dwells
in pairs in burrows of its own digging, and wanders abroad
at night in search of carrion like a hyena, it cannot manage
tough food, and subsists largely by digging termites out of
their hills. Schulz,[152] who calls this animal "ant bear," says
that the natives of the dry deserts between the Zambesi and
Chobe rivers go down its hole, one man holding to the legs of
another, and a third at the mouth of the hole holding the latter's feet, to get wet earth from which to squeeze moisture and
so save themselves from famishing of thirst.

This aard-wolf, for which some naturalists make a separate family (Pro-
telidæ), stands intermediate between the mungooses and the hyenas, and
seems to reproduce pretty closely a bone-breaking animal well known as a
fossil in the early Pliocene rocks of central Europe and Asia, named Ictitherium, in which the characters of the Viverridæ and the Hyænidæ are
so blended that they cannot be separated. After him, however, we find a

line of fossil animals developing the hyena side, and departing more and more from the civet-cat type, until they lead to the modern hyenas and the aard-wolf.

The hyenas compose a family of only three living species, but many fossil ones (none American), leading back to Pal-hyena and Ictitherium. They have a bulky body, supported by muscular legs, and big, dog-like heads, with very strong jaws and thirty-four massive conical teeth, so that "a hyena is able to crunch in its jaws the shin bone of an ox almost as readily as a dog can crush that of a fowl." The whole frame, indeed, is built for strength. F. C. Selous describes how in the Mashuna's country one night a big, spotted hyena sneaked into his camp where a crowd of men and dogs were lounging around the fire, and seized and carried away a green eland hide which must have weighed forty pounds; and although the thief was at once chased it dragged that burden three hundred yards before the dogs could catch up with it. They are scavengers, not hunters; and go forth by night to feed upon what their betters leave, or to pull down some small or disabled animal. Their courage is seldom great, but with their timidity goes a certain cunning and half-stupid boldness which leads them to make daring forays on occasion; but when caught they submit abjectly.

The most widely known one is the striped hyena, one of the smaller species, measuring about three feet from the nose to the rather short tail, and weighing sixty to seventy pounds. It is scattered from southern India eastward to the Caucasus, and down into Arabia and Africa, as far as Somaliland and the Sudan. It has sloping haunches, high, pointed ears, and a yellowish gray coat, bristling along the spine, and marked with narrow, transverse stripes of blackish and tawny. It frequents open, rocky country for the most part, and where there are caves, ruins, or rock-cut tombs, will often take permanent possession of one for a den instead of digging a burrow.

Hyenas.

Here, in the course of years, accumulates a grisly collection of broken bones; for often it can find nothing better than a skeleton which the jackals and vultures have picked clean, leaving the bones to be cracked for their marrow in the vicelike jaws of this slinking marauder. This hyena is a solitary animal, more than a pair being rarely seen, nor are even they often visible, since their visits to cultivated districts are, as a rule, made only during the dark hours. In Egypt they commonly select some hill in the desert, the weathered beds of which afford the only protection against the sun. "They sleep hard throughout the day, selecting that part of their domicile which affords the greatest comfort, taking into account the direction of the wind, heat of the sun, etc. . . . When disturbed they show no fight, but only an anxiety to make off with all possible haste." Anderson [55] further observes that the animal keeps its coat very clean, and is usually silent. In Asia, as in Egypt, this hyena is more hated than feared, and both Hindoos and Arabs charge it, probably with truth, with digging human corpses out of graves and devouring them. Hence the Hindoos are likely to put a captured one to death by torture. The Arabs do not do this, but cherish many superstitions about the beast, as that it changes its sex from year to year; that its humanlike howls are a lure for the unwary; and that it has in its eye a stone which if placed under a man's tongue endows him with the gift of prophecy. The Arabs of Mesopotamia say it understands Arabic; and when they creep into its den, and put a rope around its craven neck, they flatter it with apologies and compliments as they haul it out, and imagine it fooled into its cowardly acquiescence. Yet Anderson found the Nile men very keen to obtain its heart, which they eat, believing that they thus absorb the "courage" of the brute. They also save the whiskers to wear as a charm. This hyena frequently seizes dogs or even sheep and kids, and rushes away to its den, whence they are sometimes recovered with no serious injury, if quickly followed; but it never attacks larger animals or human beings.

The brown hyena, or "straand wolf," is a related species native to the southern and eastern coast-regions of Africa, in which the dorsal crest becomes so long as to hang like a mantle, concealing the body and neck on each side; this mantle is dark elsewhere but nearly white on the cheeks and throat, giving the effect of gray side whiskers to the face. Not much is known of its manner of life.

More familiar to readers of books of travel is the spotted

hyena, the biggest, strongest, and most dangerous of the three. It ranges throughout Africa south of the Sahara, and in prehistoric times into south-central Europe and Asia, as is proved by remains formerly separated as the cave hyena.[83]   The Dutch colonists call it "wolf," or "tiger wolf," the leopard being to them a "tiger." This repulsive and troublesome brute stands about two and a half feet high at the shoulder, and five and a half in total length, of which the bushy tail takes about fifteen inches. Its unkempt fur, coarse and bristly, is dun, irregularly blotched with circular blackish spots. This species also lives in a den in the rocks or underground, and prowls for carrion; but it kills for itself and gains courage by numbers, since it goes about in small packs, uniting to reach their prey by a rude sort of strategy and then overcome it by brute ferocity.   They play havoc with sheep — or, rather, used to do so, for now they are nearly killed out of settled parts — and get many victims among the small native cattle and donkeys.   The early travelers, like Livingstone and Harris, say much of such losses, which frequently extend to human beings, many children in southern Egypt being carried off, even nowadays, or so mauled that their faces are mutilated for life.

Spotted Hyena.

A traveler in Somaliland in 1892 had a spotted hyena attack and nearly kill one of his camels in broad daylight. It was one of a pack of six, all old males, which had so terrorized the neighborhood that women or children did not dare go about. Mr. Clarke shot the others, one by one; and each time the living came and lugged away the dead and hid the bodies under bushes, keeping off vultures, but making no motion toward eating them, as is their usual custom.

The terrific noise made by these creatures seems to baffle adequate description, — a weird, hideous, coughing laughter which, when a pack joins in, makes so horrible a din in the darkness of a mid-African night as to drive the lonely wayfarer mad. Yet in the early days hyenas swarmed all over South Africa, not only because game was abundant, but because the Kaffirs never destroyed them, holding them sacred as the means of disposing of their dead, since only their chiefs and young children were buried — in the ground.

The Fur Bearers

There now present themselves a company of small carnivores, whose coats are of that soft and thick pelage which we call *fur*, — the martens, weasels, badgers, ratels, skunks, otters, and their kin of the family Mustelidæ. Their structure in general is near the civet type; and the "testimony of the rocks" shows that if this line be not an ancient branch from the civet stock, at any rate it has sprung from the same root. In the Upper Eocene formations of France, for example, are found such small, tall-legged animals as the genus Plesictis, which seem to be generalized civet cats (viverroids) with features, especially as to the teeth, now distinctive of the Mustelidæ; and after them appeared others in which these features were more developed, until in the Miocene and Pliocene eras came true weasels, badgers, otters, etc., at first in Europe, but soon spreading all over the northern hemisphere. None of these was of an existing species, or even as a rule of any existing genus, but there is no doubt of their near relationship. The family falls into three sections: the martens, grisons, weasels, and wolverines (Mustelinæ); the badgers, skunks, etc. (Melinæ); and the otters (Lutrinæ). They constitute an army of sharp-toothed, keen-witted, bloodthirsty devourers of the small life of the world, doing in the North the police work which in the Oriental tropics is committed to the civet cats and mungooses.

These are the animals whose coats, acquired to keep themselves warm amid arctic frosts, make our most beautiful furs, as sable, marten, mink, ermine, and the rest. The sable is

CANADIAN PINE MARTEN AND SQUIRREL.

Siberian, the marten is North European, and its American brother is the pine marten, or "sable," of the Canadian forests.

Sable. The three are scarcely distinguishable, each averaging about eighteen inches in length, plus seven or eight inches of tail, and are brown, somewhat lighter below (throat and breast-spot orange in the Canadian sable), and variable according to age, sex, and season. The winter fur is thick, soft, an inch and a half deep, of richest hue, and has scattered through it coarse black hairs which the furrier pulls out; the tail is somewhat bushy. The body is elongated and supple, the legs short, and the toes separate, with sharp, long claws, as behooves so expert a tree climber. The martens exhibit great agility and grace in their movements, and live usually in trees, furnishing with a bed of leaves a lofty hollow in a decaying trunk or sometimes a rocky crevice. Here the young are brought forth in litters of six to eight early each spring.

Europe has also a "beech," "stone," or "sweet" marten of duller hue and with a white breast; and in India the local marten is blackish brown above and the breast orange-yellow; while North America contains the giant of the tribe in Pennant's marten, named by the early French Canadians pekan, and by modern trappers "fisher," "black cat," or "black fox," — it being none of the three! In general manner of life all these fur bearers are alike, yet with many a specific or individual peculiarity, as one may learn who will talk with hunters or read the books of Pennant,[174] Hearne,[181] Richardson,[183] De Kay,[182] Audubon and Bachman,[90] and the narratives of the fur country. The most pertinent parts of these accounts have been brought together by Dr. Elliott Coues, whose "Fur-bearing Animals" [175] is the foremost authority on the group.

For two hundred and fifty years the Canadian marten has supplied, as had the sable for perhaps as many centuries, the most valuable furs sent to market, excepting a few rarities like sea otter. Originally this marten occurred wherever forests grew, from the central United States to the arctic coast; and was so plentiful that periodically it overflowed certain districts and spread in hordes, scattering **Marten.** far and wide in search of food. On the other hand, periods of astonishing scarcity of martens occur every eight or ten years, no cause for which is known.

"This species everywhere rapidly fades away before the approach of civilization. They keep mostly to the trees, and hence like the denser parts of the forest, but they constantly descend to the ground for food, especially in winter, when they regularly hunt for hares and grouse of all kinds, trailing them with nose to the track like hounds. Their broad feet enable them to move rapidly, even over soft snow. They also hunt persistently for squirrels, chase them in the trees and on the ground, and enter their nests. To this fare is added whatever mice and birds and small fare comes their way. Martens have little to fear from native enemies; the much larger fisher is said to kill them, and the great horned owl may now and then pounce on one, but very few of the carnivores care to taste their flesh unless driven to it by extreme hunger. They are trapped from November until toward March, when their coats begin to become ragged and dull in hue, and with the approach of the rutting season they are no longer attracted by the baits offered by trappers." [20]

Pennant's marten, or the "pekan," is an American species remarkable for its great size — about twenty-four inches, plus thirteen inches of tail — and for its doglike head. It has always been rare near settlements, **Fisher.** has long been nearly extinct south of the Hudson Bay watershed, and now is a great prize for the trapper even in the far northern wilderness. Though long known as "fisher," it certainly does not catch fish; the name may have originated, as De Kay suggests, because it constantly stole the bait from mink traps, and raided the Indian's stores of frozen fish. It does worse mischief than that, however, for it will follow a line of marten traps and rob them of both bait and catch with the skill and immunity for which the carcajou is infamous.

In general habits and food the fisher is, in short, an exaggerated marten, which keeps more to the ground and prefers the wet rather than the dry parts of the forest, and has a special taste in summer for frogs. Wonderfully quick and strong in leaping, or for a short run, either on the ground or among tree branches, it makes easy prey not only of squirrels, mice, etc., but of such larger creatures as the muskrat, coon, skunk, and porcupine — the last named by Richardson as its favorite food, procured by "biting the belly." Audubon questioned this statement — "in what manner it is able to overturn the porcupine"; but the explanation is that the attempt is made only in winter, when the fisher bores his way through the snow and comes up beneath the porcupine, who sits on the surface thinking itself secure in its armor of quills, and unsuspicious of the burrowing strategy of its wily foe. Even the bear, according to Colonel Brackett, U.S.A., is likely to be despoiled of her baby cubs by this hungry prowler when she leaves them alone in her den. Its own young, born usually in a hollow tree or log, number two or three. When attacked by men or dogs it fights with the ferocity of a wildcat and the deathless courage and tenacity of a weasel.

Wolverine. This big species stands between the typical martens and a still larger and more powerful mustelid common to both hemispheres, and called glutton in the Old World and wolverine, or "carcajou," in the New. Were one to judge of it by the stories of the forest people alone, it could hardly be considered anything else than a sort of devil on four legs, with a heart as full of malice as its brain is surely

THE WOLVERINE OR GLUTTON.

full of wit. This is no worse, nor more erroneous, than the animal's reputation in Europe, where the glutton is represented in old books as a ravenous and disgusting monster of ferocity and cunning. In reality the creature is simply, to use the phrase of Dr. Coues, whose book [175] devotes a long chapter to the animal's diabolical record among the trappers, an uncommonly large, clumsy, shaggy marten, of great strength, and displaying extreme perseverance and sagacity in procuring food where the supply is limited and precarious.

Two smaller but very savage and troublesome relatives of the martens dwell in Central and South America — the tayra and the grison, or hurón. Both are terrestrial and mainly nocturnal, and are remarkable for being darker on their ventral than on their dorsal surfaces. W. H. Hudson says that on the pampas the black tayras hunt in companies, and are often seen; "and when these long-bodied creatures sit up erect, glaring with beady eyes, grinning and chattering at the passer-by, they look like little friars in black robes and gray cowls; but the expression on their round faces is malignant and bloodthirsty." These are weasel traits rather than those of martens, and result from their unmartenlike, terrestrial mode of life.

The weasels, ermines, stoats, polecats, minks, and the like form a group distinctly northern, although one species ranges southward into the Andes. Slender, lithe, perfectly toothed, sharp-clawed, secretively colored, **Weasel Tribe.** and endowed with strength, speed, cleverness, and indomitable courage, the weasels are the scourge and terror of all the small ground-keeping animals, and do more than any other class of agents to restrain mice, gophers, and similar nuisances. Some or all can climb, but their preference for the ground distinguishes them from the martens, as also do the comparatively short tail, close fur, three instead of four premolar teeth, and the presence of anal glands whence they may discharge a fetid odor. This musky, nauseous secretion is most copious and evident in the large European polecat, but most distressing to human nostrils in an old mink; and ordinarily it is not very noticeable in a weasel. Its emission is under control, and becomes perceivable mainly when the animal is excited or alarmed. Its service seems to be that of attracting the sexes; and trappers save it to put upon their bait as an additional allurement.

The polecat, or "foumart," of Europe is about two feet long, of which the bushy tail occupies 5–7 inches, and its fur is long, loose, dark brown, and known as "fitch." The Siberian and Tibetan polecats are similar species, and a smaller mottled kind is common from the Danube to the Indus. All are more dreaded by gamekeepers and farmers who wish to raise game and poultry than are any other animals; and the wild polecat has become nearly extinct in western Europe, but survives, and its bloodthirsty zeal is utilized,

Polecat.

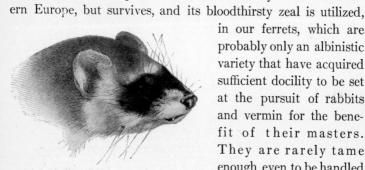

BLACK-FOOTED FERRET.

in our ferrets, which are probably only an albinistic variety that have acquired sufficient docility to be set at the pursuit of rabbits and vermin for the benefit of their masters. They are rarely tame enough even to be handled in safety, although the breed has been semidomesticated for centuries, and this, no doubt, is about the extent to which the ancient Romans and Greeks "trained" the stone martens they used as ratters.

Our plains are the home of a relative, buffy or whitish in general hue, with a dark, saddlelike patch on the back, the face crossed by a broad band of sooty black, and the feet and outer end of the thin tail black. This is the black-footed ferret, which, described and figured first by Audubon, eluded further observation for many years; and even now is not well known, though it is plain that it preys chiefly on prairie dogs.

In the older books, even down to and including Coues's "Fur-bearing Animals," the North American weasels were considered to be of only four species; namely, the common least- or short-tailed weasel of the East; the ermine; the long-tailed northwestern weasel; and the bridled weasel living on the Pacific coast and in Mexico. But, in 1896, Outram Bangs and C. Hart Merriam examined the collections of skins and skulls in the National Museum at Washington and elsewhere, and announced that we had twenty-two species and subspecies, none precisely the same as those of Europe. Most of them, however, belong to the West and far North, and naturalists of a less radical school will probably refuse to admit so much specific distinction. At any rate, they differ little in general character, and such peculiarities as belong to each Merriam connects with their food. Thus he finds that the group of northern weasels represented by *Putorius cicognani* flourishes only in the country where the meadow mice (Microtus) abound; the large western weasel, *P. longicauda*, does not range much outside of the re-

gion inhabited by the pocket gophers on which it feeds; the black-footed one frequents only the prairie-dog country southward; and "in the far North, where the frozen tundras are inhabited by

CALIFORNIA BRIDLED WEASEL.

lemmings as well as voles, two weasels are present: the tiny, narrow-skulled 'rixosus,' which feeds mainly on mice, and the large, broad-skulled 'arcticus' [analogue of the true ermine] on lemmings and rabbits." With these fine points of classification we need not here concern ourselves. A weasel, in the Old World or in the New, in Labrador, or Florida, or Mexico, on the Yukon as on the Hudson, is substantially the same, — a keen, agile, relentless, indomitable hunter, within his powers a being of the highest type of effectiveness.

"Swift and sure-footed, he makes open chase and runs down his prey; keen of scent he tracks them, and makes the fatal spring upon them una-

Weasel Traits. wares; lithe and of extraordinary slenderness of body, he follows the smaller through the intricacies of their hidden abodes, and kills them in their homes. And if he does not kill for the simple love of taking life, in gratification of superlative bloodthirstiness, he at any rate kills instinctively more than he can possibly require for his support. I know not where to find a parallel among the larger Carnivora. Yet once more, which one of the larger animals will defend itself or its young at such enormous odds? A glance at the physiognomy of the weasels would suffice to betray their character. The teeth are almost of the highest known raptorial character; the jaws are worked by enormous masses of muscles covering all the side of the skull. The forehead is low and the nose is sharp; the eyes are small, penetrating, cunning, and glitter with an angry green light. There is something peculiar, moreover, in the way this fierce face surmounts a body extraordinarily wiry, lithe, and muscular. It ends a remarkably long and slender neck in such a way that it may be held at a right angle with the axis of the latter. When the creature is glancing around, with the neck stretched up, and flat, triangular head bent forward, swaying from one side to the other, we catch the likeness in a moment, — it is the image of a serpent." So writes Dr. Coues.[175]

Out of the many things which might be said further in respect to these interesting little bandits, whose bright eyes gleam out at you from a cranny in a lichen-scaled wall "like dewdrops caught in a spider's web," as Rowland Robinson pictures it, one thing only can be given space — the change of color from summer's brown to winter's white and back again each year, which so many undergo, and which gives value to ermine.

"Ermine" is the modern form of the ancient Teutonic name of the weasel known in Great Britain as "stoat"; but the term is rarely used anywhere now except for the fur of its white winter dress. The pelts come to market from Alaska, Canada, Lapland, Russia, and Siberia, and are used not only for ladies' garments, but for the robes of kings and

Ermine. nobles, and for their crowns and coronets. This came to be a matter for royal regulation in England from the time of Edward III, various ranks of officers being designated by the way the ermine tails were arranged. It was especially prominent in the regalia of judges; and the idea survives in our figurative expression "the ermine" for the judicial office. Its use as a symbol of rank led to a recognition of ermine in heraldry as one of the eight "furs," represented by an arrangement of points indicating the black-tipped tails which, in making up ermine fur, are inserted ornamentally in contrast with the pure white of the field.

A WEASEL IN THE "ERMINE," OR WINTER, DRESS.

The ermine weasel in summer is brown, individuals differing in color from light yellowish to a rich dark mahogany hue, according to locality, freshness of the coat, health, etc. The chin, throat, and inside of the limbs are sharply white, and the chest and abdomen are sulphury yellow — neither white, as in the southern weasel, nor orange as in the plains and bridled weasels, the last (of the Pacific coast) further distinguished by its beautiful black-and-white face. The end of the tail in every species but one is black; the exception is the tiny *P. rixosus* of the Canadian Northwest, which is only six inches in total length, and the brown of whose summer coat continues to the tip of the tail. This last is the smallest carnivore.

Now, in common with many animals of boreal regions, this coat is shed in the late autumn and rapidly **Winter** replaced by a much longer and denser one for win- **Whiteness.** ter wear, which in northern weasels is wholly white except the black tail end. This change of color takes place in all weasels of both continents wherever the climate is so cold that snow lies continuously on the ground from autumn until spring. The British stoat and our own weasels remain brown in winter (though paler) south of the line of persistent snow, and turn white north of it, and also on lofty (and consequently cold) mountain tops. On the Cascade Mountains along Puget Sound you may collect in winter brown weasels in the coast valleys, drab ones halfway up the range, and pure white ones on the summit. The change in color appears to be wholly beyond the will of the animal, and to be due to the shedding of the old hairs and their replacement by hairs which come in wholly white, but it appears that the process may be hastened by the early arrival of cold and snow, or retarded by a late season. The same molt takes place in warm regions, but there the new hair comes in brown instead of white. Nevertheless it is impossible to dismiss wholly the old belief that the change is brought about in some cases at least by the gradual blanching of the hairs; for we cannot dispose of such facts as Dr. Coues's statement that he had *seen* many autumnal skins in which the hairs were white at the roots and dark at the tips. A very full discussion of this subject may be found in Poulton's [178] and Beddard's [179] books on animal coloration, and in Lydekker's "Mostly Mammals."

As to the purpose of the change, it seems evident, at least, that it is beneficial in two ways. First, in screening the weasel from the eyes of both its enemies and its prey, by making it unnoticeable amid the snow; and second, in helping it to retain its bodily heat, which would be radiated more rapidly by a dark dress than by a light one. How far the former advantage is neutralized by the fact that its principal victims in winter, the hares, lemmings, and ptarmigan, are equally "invisibly" white, the reader may determine for himself.

The mink is the last, and one of the most important and interesting, of this tribe, — a musteline with toes somewhat webbed, and of stouter build than a weasel, about twenty-eight inches long, a quarter of which belongs to the somewhat bushy tail. Normally in the East it is chestnut-brown, with a white spot on the chin and sometimes others below, and the tail darkening toward its end.

Mink.

The animal is distributed practically all over the continent, regardless of civilization, which interferes little with its making a living. Alaskan and Pacific-coast examples are larger and darker, while those of the Gulf states are lighter both in weight and color. A second, rather small, species is found in the South Atlantic states, russet in color, with irregular white markings on the chin and under parts, and the tail chestnut toward the tip. A mink is well known in northern Europe, and another species contributes fine dark pelts from Siberia. The fur of all northern kinds is of great beauty and value when taken early in the season; and the trapping of minks not only engages the attention of a surprising number of professional trappers in every part of the Union and of Canada, but puts many a dollar into the pockets of farm boys winter after winter. Moreover, in many localities, more or less success has followed the keeping and breeding of minks in captivity for the sake of their fur, and also to dispose of young ones to be trained as ratters.

Our literature of natural history, from Coues's studied monograph [175] to the half-poetic notes of Thoreau, abounds in biographical materials, — none more truthful and vivid than those in the books of W. E. Cram. [52; 100]

"Minks," says this observer, in part, "combine the habits of the land and water hunters more successfully perhaps than any other animal. In warm weather they are fond of exploring wet swamps and low lands, where they find an abundance of frogs and lizards, and dig all sorts of grubs, beetles, and earthworms from the black, peaty soil and leaf mold around old, weather-beaten stumps and rotten logs. They are most inveterate nest robbers and mousers, chasing the little blunt-headed, furry meadow mice along their runways in the thick grass being their favorite sport.

"In April the female fixes herself a cozy nest in some hole among the rocks, or inside a hollow log or stump, generally hidden away among flags and bulrushes beside a stream. . . .

"In winter, when the still waters are frozen, they haunt open rapids and warm springs in the woods, or finding entrance beneath the ice of closed brooks, make extended excursions along the dim buried channel, alternately running beneath the ice and along the brook's border where the falling away of the water has left a narrow strip of unfrozen turf beneath ice and snow. Here they catch small fish and meadow mice, or, tracing the brook's course down to the wider reaches of the river, find larger fish and muskrats to try their strength upon. Water, however, is not essential to the minks' happiness at any season, for they can hunt rabbits all winter long in the snow as successfully as the sable or fisher. . . .

"The mink is endowed with boundless resources in the face of danger as well as in the matter of getting a living. Wander where he will day or night, it is of small consequence whether the enemy that attacks him is fox, dog, wild cat, otter, or owl, he is always within a couple of jumps of some place of refuge. If the water is near, he dives without a splash and darts away like a fish, almost as much at home as the fish themselves in the swirling depths of the eddies and dim passages beneath sunken logs and driftwood, only coming to the surface here and there for a breath until the enemy is left hopelessly behind. When the water is not within reach, he can go up the nearest tree like a squirrel, or dart into any hole or crevice that would hide a rat; and lacking this, can outrun and outdodge any ordinary pursuer."

The agile, slender, short-toed, cat-clawed fur bearers we have been considering have a group of relatives which are stout-bodied, slow, long-toed, and long-clawed, and which search for their livelihood on the ground or under it, — the ratels, badgers, skunks, and the like.

This subfamily (Melinæ) is distinguished for nauseous smell and conspicuous coloration. These two features seem **Fetid Fur Bearers.** to go together, and several of these animals have long figured as stock examples of what Wallace [185] termed warning coloration. "On the back of every skunk are bold white bands and patches alternating with coal-black, making it an object visible and attractive to brute curiosity from a long distance; but, as if to increase this notoriety to its utmost, the animal always hoists its tail, and the tip of it — or, in some species, the whole of this pomponlike appendage — is glaring white. Conspicuous? You can see it bobbing along above the grass as far away as you can see anything of its size." A similar contrast of colors is displayed by most other species; but whether the signal is heeded, and these animals so escape attack by the larger beasts and birds of prey as often as the theory requires, is a more doubtful matter, which I have discussed at some length elsewhere.[36]

The characteristic odor proceeds from a pair of glands, one on each side of the vent of the rectum, and its primary purpose, no doubt, is connected with the need for the mutual attraction of the sexes in the mating season. When not excited to discharge it, few of these animals emit a bad odor, and tame skunks and badgers are no more offensive than other flesh-eating pets, even when the glands have not been surgically removed, as is often done; nor do they soil their fur or their habitations except by accident.

A connecting link between the musteline and the present, or meline, groups is found in the African zorillas, of which the best known is the Cape polecat, — an almost exact miniature of our skunk, and giving an equally offensive secretion; it and its Egyptian and Syrian cousins are noted poultry thieves, but are sometimes kept as tamed **Ratel.** mousers. An allied East Indian genus (Helictis) contains the "ferret badgers," small, bushy tailed, gayly colored, tree-climbing, omnivorous forest animals of India and the Malay Islands. Next comes the "ratel," as it is known in Africa, or "Indian badger" in Asia. It is a powerful animal, bigger than a badger and of similar shape, but black on the face and lower half of the body up to a line running from the forehead and above the small ears along the sides to the top of the tail, above which the color is gray; the creature thus looks as if it wore a white-edged blanket. Heuglin gives the Arab name as "abu djaga," and says it feeds on all sorts of larvæ and grubs, and is particularly fond of the honey and wax of bees. A hole in a hillside or river bank serves it as a den. Here a pair live in fair security, coming forth at night to search for such small mammals, birds, frogs, insects, etc., as it can catch or dig up. In the north of India the natives call it "gravedigger," and say it exhumes human corpses; but this charge is false. Its great foreclaws enable it to tear ant-hills to pieces, and to excavate the subterranean nests of bees, to which it is constantly lead by the honey-guide bird.

"I once had a pet ratel in the Punjab," writes a British officer, "which used to follow me about the house and garden like a dog, and was perfectly tame, although somewhat rough with strangers. It seldom tasted animal food, lived on sweetened rice and milk, bazaar sweetmeats, fruits of all sorts, but, above all things, was fond of raw eggs, and had one every morning for breakfast. It used to play half the day with a wanderoo monkey I was the happy possessor of, and would drive away and utterly put to flight a poor old doggie of mine who used to try to make friends. A man on the scaffold I have no doubt would have laughed to see the beejoo (for such is its name among the natives) and the black monkey endeavoring to unravel a hedgehog, an attempt which, I need not say, was never a success. This animal has the loosest-fitting skin of any mammal of my acquaintance; it seems as if he could be shaken out of his skin, an advantage probably he may be thankful for when baited or drawn by dogs, a cruel proceeding I never permitted with my Bijou, which naturally became its familiar name."

Two related animals of the East are the teludu, or stinking badger, a small nocturnal burrower of Java and Sumatra, **Badgers.** which may eject its dreadful fluid like a skunk; and the large, long-snouted, piglike sand badgers or balisaurs of northeastern India and Assam. These two bring us to the true badger of Europe and eastward, — one of the most familiar animals of the Old World. It lives in the woods, is nocturnal, omnivorous, and brings forth its young in a deep, winding burrow permanently occupied, — three or four at a time, born naked and blind, after gestation lasting twelve or sometimes fifteen months. Four other species are found in Asia, one peculiar to Japan; and extinct species are known as far back as Pliocene strata.

To this animal our language owes the expressive verb "to badger"; that is, to harass; and it comes from a practice in which our British fore-fathers took great delight — badger baiting. "In order to give the better effect to this diversion," Strutt [196] explains, "a hole is dug in the ground for the retreat of the animal; and the dogs run at him singly in succession; for it is not usual, I believe, to permit any more than one of them to attack him at once, and the dog which approaches him with the least timidity, fastens upon him the most firmly, and brings him the soonest from his hole, is accounted the best." But in its later times — and the "sport" lasted in

Copyright, N. Y. Zoölogical Society.
THE AMERICAN BADGER.
Sanborn, Phot.

country places until the beginning of the nineteenth century — the poor creature was no longer treated with such fairness, but was put into a barrel laid upon its side and attacked by an unlimited number of dogs, among which it was able, often, to do much execution before overcome, thanks to its powerful jaws and sharp teeth. Old books show that this animal was formerly called "grey" or "brock" (still heard provincially), and that in Italy and France its flesh was considered a delicacy when made into hams or bacon; also that the skin when dressed with the hair on is impervious to rain, and was a favorite covering for trunks, while out of the hairs them-selves are made artists' brushes.

Our American badger resembles the European one in appearance and habits, but is smaller, has different teeth, etc. When this country was first explored badgers were met with everywhere in open lands from the Alleghanies to the Pacific, and as far north as Peace River. Wisconsin took its name, "Badger State," after them. Now they have disappeared from the prairie states, and are rare except in the high, dry plains, where gophers and prairie dogs remain to support them.

The badger is truly a "beast of the field," — digging or stealing underground holes, and preying upon everything it can catch or conquer.
American Badger. Its body is two feet long, extraordinarily low-hung and broad, and when it is curled up asleep, and its long fur is erect, it looks like a well-stuffed cushion. The legs are short and firm, and the large feet are furnished with long and very strong claws, making them powerful digging tools. The head is broad, massive, and doglike, with round, furry ears, a hairy muzzle, and jaws filled with formidable teeth, scarcely less terrible than those of the wolverine. " The whole squat, compact, large-boned, massively skulled form indicates great muscular power; and it is controlled by a capable brain and an indomitable spirit. . . . The loose fur is a ' grizzle of blackish, with white, gray, or tawny,' each hair having all these colors on some part of its length, and the whole blending handsomely."

The badger feeds upon whatever animal food he can kill or catch that is not carrion — principally the ground squirrels, gophers, and field mice among which he lives. It is beyond his ability to chase and catch these nimble fellows, for the badger is slow and clumsy; but it "is the work of a very few minutes for this vigorous miner to so far enlarge their burrows that it can reach the deepest recesses." His hunting is at night.

The entrance to its own burrow is large, and the tunnel reaches below the frost line, and may be almost any length. The animal changes its abode frequently, and constantly digs more holes than it needs, thereby saving a good deal of labor for coyotes, foxes, ferrets, snakes, owls, etc., which take possession of its abandoned intrenchments. Godman tells us that three or four young are born in summer, and that the period of life may reach fifteen years. In the United States the animal is more or less active all winter, being able to search out or dig out enough sleeping ground squirrels, marmots, etc., in spite of the frost, to satisfy its needs if not its appetite. Farther north, however, the greater cold and enforced famine induce or compel it to pass in semitorpidity the more severe months.

The fullest accounts of badger life are to be found in Coues's "Fur Bearers," and in the works of Audubon,[90] Godman,[91] and Richardson;[188] and a chapter in my "Wild Neighbors" contains a biography in which the animal's traits are described and discussed at length.

Last of the mustelines is the skunk — an animal exclusively American, and covering under its name many species and a multitude of misdemeanors. Considering diversities **Skunks.** in climate and food, the habits of all are essentially the same. The common eastern skunk is about the size of a cat, but more robust, and with taller hindquarters and a pointed, somewhat piglike snout; this form, and the planti-

THE COMMON EASTERN SKUNK.

179

grade feet, account for that mincing gait characteristic of it. His fur is long, thick, and glossy black, variegated with pure white, and is in constant demand by fur buyers, so that the animal is incessantly trapped in all parts of the country. The white runs in a narrow stripe up the nose, expands behind the ears into a saddlelike patch on the nape of the neck, then narrows backward over the shoulder, and there divides, a stripe curving backward and downward on each side, leaving an intensely black, wedge-shaped tract between them, continued over the upper surface of the bushy tail; the under surface and tip of the tail are white. This description will apply in a general way to any of the nine species which a recent monograph [186] of the genus Mephitis (or Chincha) enumerates in North America; and all the species are extremely variable.

The skunk is probably as numerous in most localities as ever it was, since its food resources are increased rather than diminished by rural civilization, while its natural enemies are reduced. Of mankind it seems perfectly fearless, and when one is met in the road (usually toward evening, when it begins its nightly wanderings) it keeps steadily on its course and the man, if he is wise, does not dispute as to right of way. It habitually digs a deep burrow for a home, but may take possession of a woodchuck's hole, a cave, hollow stump, or stone wall, and often seeks a lodging beneath a house or barn, making its presence known sooner or later during the winter by a stench that compels the landlord to evict the intruder straightway.

An annual litter of six to ten "kittens" is produced; and these young skunks, when taken early, have been tamed and enjoyed by many persons, notwithstanding, as Godman puts it, that "such a pet requires very cautious management." No one has had so much experience, or has so well recorded it, in this direction, as Dr. Merriam, who declares that as pets skunks are attractive in appearance, gentle, cleanly, playful, and sometimes really affectionate.

The staple food of skunks in summer is insects, mainly beetles, grass-hoppers, and the like. The number of insects a single one will destroy is enormous, and mice are also pursued with avidity and success. The pro-digious harm both the insects and the mice do to crops, orchards, grass, etc., is expressed in appalling statistics; and the skunk is one of the most effi-cient aids of the harassed agriculturist, yet, because it occasionally raids

A LITTLE STRIPED SKUNK OR PHOBY CAT.
This is the animal called " civet cat " by the fur-trappers of the southwestern States.

a poultry yard, it is killed on sight by the average farmer, whose prejudice is as large as his ignorance. Western skunks capture the destructive striped gophers and prairie spermophiles, while even rabbits are now and then followed and attacked. These timid animals have a habit of running into any sort of a hole, and frequently enter one at the other end of which dwells a skunk, fox, or badger, which makes short work of poor bunny, and, I hope, is properly grateful to the providence that thus sends a meal home in its original package. Reptiles, also, form a share of the skunk's subsistence, — toads, frogs, salamanders, and serpents.

To the skunk's power of hurling an acrid and terribly stinking liquor from its anal glands great attention has been paid by everybody. Coues[175] and Merriam[48] furnish complete technical information as to the matter; and in "Wild Neighbors" I have sketched this information in detail, and discussed the effect of the possession of this extraordinary "weapon" upon the nature and habits of the creature whose audacity seems merely the expression of perfect self-confidence.

A closely allied genus (Spilogale), the little striped skunks, inhabits the warmer parts of the continent and contains several species. These are decidedly smaller than Mephitis, and instead of two broad white stripes have four narrow and often broken white stripes upon the shoulders, while the sides and rump are marked with transverse curving lines and irregular spots. One handsome species is distributed through most of our southern states. Finally, we have in Texas, and thence southward, the white-backed or hog-nosed skunks, or mapuritos of the genus Conepatus, which are of large size, and black, but with the whole back blanketed with white much like a ratel. The head is narrow, the snout long and somewhat piglike, usually worn on top by much probing and rooting; and the tail is a short, stubby brush. The familiar Texan one[68] subsists mainly on large burrowing beetles and other noxious insects, varied by cactus fruits and berries. Its gland-discharge is vile and copious.

The otters and sea otters must be separated as a subfamily (Lutrinæ) on account of their adaptations to an aquatic life and diet. Their lineage is ancient, going back at **Otters.** least to a Lower Miocene fossil ancestor, Potamatherium — a near relative of the civets of its period. Otters are distributed all over the world except Australasia, in about ten species, all very much alike. They have an elongated, flexuous body, a tail very strong and broad at the base and tapering roundly to the end; short, stout limbs and webbed feet; and a bulldog-like head, with powerful jaws, bristling whiskers, small black eyes, and little pointed, closable ears. Males will average about three and a half feet in total length and weigh eighteen to twenty-four pounds; females are smaller.

As the otter lives exclusively on fish, it is rarely met with far from a stream or pond, and frequently disports itself in the sea. As much at home in the water as the fish it chases and

OTTER AND FISHER.

captures by a speed and agility superior to their own, it yet must bring its catch ashore to be eaten and leaves the tail as a memento of the meal. Unfortunately it sees no reason to discriminate between those fish in which the angler is interested — often financially — and the baser sorts; and therefore in Europe, or wherever trout and salmon are "preserved," the otter is regarded as vermin and vigorously persecuted. The chase of it then becomes of itself a sport of no mean kind, calling for the aid of specially bred hounds of great endurance and courage, since the otter is wily in eluding capture, must be followed fearlessly into bad waters and dangerous retreats, and when cornered is capable of fierce and bloody resistance, taxing the skill and pluck of both dogs and men until dispatched by the thrust of a spear. Nevertheless otters have been tamed and taught to fish and to bring their catch ashore, or to swim about and drive fish into nets. This art is an old one in the Orient, and occasionally practiced in Europe. As pets otters are most amusing, being fond of romping with the dogs, and showing much intelligence and affection toward their masters. The mediæval Catholic Church declared the animal, in view of its aquatic life, to be "fish," and so permitted the eating of its flesh on fast days; thus enabling the Carthusian monks to indulge in it without violating their rule of abstention from flesh, as readers of Izaak Walton's genial philosophy will remember.

The fur of otters is of very fine quality, dense, grayish at the base, and rich, shining dark brown on the surface. Its value is now very great, as otters are fast disappearing, though a few manage to exist, by nocturnal, secretive habits, even in long-settled countries. But the Brazilian otter, which is the largest and fiercest of its race, hunts wholly by day, and "works" its rivers in large companies.[10]

Our North-American otter, though closely similar in most respects to the European one, has certain noteworthy peculiarities, extensively treated by Coues[175] and other American naturalists. The species was originally scattered over most of the continent, and some still linger in every state, but trapping for them is unprofitable now except in the far North. Merriam says that in summer in the Adirondacks they live very largely on crayfish; other writers mention a wide variety of food beyond fish. In winter they wander widely, starting on excursions which require them to make long overland trips through the snow from one frozen river or lake to another, in order to get a requisite amount of food. A striking characteristic of our otter is its playfulness, so that, as Hornaday remarks, a single otter is worth more to a "zoo" than a score of beavers, because it is constantly amusing. For one trick it is famous — its sliding. When in winter the animal is in a hurry, **Otter Sliding.** it has a way of making a few leaps and then hurling itself forward on its belly over ice or snow, especially down an incline. But it also does this "just for fun."

"Their favorite sport," as Godman describes this diversion, "is sliding, and for this purpose in winter the highest ridge of snow is selected, to the top of which the otters scramble, where, lying on the belly, with the fore feet bent backwards, they give themselves an impulse with the hind legs and swiftly glide head-foremost down the declivity, sometimes for the distance of twenty yards. This sport they continue, apparently with the keenest enjoyment, until fatigue or hunger induces them to desist."

THE SEA OTTER.

Usually the termination of the slope must give them a long skate across the ice, or a plunge into the water, in order to be satisfactory; but the sport still attracts them where there is no snow or ice at all, for Audubon describes mud slides on the stream banks of the southern states, and along the dikes of the rice fields, where slippery soil answers all purposes, and deeply worn troughs attest the frequency of the play. His account of one of their dens in the hollow base of a tree in a swamp is also of great interest.

A very remarkable animal is its oceanic cousin the sea otter, whose skin is now by far the most costly of furs. Its home is the North Pacific, where primitively it inhabited the Kamchatkan coasts, and the islands and shores on the American side south to California. At favorable places it was in plenty, so that voyagers and traders toward the end of the eighteenth century gathered thousands of cloaks made by the Indians from its skin (less valued by them than some others), besides bales of fresh pelts bought for a trifling price. Within a few years, however, hunters had driven the excessively wary otters from all but a few remote and rocky islets in Bering Sea; and such as still remain alive must be sought in the open ocean, since none now comes ashore, even about the desolate Senaach Rocks — their last refuge as a nursery for young.

Sea Otter.

All modern accounts of the animal are derived from the masterly studies of its life history made by Henry W. Elliott[188] during his residence in the Aleutian Islands from 1872 to 1874, supplemented by Scammon's[189] observations at sea; both are extensively reproduced by Coues.[175]

The sea otter is a truly pelagic animal, rarely ever landing farther than to climb upon outer rocks and reefs, amid the dash and thunder of the surf. An adult will measure three and a half to four feet from the nose to the tip of the tail, which is short and stumpy. The general form is like a beaver's, and the skin is far too large, apparently, for the body, lying in loose folds, and likely to be greatly stretched in removal. The limbs are short, the fore paws small and feeble, and the hind feet enlarged by great enveloping webs into a semblance of flippers — powerful swimming paddles. Its senses of smell and of hearing are surpassingly acute, and with no other fur bearer must the hunter — for trapping is out of the question — take such extraordinary precautions against alarming the game. Although "pups" were obtained every month of the year, and used to be brought ashore, the Alaskans from the first reported that they had never known one to be born on land, and were of the opinion that the birth was always when the mother was resting on a bed of floating kelp. Nowadays, certainly, no birth occurs in any other situation; and the whole life of the majority of sea otters is passed in the open ocean. A single offspring is the rule, and its first coat is gray. "From this poor condition," says Elliott, "they improve as they grow older, shading darker, finer, thicker, and softer, and by the time they are two years old they are 'prime,' though the animal is not full-grown until its fourth or fifth year. The best specimens are deep liver-brown everywhere silvered or 'frosted' with the hoary tips of scattered long hairs." A fine skin is now worth in London (the central fur mart) $500 or more, previous to any furrier's preparation; and some single pelts have sold as high as $1400. Only about 400 pelts reached London in 1904.

"The sea-otter mother sleeps in the water on her back, with her young clasped between her fore paws. The pup cannot live without its mother. Their food is almost entirely composed of clams, mussels, and sea urchins, of which they are very fond, and which they break up by striking the shells together, held in each fore paw, sucking out the contents as they are fractured by these efforts. They also undoubtedly eat crabs and fish, and the juicy, tender fronds of kelp."

The Dog Tribe, — Canidae

In taking up the dogs and their kin of the family Canidæ, we study the oldest and most central stock of the Carnivora, — the animals most intellectual and most closely connected with man. The dogs display, says Cope, superiority to all other families in the character of the brain: "There are four longitudinal convolutions of the cerebral hemispheres, while the other families have but three." But studies of the skulls of fossil dogs show that their brains were much inferior in organization to those of recent examples of the family.

As to the origin and ancestry of the dog tribe, Cope shows the probability of their descent from the Miacidæ, the latest and most specialized of the creodonts (see page 80). Cynodictis of the European Eocene, says Woodward, may not only be an ancestor of Canis, but would serve almost as well for a forerunner of the Mustelidæ and Viverridæ. **Evolution.** Huxley declared [191] that Cynodictis not only lay in the direct ancestry of the Canidæ, but "represents pretty closely the stock from which the branch of the Viverridæ arose, subsequently to give rise to the Felidæ and Hyænidæ." The most conspicuous feature connecting all these animals whose ancestry is so commingled is the bulbous, bladderlike inflation of that part of the skull (auditory bulla) which on each side contains the internal apparatus of the ear, and acts as a resonant sounding-board, increasing greatly the hearing power. This apparatus and sense are perfected in this family; and there is good reason to believe that the Carnivora as a group have sprung from a common source. Notable among Miocene fossil genera is Amphicyon, whose remains are found in North America as well as in Europe, varying from the size of a kit fox to that of a grizzly, and it may be termed a "bear-dog." At the same period there abounded on both continents the genus Galecynus, containing many generalized species, all of moderate size and a foxlike aspect. This type prevailed throughout the Miocene epoch, and then gradually gave place to descendants which in their central line seem to have developed into true dogs (Canis), although Galecynus also gave rise to a series of larger and different animals (as, in North America Temnocyon, Enhydrocyon, and Hyænocyon of the Miocene rocks), most of which presently became extinct. The genus Canis seems to have been developed from Galecynus, which disappeared at the close of the Miocene, since which Canis has persisted and spread to all parts of the world. In its early history the family branched into many forms, experimentally, as it were, most of which died out within the Tertiary period. Among these side lines is one represented by the early Miocene genus, Oligobunis, — a powerful predatory beast from which, it is believed, has descended the South American bush dog (Icticyon); another branch gave rise to the Ælurodon of the later Miocene formations of our plains, whose teeth and jaws show it to have been a big, muscular animal with the bone-crushing, scavenging habits of a hyena. The dominant type, however, proved to be that leading to the dogs, Canis; and the process of development has been in perfecting their running and biting powers. They have become better hunters by lengthening the legs, reducing and strengthening the toes, which in the early bear-dogs were partly or wholly plantigrade, and by the lengthening of the jaws and coincident reduction in number and increase in size and sharpness of the teeth; along with this has gone an enlargement of the skull and a development of the brain beyond that of any other kind of carnivore.

Our friends the dogs should lead the list by right of their advancement, but it will be better first to examine some of their wild prototypes, especially the wolves, the most typical and powerful of the canine race.

The great gray wolf, still more or less prevalent throughout

Wolf.   almost the whole northern hemisphere, measures in its largest subarctic form about three and a half feet long, exclusive of the somewhat bushy tail, which hangs to the hocks, and weighs one hundred and fifty pounds or thereabout. This northern wolf has an under fur of slate-gray not found in southerly examples, and is typically of a rufous or yellowish gray above, more or less grizzled, while the under parts are whitish, and the tail is often tipped with black. These hues are paler in northern than in southern specimens, and the latter are also inclined to be smaller; in many warm regions totally black races are known, and the black wolf of Florida is considered by Merriam a distinct species; as also are the great pure white wolf of our Arctic coast and the wolf of Japan. In general the animal is a creature of wooded mountains, — a "timber" wolf.

In summer a pair will retire to some cavern or convenient shelter, often dug by the mother herself, and there six to ten whelps are born, but usually only two or three survive to full age. At this season small game is numerous everywhere, and the animals, wandering about alone by day as well as by night, pick up a good living with little trouble, and grow fat, indolent, and cowardly, or at any rate peaceful. As the summer closes and the whelps grow the parents take them out with them and show them what is good to eat and how to hunt for it. With the onset of winter times become harder, the small creatures disappear, and then the wolves must arouse their strength and intelligence to outwit and overcome the larger animals, — the wild cattle, deer, antelopes, and the like upon which they prey.

The peaceable disposition of summer changes as the snow fills the forests, the cold gales moan through the trees, and the long, dark nights enshroud an almost dead world, into hungry ferocity and a force of craft and caution born of the direst need, breeding a daring which at last makes the animal formidable to man himself. Much exaggeration has crept into the popular history of wolves, from the superstitious tales of old, which fill so many pages of Gubernatis's[208] curious books, to the stirring romances of "Wolf" Seton; but basis enough remains to make it certain that travelers through the wintry wilderness of Canada or Russia have more than once been attacked, pulled down, and killed by these beasts, whose boldness, endurance, and persistence in pursuit when crazed by famine, are almost boundless. Nevertheless more persons have been scared than hurt; and that mainly by the terrific howling which multiplies itself by its rapid, echoing volume, until it seems as though a dozen wolves were clamoring in concert.

Copyright, N. Y. Zoölogical Society. Sanborn, Phot.

GREAT GRAY OR AMERICAN TIMBER WOLF.

It is in winter, mainly, when the larger animals must be depended upon, that the wolves form themselves into "packs" and assist one another. To this class of animals **Hunting in Packs.** hunting is truly "the chase," for their method is, having found their quarry (in which the good nose for a trail and the keen hearing assist them), to keep it in sight and run it down. The endurance of their gallop is astonishing, yet most deer, antelopes, and horses can outspeed and outswim them, and would usually escape a single wolf. Therefore two, or sometimes many, unite, and by relieving one another, cutting across corners, surrounding a pond in which some fleeing victim has sought safety, or otherwise acting in concert, will exhaust and pull down an animal large enough to furnish a meal for all — if the later ones are not too slow in arriving! A band of arctic wolves will depopulate a district of reindeer in one winter; only the polar bear and the musk ox can hold their own against them. Very pretty tactics are often employed, especially by coyotes, whose work must be doubly strategic because done in the open. Plainsmen still call a particularly big old gray wolf a "buffalo runner," recalling the time when the principal prey of those of the West was the bison. "The wolves seldom molested the buffaloes unless they were disabled by wounds or sickness. The young calves were what they were after when they skulked through the herd, dodging the old bulls and angry cow buffaloes in the tall bunch grass of the plains."

Dwellers on the frontier, or in thinly settled and mountainous districts, suffer much from the depredations of the bigger wolves, which maim more than they kill and eat, when famine, or the lesson learned from some previous success, leads them to attack domestic animals. This destructiveness, and the value of their pelts, have led to their extermination throughout the more thickly settled parts of both the United States and Canada, and even in the far West they have become scarce since the disappearance of bison, elk, and blacktail. A black variety still haunts the recesses of the Florida everglades. In the ranching districts, however, cattle and sheep keep many bands alive wherever there are rocky fastnesses to which they may retire, in spite of the traps, poisons, and guns which they understand so much better than did their forefathers; but they are not as adaptable, clever, and safe as the coyotes. In Europe, as we learn from Harting,[109] Aflalo,[101] and other authorities, they still **Historical.** persist on the continent even in France and Spain, wherever a rough country gives them harbor, whence they may race forth on winter nights to ravage the farms and pastures;

and official returns show that more than half a million head
of cattle and smaller live stock are annually destroyed by
wolves in European Russia alone.

"In Saxon times wolves were very abundant [in Great Britain]; and
even so recently as the reign of Elizabeth they were to be seen on Dart-
moor and in the Forest of Dean. In the New Forest they were hunted in
the twelfth century. It would seem that the last English wolf was slain
some time during the reign of Henry VII. In Scotland, however, they
persisted very much longer. So recently as 1743 was the last killed. But
before this period they had begun to get exceedingly scarce, for the price
of a skin in 1620 is quoted at £6 : 13 : 4. In Ireland wolves lingered yet
longer; about 1770 is believed to be the date of their final extinction in
that island. . . . Much legend has collected around this fierce carnivore.
Aristotle, usually accurate in the main, still states more of wolves than experience warrants." Pliny, unable to sift truth from falsehood, was in this
matter "an eager listener to all old women's tales." Ælian added to his
marvels and asserted that the wolf cannot bend its head back; if it should
happen to tread on the flower of the squill it at once becomes torpid. So
the wily fox, fearing his more powerful enemy, takes care to strew his path
with squills. The conversion of men into wolves was a well-known superstition, dating from Grecian and Roman times; it formed the basis of much
of the witchcraft persecutions of the Middle Ages and onward, and has
left its mark in folk-lore, *e.g.* the Wolf in "Red Riding Hood." [37, 208]

Of our western coyote, red, barking, or prairie wolf, one
might write a long chapter, but its biography is easily accessible
in many books; and I myself have written it at
Coyote. length in my "Wild Neighbors," under the caption
"The Hound of the Plains." Formerly this wolf (or wolves,
for the old *Canis latrans* has latterly been divided [98] into a
dozen or more species) was to be found from the Ohio prairies
west to the Pacific, and from Great Slave Lake to Guatemala;
but now none is seen east of the dry Plains, where it continues
to maintain itself because its natural enemies have been killed
off, and because it is extremely clever in raiding the farmers'
poultry yards, pigsties, and lamb-folds; in fact, in some regions
it interferes seriously with ranching industries — far more so

than does the timber wolf. On the other hand it does good service by its ceaseless destruction of rabbits, prairie dogs, and similar pests, as has been well shown by Lantz.[193] No livelier

A FAMILY OF COYOTES.
From a photograph of a mounted group in the National Museum.

account of coyote hunting exists than that written by President Roosevelt of his sport in 1905.[128]

South America has certain other wolves and "fox dogs" not very well known. The most remarkable one, perhaps, is the maned or red wolf of the forests north of the Pampas, which is about the size of the common **Fox Dog.** wolf, but not so heavy, its height being due to its long, ungainly legs, which give it a stilted appearance. In the Falkland Islands there formerly dwelt an isolated, burrowing, coyotelike "antarctic" wolf, long ago exterminated. The fox dogs proper form a group of small canine animals, five species of which are recognized by Mivart.[192] They are much alike in their foxy appearance, though rather larger in size than a fox, and more variegated. The crab-eating fox dog is common throughout the forested parts of the whole Amazon basin, and gets its name from its fondness for crayfish; it often collects in packs and runs down deer. Azara's dog, or the colpeo, is known throughout the whole continent east of the Andes, and has been well described by Azara,[131] Hudson,[35] and others. It has much the habits of coyotes, but takes more rapidly to life in forests. Everywhere it is foxlike in its fondness for poultry, and in Paraguay destroys a great amount of sugar cane, while eating but a little.

In the small reddish variety of wolf native to India [19] we have a form which seems to bridge the narrow gap between wolves and jackals,—the latter, small, active, noisy, wolf-**Jackals.** like animals inhabiting Africa and southern Asia. Many kinds of jackals are known — none better than those of Egypt and Syria, especially *Canis lupaster*, upon which Anderson furnishes the following notes: —

"They live in the desert surrounding cultivated land, and descend from the gullies and hills at sunset, making their way into the palm-groves and gardens, where they often make night hideous with their howls. At Dakhel they appear to live chiefly on fruit, which is plentiful, and consists of dates, mulberries, apricots, etc., at different seasons. In the north of the Fayum the jackals . . . live entirely on fish. . . . Unlike the hyena, they often congregate together at night near one's tent, and keep up an infernal din for hours; their cry is usually a long howl broken into a number of yelping notes at the end. Like hyenas, the jackals do not penetrate any distance into the desert."

In South Africa the red jackal and the side-striped jackal are prevalent, and do much damage to sheep, poultry, etc., and like our coyote are successfully kept out by wire fences, which they will not jump. The well-known Abyssinian black-backed species [23] has similar traits; and that country has also a rarer and very interesting wolflike jackal called the kaberu. The most familiar of the Asiatic jackals is the common pale yellowish or "golden" one, traceable in a great variety of color disguises from Greece to Ceylon and northern Burma, in all sorts of country and even within the confines of large cities. More than others, the Indian jackal associates in packs, which use most effectively their native craft to drive from its covert, and in the precise direction they wish, any luckless axis, black-buck, or similar game, upon which they fix their attention; meanwhile one or more jackals have crept far ahead, and lie ready to spring upon the wearied and badgered quarry the moment the maneuvering pack has driven it within reach.[194]

"In the towns and villages of India the jackals act as efficient scavengers. Occasionally they take to killing poultry or lambs or kids; and Jerdon states that weakly goats and sheep often become their prey, while wounded antelopes are tracked down and killed. Among vegetable foods the chief seems to be the so-called ber fruit; but Professor Ball reports that in certain districts jackals do enormous damage to the sugar plantations, biting ten or a dozen canes for one they eat. Like the civet cat in Java, jackals in the Wynaad district of Madras feed on the ripe fruit of the coffee plant."

With the jackals we come to the end of the great genus Canis, but there remain in the "thooid" section of the family several

DINGO.

other animals which demand mention, such as the queer little raccoon dog of China; the dingo [20, 261] of Australia, which there both runs wild and is kept as a pet among the blackfellows, by whose ancestors it was probably introduced thousands of years ago; the long-bodied, short-legged, primitive bush dog of Guiana; the still more primitive and fenneclike Lalande's dog, or "bakoor jackal" [191] (Otocyon) of the South **Hyena Dog.** African deserts; and the African and East Indian hunting dogs. The hunting dog or hyena dog of Africa differs from the type in having only four toes on any foot and by its dental formula, — p. $\frac{4}{4}$, m. $\frac{2}{3}$; and it so resembles a hyena in

Copyright, N. Y. Zoöl. Society.   Sanborn, Phot.

AFRICAN HYENA OR HUNTING DOG.

general appearance that at first it was classified in that family. It ranges the country in swift-footed packs dreaded by every creature both of the forest and the veldt, and every writer adds to their evil reputation for both strategy and ferocity. Selous relates that he has seen a herd of buffaloes put to flight by them; and the negroes say the lion himself fears these brutes. H. A. Bryden thus describes their method of attack: —

"A pack of European hounds press their game steadily until it is run to a standstill, and overwhelm it in a body. But the 'wild honde' hunts quite differently. Each of the fleetest hounds in turn, or as it gets a chance, races up to the game and tears with its teeth at some portion of the hinder parts; the flanks and under parts and the hock tendons are favorite places. By this method the unfortunate antelope is finally overcome. As its paces become shorter and more feeble, the attacks grow fiercer and more deadly, and finally, maimed, hamstrung, and partially disemboweled, the quarry is pulled down and devoured."

This animal has been such a nuisance to both settlers and sportsmen that it has been killed at every chance, and is now uncommon. A century ago it ranged even into Egypt; and it is the party-colored, prick-eared dog represented in the ancient mural paintings at Beni Hasan and elsewhere.

The Asiatic wild dogs form the genus Cyon, peculiar in having only two molars in the lower jaw, and otherwise. It contains two or three species, one of which is Siberian, and closely resembles a small Eskimo sledge dog, except that its bushy tail does not curl. With its long, thick hair forming a real mane around its neck and face, foxy red in summer and yellowish white in winter, and its compact, robust body and short muzzle, this is among the most doglike of all its wild tribe. It is most common in forested mountain ranges and hunts in packs, chiefly after deer. At the other extreme is the wild dog of the Malay Archipelago, which is thinly haired and gaunt, as becomes a native of those hot islands. More widely known than either of these, however, is the wild dog of India, called "dhole" in the South and "buansuah" in the North. Like the others it is normally rusty red in color and makes its lair in rocky jungle, whence, more often by day than by night, it makes its forays, sometimes alone, but usually in a pack from which even the tiger and leopard flee. Doubtless they have good reason to fear such an unequal combat, as have big cats in other countries; and herein lies the root of the deeply planted antipathy between the two races, and the explanation of the ease with which a few curs will "tree" a jaguar or make a lion turn tail. According to Blanford [19] these dogs avoid the neighborhood of man, and consequently rarely attack domestic animals; "occasionally, however, they kill sheep, goats, and cattle, and Jerdon mentions one instance, and M'Master another, of their pulling down a tame buffalo." They worry their quarry to death exactly as does the hyena dog.

I have now passed in review all the kinds of canine animals from which our domestic dogs might have been derived; for it is certain that foxes have had little if any part in their formation.

It is probable that the dog was the first, as it is the most universal, of domesticated animals. I believe that, almost from his beginning, man made a companion of something

Pedigree of Domestic Dogs.

of the kind: perhaps, however, it would be nearer truth to say that the dog made a companion of him, for a striking characteristic of this fine animal is that he attaches himself voluntarily to mankind. This disposition has, no doubt, been greatly intensified by centuries of domestic associations, yet such a tendency must have been inherent in the stock. Wolves are far less likely to attack human beings than are any other Carnivora; their whelps are the easiest of all to tame; and the wildest dogs stay about the camps of their owner, or follow him in his wanderings, though their reward be scant in prosperity, and in adversity their confidence is betrayed in order to provide him with a meal.

The origin of our house dogs has been the theme of copious

speculation. Their world-wide presence — for, excepting in the South Sea Islands, the natives of every part of the globe have possessed them from time immemorial; their extraordinary diversity — more than two hundred well-recognized breeds, besides countless mongrels — and the fact that this diversity seems to go back beyond the utmost horizon of history;

"WAGGLES," THE AUTHOR'S FOX TERRIER.

the unlikeness of most modern dogs to any existing wild canine animal — all have been difficulties in solving the problem. An examination of skulls and teeth, such as was made by Windle,[195] shows that we may leave out of account in reconstructing their pedigree everything outside of the genus

Canis. Still further clearance may be made by setting aside dogs that we know to be simply tamed examples of local wild species. Such were the original arctic sledge dogs, — half-tamed gray wolves, — and the stock was constantly kept up to the mark by crossing with wild wolves. Similarly, the dogs found with the Indians of our Northwest were tamed coyotes; those of India — as remains apparent in the Oriental pariahs — are descended from captured East Indian wolves; those of the African negroes from one or another local jackal; those of the South American Indians from the maned wolf or one of the fox dogs; and other cases might be added. Everywhere it is reported that although suspicious and snappish toward strangers these tamed wolves, jackals, etc., were closely attached to their owners, in spite of the neglect and abuse with which they were usually treated. Experience gained in zoölogical gardens shows that the young of all kinds of wild canids respond eagerly to any friendly advances we may make. This must always have been so; and I have no doubt, as has been said, that from the beginning of his history man in all parts of the world made friends with some canine animal of his neighborhood, including, very likely, kinds which became extinct long ago, leaving as their traces features and traits in our dogs which otherwise we find it hard to explain.[244] These early camp dogs would become modified by interbreeding and by the influences of captivity; and as their vagabondish owners wandered about would be crossed not only with divers sorts of tamed dogs, but with the wild stocks of new countries; and this complication would increase as civilization extended. The dog as we know it, then, appears to be a composite from many lines of canine ancestors, and his present existence and variety are due to the unusual capability in this race for hybridity; while his natural ability to learn may and should be developed far beyond present attainments.

Though we are accustomed to think of the dog of primitive man as an aid and companion in his hunting, it is doubtful whether it was of much **Dogs of** real value in that way. It might help in running down a **Early Man.** deer or overcoming a boar, but the everyday hunting of a man armed only with bow and spear must be by cautious methods of stalking his game, and here a dog would be likely to do more harm than good. It is only since the invention of firearms that hunting with dogs has become

THE SETTER, — A HIGHLY DEVELOPED TYPE OF HUNTING DOG.

general, and the pointers and retrievers of our time are of very recent origin. The earliest men no doubt valued their dogs principally as a reserve food supply; and secondarily, taking advantage of that sense of proprietorship innate in the animal, because they were useful in protecting the camp against inroads of wild beasts or forays by human marauders. Man, and especially a weary savage, is a heavy sleeper, so that it was well to have a friend in camp who slept as lightly as does the dog. And when the depth of winter or other occasion of want and perhaps famine arrived, and it began to be needful to sacrifice their guardians for food, the first to go would be the ones least helpful and cared for. A dog whose gentler nature had made it the pet of the children would be hidden and shielded by them when the father's stone ax was lifted; and, turning toward others of the pack, he would strike down last of all that animal which had courageously befriended him in some encounter with a bear, or which was the keenest of the crew in scenting and announcing danger. Savages, though rude and thriftless, are not fools in such matters, so that an accidental, yet effective, selection of the better dogs along various lines must have begun almost at the first. Thus certain varieties would be developed and maintained with more or less distinctness and permanence during the rude stage when all men were nomadic hunters, and when there would be no other domestic animal. Evidence of the truth of this supposition is at hand. Remains of dogs are mingled with human relics of the earliest Stone Age, and in the later Polished-stone period, represented by the Swiss lake dwellers. As to the origin of the two hundred or more specialized domestic breeds of the present time, some of which are quite modern while others date back thousands of years, little can be said with confidence. One of the latest discoveries is of the remains of a distinct canine species, allied to the dingo, which was domesticated in what is now Russia by men of Neolithic time, and perhaps contributed to existing varieties.

"In the Roman period not only were sight hounds and scent hounds fully differentiated, but there were also various kinds of lap dogs and house dogs, although none quite like our modern breeds. Even as far back as about 3000 B.C., Egyptian frescoes show not only greyhound-like breeds, but one with drooping ears like a hound, and a third which has been compared to the modern turnspit; while house dogs and lap dogs came in soon afterward. Whether any of these are the direct ancestors of modern breeds, or whether all such have been produced by subsequent crossing, is a very difficult question to answer."[65]

The foxes so differ from the wolfish branch of the Canidæ in anatomy, especially of the skull, that Huxley made them a distinct group under the title "alopecoid"; but paleontology now shows a closer connection between **Foxes.** the two than he knew of. Some zoölogists, as Mivart,[197] set them aside in a genus Vulpes, or even separate them into several genera, but with Beddard we may include them in Canis. The type is that of a smaller, more agile and delicate animal than a wolf or jackal, with a broader skull and sharper muzzle, larger ears, a longer, more bushy tail, and usually longer fur. Weaker than its wolfish relatives, though endowed with great swiftness, and used to playing the double rôle of hunter and hunted (for foxes are regularly chased by wolves and big cats), its brain has been developed to a high degree to make up for its bodily deficiencies, and shows capacity for further development; yet, says Beddard, "the sagacity of the fox appears to be a little more proverbial than actual," and certainly is far more apparent in populous countries than in a wilderness. This fact is of itself, however, a tribute to the animal's intelligence as betokening a quality of mind above mere native half-instinctive knowledge, for some kinds of foxes display notable quickness in meeting the new problems presented by the clearing and cultivation of the wilderness, and the rising of man, with his guns, traps, and poisons, to the rank of chief enemy, — an entirely novel state of things.

The literature of fox hunting in Great Britain teems with illustrations of the animal's wiles in "saving its brush" in the face of the persecution to which for two hundred years or more it has been exposed

Sagacity. by that sport, and many of the incidents recorded are truly remarkable; yet undoubtedly the British fox would long ago have been exterminated were it not regularly bred and "preserved" there. In other countries, however, where little or no help is given by either law or public opinion, the animal holds its own among men by its quickness in "catching on," and by its cautious, keen study of each new thing it encounters. Man may be sure he has never studied Reynard so closely as Reynard has studied him! Even here, nevertheless, exaggerations and misstatements have crept in, else we must believe that the foxes had grown so wise long ago that the supply of their pelts must have ceased; at least so exalted a view of their ability as that, for example, in Seton's [198] "Springfield Fox" must be rejected, like much else in that author's fascinating but uncritical writings. The fact remains, all the same, that foxes generally are notably clever and quick-witted; and that they often, but not always, show astonishing skill and appreciation in coping by new and improved strategy with some entirely novel situation, where life will be the forfeit paid for a blunder.

The typical species — *the* fox of ordinary speech — is the red fox. Inhabiting the whole northern hemisphere, it varies immensely in both size and color, and has been given many local specific names; but it is probable that the "common red fox" of Europe, Africa, Asia (south to and including the Himalayas), of Japan, and of all North America, form only one ancient and diversified species, whose ancestors were of a circumpolar stock. Our American form seems especially variable, since its typical yellowish red, darkest on the back and shoulders, may be very bright or very pale; or may have the markings on the spine and withers very dark and distinct, making it a "cross fox," or be totally black with a white-tipped tail; or black with the tips of most of the hairs white, giving the fur a frosted or "silver" appearance. Such extreme variations are rare, and, making the pelt very handsome, are highly prized by furriers; but they may occur in the same litter with normally reddish ones. It must also be remembered that a good many English red foxes have been imported and turned loose in the eastern United States, particularly in Maryland, to increase the supply for the sport of fox hunting, and also in response to a popular idea that the British fox, as a result of inherited experience, knows how to play his end of the game better than does his American cousin. This sport has been practiced after the British fashion in the Middle South since Colonial times, and has produced a special American strain of fox hounds.

American Red Fox.

Foxes everywhere are naturally burrowers and nocturnal hunters of ground-nesting birds from ducks and geese to sparrows, and of their eggs; rodents of every sort, frogs, lizards, insects, and in summer and autumn fruit and berries. Some of the prey is got by running it down, for the fox is fleet; some by digging it out of its underground holes; some by stalking it with crafty caution; some by lying apparently dead until the victim approaches near enough to be seized by a catlike pounce. These are the essential tactics of its food getting in all lands, the fare and the method varying with the country; and endless stratagems match the native precautions of the small quarry. All the larger cats and wolves are its enemies in the wilderness, and the skill in avoiding them inherited from innumerable ancestors serves it well when in civilized lands the fox finds troops of dogs set upon its track.

Standard works are supplemented by admirable essays on the American fox by Thoreau, Burroughs, Lottridge, Robinson, and others who know him well; none is more complete and intimate than the history given by Mr. Cram,[52, 100] who asserts that in New England, at least, the foxes in cultivated districts are far more highly developed in intellect than are those of the outlying parts, or than were the foxes of a century ago. They are the most bold, skillful, and inveterate of poultry thieves, and will sometimes take as many as "thirty pullets in a single night"; and often half or more of the booty of such a raid will be found in a pile in some hiding place, which goes to show that the foxes of all cold regions probably store surplus food. In return for levying upon his chickens (or, in Europe, upon the pheasants and other treasures of the gamekeeper) the animal aids the farmer by destroying numberless rats, mice, gophers, and similar pests.

There is in California another species of fox, — the big-eared; and Alaska is said to have two more, but we know little about them. On the Plains scampers the kit fox, now becoming rare, which is only two thirds the size of the red fox, though nearly as tall, and frosted red buff in color. It frequents the prairie-dog towns, feeds largely on these and associated rodents and birds; is an expert burrower, and very alert and wary, to which it owes its safety rather than to its reputed excessive swiftness.

Very different from any of the foregoing is the gray fox, now

Gray Fox. altogether a denizen of Dixie, having disappeared from most of the North where the red fox holds its own so well. This seems to be the result mainly of a competition in brains, the gray fox not having the quick-witted

AMERICAN RED FOX.

A little farther

Ernest Seton

adaptability and fearlessness of the red; but it is due in part to the gray's less strength and fecundity, its young rarely exceeding four or five annually, whereas the litter of the red often numbers seven or eight. Otherwise the gray fox seems to have several advantages. It is decidedly smaller and less conspicuous, being silver-gray, darker on the back, and tinged with

Copyright, N. Y. Zoölogical Society.   Sanborn, Phot.

A GROUP OF GRAY FOXES.

rufous on the ears, sides of the neck, breast, and under parts, while the tips of the ears, top of the nose, chin, and feet are black. It is a woodlander, and seems incapable of adapting itself to the cleared districts in which the red fox so easily makes itself at home; climbs trees almost like a cat, and takes to them naturally for safety or to get grapes and persimmons to eat. There, too, it makes its home in a hollow stump or log, not digging a burrow, for the weather of its southerly habitat, and the later date of its breeding, do not require for its young the warmth of an underground nursery; and all the year round it can supply itself with food by its own cunning tricks, while the red fox must wander over many miles of country. The ground-breeding game birds and waterfowl and their eggs form its principal fare, perhaps, in summer, when hens or turkeys straying in the woods are likely to be seized; but rarely is the poultry disturbed on the home roost, nor can such worse depredations as killing young pigs, lambs, etc., be laid at its door. Audubon, whose account of this to him very familiar animal is circumstantial, speaks of it as a "pilfering thief" and of the red fox as a "daring and cunning plunderer." Gray foxes will run before hounds only a short distance, doubling constantly and for a short time, when they either "hole" in a tree or climb one; while a red fox may run straight eight or ten miles away and then back in a parallel course.

Extremely interesting is the arctic fox, of the polar regions right round the world. It is a shy, swift little beast with blunt nose, short rounded ears, a very long bushy tail, **Arctic or** and the soles of its feet well shod with moccasins **Blue Foxes.** of hair, giving them a firm hold on the slippery rocks, snow, and ice, over which it leaves its tiny tracks from Labrador to the Lincoln Sea. Every arctic explorer from Steller [203] down has had much to say of this animal, the accounts given by Richardson,[183] Feilden,[202] and Nelson [201] being especially full and good. The most remarkable feature of its history relates to its varying phases of coloration. During the short arctic summer its dress is brown with the under parts lighter, often drab. In autumn this coat is replaced by one of pure white, beneath which is a fine wool; and this warm, white dress, invisible against the snow, is the normal winter hue of the great majority of arctic foxes. A small proportion, however, are never either white or dark brown, but are slate-gray all the year round. This double phase may occur anywhere, one or two, perhaps, arising from a litter that becomes white; but in some rather southerly places the "blues" prevail, forming a local race. Such is the case in Greenland, Iceland, and in the Aleutian Islands, where blue foxes are now carefully preserved and cared for in a semidomestic condition, for the sake of their highly valuable fur, a certain number being killed annually.

In Alaska these foxes occur everywhere, but prefer rocky ledges, or the precipitous seacoast, where they can find snug shelters. Nelson's party, scaling the unvisited cliffs of Herald Island, found them in prosperous possession. Their burrows pitted the hills, each bedded with moss; and the animals sat about squeaking surprise rather than protest at the intruders. "During summer they fare sumptuously upon the breeding waterfowl, eggs, and young birds, which are found everywhere; but in winter comes harder work, and the ground is more carefully searched for stray mice, lemmings, or an occasional ptarmigan. In early spring, toward the end of March, when the seals begin to haul up on the ice and the first young are born, thousands of these foxes go out seaward and live upon the ice the rest of the season. The young seal's offal left by hunters and from other sources gives them more food than the shore affords at this time. . . . In fall a dead whale or other large sea animal cast ashore forms a general feast for all the foxes and ravens from the country round till its bones are polished. . . . The young of this species are born in May and June. . . . The young are covered with a dingy or smoky plumbeous fur all summer until the last of September or first of October, when the white winter fur begins to appear. In spring the fur gets worn and is harsh and worthless by the middle of April; it becomes prime again about the end of October."

For the most northern adventurers, which spend the winter on Spitzbergen, or even some more remote arctic island, no food whatever save an accidental find of sea-carrion is available during the dark half of the year; and so they have learned to lay away stores of food. While the brief summer lasts, these foxes are ceaselessly occupied in feeding on birds, eggs, and lemmings, and grow replete with fatness. As cold weather approaches they kill lemmings industriously and pack their bodies away in rock crevices and in câches beneath the snow, where they freeze and are drawn upon from day to day. The foxes of southern Alaska and other southerly regions do not seem to store such supplies, and are often driven by famine to enter native villages and encampments in search of scraps, and so fall victims to the dogs.

FENNEC; OR, DESERT FOX

EAST AFRICAN JACKAL

Several other foxes inhabit the Old World, but none calls for particular mention. The arid highlands of southwestern Asia have two or three small, pale, mice-catching species, of which the best known is the corsac. Another small and pretty kind of fox is common throughout India, and, since it runs freely and doubles like a hare, affords some sport by coursing it with an inferior breed of greyhounds, for first-rate hounds would overtake it too quickly to make the chase interesting. More attractive, however, are the exquisite little fennec foxes, four species of which dwell in the African deserts.

Fennec.

The one best known, the fennec proper of the Sahara and eastward, is the smallest of the Canidæ, the head and body measuring only fifteen or sixteen inches, and the tail six and three-fourths inches, while the sharp-nosed, big-eyed, "cute" little face is surmounted by immense ears, each larger than the whole countenance. These great ears are associated, as is the general rule, with the excessive inflation of the "bulla," or ear cavity, which gives such peculiar and picturesque breadth to a fox's face; and both structures indicate extraordinary powers of hearing. The general cream-color of the fur harmonizes the animal protectively with the sands, but the throat, cheeks, eyelids, and furry borders of the tall, pointed ears are pure white. These delicate and gracefully pretty little creatures are true desert dwellers, existing in the sandiest wastes as well as about the oases, and making deep burrows, sometimes in large colonies, and dug with amazing quickness, in which they spend the heat of the day, and whence they steal forth at night to hunt in packs after the jerboas, spiny mice, lizards, and other small prey upon which they subsist. "The inside of the burrow is lined with feathers, hair, and soft vegetable substances, and is remarkable for its cleanliness." They seem capable of going long periods without water, yet drink eagerly when they find a pool. All feed much in the proper season on dates and other fruit; and it is quite possible that the poet of the "Song of Solomon" had it in mind when he sang of "the foxes, the little foxes that spoil the vines."

None of this fox group seems to have had any part in the composition of the domestic dog. Foxes do not tame well, nor are they likely, or apparently able, to cross with dogs, for none of the few alleged instances of hybrids seems trustworthy. On the contrary, various wolves and jackals not only may cross in their wild state, but all produce fertile offspring when mated with any race of domestic dogs.

Bears, Raccoons, and Coon-Bears

In tracing the ancestry of the Canidæ, mention was made of the Miocene fossil genus Amphicyon as combining with canine features those later to become characteristic of the bear family (Ursidæ). This genus and related forms, such as Hemicyon, and Hyænarctus, so completely fill the gap, structurally speaking, between modern bears and dogs, that it is plain that the ursine line developed from among them.

One of the more prominent of the later ancestors was Arctotherium, — the genus of the arctotheres, — which seems to have originated in southern South America, where it was a contemporary of the saber-toothed tiger, megatherium, and those other huge animals of the Pleistocene which made the fauna of the Pampas of that time so remarkable. It had a great broad head, short, snub-nosed muzzle, and sharper, more doglike teeth than bears, showing that it was more carnivorous. Toward the end of the Pleistocene one species, probably a migrant from the South, dwelt in California, and is described by Cope [204] as "the most powerful carnivorous mammal which has lived on our continent";. it was as big as a grizzly, had a face like a bulldog, and died out with the disappearance of the huge, slow creatures on which it preyed, more by main strength, I guess, than by any exercise of activity or intelligence.

The nearest existing representative of these ancient forms is the little-known Æluropus of eastern Tibet, — a bulky, broad-faced, vegetable-eating, bearlike creature, grayish white except the legs, shoulders, ears, and rings around the eyes, which are black. This curious relic of a bygone time stands between Arctotherium and Hyænarctus; and between the latter and Ursus, the genus of modern bears, stands in Cope's view Tremarctus, with two species, one fossil and the other living in the quaint little "spectacled" bears of the Peruvian Andes, about which little is known.

Æluropus.

Not until the Pliocene in the Old World and later in the New did the true bears (Ursus) appear, so that this is perhaps the youngest branch of the Carnivora; and while highly specialized in many particulars, *e.g.* loss of tail, they retain many primitive features, such as the plantigrade walk. Of the various extinct species, all large in size, the most important is the cave bear of Europe, whose remains are extremely numerous in cavern floors [88] and other recent deposits, mingled with evidence that it persisted until long after man began to roam its forests; and he undoubtedly extinguished its line. It was so like a grizzly, judging by its bones, that some naturalists have asserted that the grizzly is its direct American descendant. These caves also contain skeletons of the brown bear, proving that its distribution was in the past far more extensive than now; in fact, it was not until shortly before the Norman Conquest that it was exterminated in the British Isles, which had furnished in great numbers the "Caledonian bears" so popular in the arena shows of imperial Rome.

Bears are massive, clumsy beasts, with thick limbs, big, strongly clawed, plantigrade, naked-soled feet, and an ability to take the world as they find it. It is in the skull and teeth that a bear diverges most from other carnivores. In-stead of having a

GRIZZLY BEAR.

greatly inflated tympanic bulla, associated with big ears and implying the quick hearing so notable in dogs, cats, etc., this bulla is small and flattened. The teeth have a general resemblance to those of dogs, but the broad, flat-crowned molars are more adapted to grinding than to cutting, and the flesh teeth are more massive and blunt. Other family peculiarities are the extreme shortness of the tail, the coarse hair, and the likeness in color and aspect, so that their classification is still in dispute.

European zoölogists regard all brown bears of both continents as a single species with numerous local varieties; while American systemists now divide those of America into seven species, besides half a dozen black species. For our purpose the list may stand as follows : —

Classification.

1. *Polar or Ice Bear:* long-bodied (about nine feet), long-necked, yellowish or white the year through; arctic regions.

2. *The Brown Bears* (including Alaskan brown bears): largest and heaviest of the tribe, yellowish or grizzled to dark brown or dull purple; Europe, northern Asia (except Japan, — see No. 5), and Alaska.

3. *The Grizzlies* (including the "Barren Grounds" but not the "Cinnamon" varieties, since the latter is simply a reddish phase of either a grizzly or an American black bear): large, massive, broad-headed, more or less hoary; western United States and northwestern Canada.

4. *American Black Bears:* smaller, head more pointed, flat profile; sooty black to red brown, snout yellowish; hind feet smaller than fore feet; North America generally.

5. *Asian Black Bears:* like No. 4, but breast marked with a light-colored inverted chevron; fur (as in No. 4) comparatively thin, glossy, and without dense underfur; Himalayan region, Japan.

6. *Glacier Bear:* see page 220.

7. *Sun Bear:* see page 220.

All the foregoing are of the genus Ursus; dental formula: i. $\frac{3}{3}$; c. $\frac{1}{1}$; p. $\frac{4}{4}$; m. $\frac{2}{3}$; but several or all premolars may be small, and shed before maturity.

8. *Sloth Bear:* small (about five feet), head pointed, lips long and mobile; tongue very long and protrusile; claws white, very long; fur coarse, long, especially on shoulders, blackish gray on muzzle, and whitish in a crescent on the breast; all India and Ceylon.

9. *Andean Spectacled Bear:* see page 211.

10. *Tibetan Party-colored Bear* (*Æluropus*): see page 210.

Bears are rather solitary, the males wandering about alone, the females accompanied by cubs often as big as themselves. The young, two as a rule, are born in midwinter in the family den, which may be a rocky cave or the hollow of an old tree, the center of a dense thicket or simply a bed beneath the snow. The cubs at birth are surprisingly small — not larger than rabbits — and are naked, blind, and very slow to develop; hence the mother is extremely solicitous about them, and heedlessly brave in their defense. Most of the instances of unprovoked attacks by bears have been cases of mothers who saw or fancied their babies in danger.

Although courageous and able to overcome the greatest rivals or foes, the weight and indolence of bears forbid their chasing the large grazers, while the agile small ones mostly keep out of their way; hence the flesh **Character.** they get is mainly that of animals too young to escape, or such as chance throws into their grasp. When lurking near settlements, they are likely to make forays upon the farms, and to carry off colts, calves, lambs, or pigs, especially the last, — and a bear climbing a rickety rail fence or stalking away through the moonlight with a squealing porker under his arm is a sight to see. A bear is a comical creature anyway, and never more so than when it feels good-natured and is amusing itself in cumbrous play. It can, when in a hurry, gallop as fast as a pony, but is too heavy to keep up the gait long, and usually its pace is a fast shuffling walk, leaving very manlike tracks. In the wilderness it tears open the houses of the beaver, muskrat, pack rat, and other hibernacula, and devours the tenants unless they get away. Thus Osgood [206] describes how an Alaskan bear pursues the ground squirrels there in spring: —

"Sometimes he slips along the hillside and tries to catch the squirrel by a sudden pounce, but this usually fails. When the squirrel dodges into its near-by burrow new tactics are adopted. The bear immediately begins to dig, throwing out big turfs and clods at each stroke, using the left hand chiefly, and watching the hole intently all the time. While this is going on the squirrel sometimes runs out between the legs of the bear and makes for another hole. Possibly he is caught by a quick pounce. If he escapes, excavations begin immediately at the new hole. The bear digs for a few strokes, and then stops to poke his nose into the hole and sniff. Finally his efforts are successful, and the luckless squirrel is devoured."

No wonder they are given to tearing down câches! Carrion is another important resource; and when a large carcass is found they scrape a shallow pit near by and half bury, half cover it for future use — a practice of which hunters take advantage both for sport and to poison the animals for the sake of getting their always marketable skins. The polar bear, in fact, must depend largely on the washing ashore of dead animals. This and other far northern species, however, hunt for live walruses and seals, traveling in winter scores of miles across the sea ice in search of them, but in summer finding them more conveniently. "The seal is basking on the ice. The bear at a proper distance quietly enters the water swimming toward its prey, keeping well below, and only occasionally allowing the nose to touch the surface sufficiently to catch a breath. At last it rises just beneath and in front of the seal, whose capture is certain." They also seize porpoises and other small cetaceans, and quantities of fish.

Fish, indeed, form a staple article of food wherever they can be obtained. The most businesslike fishing seems to be that for salmon by the bears of Alaska and Kamchatka, whose paths along the banks of favorite rivers are beaten roads. Both Guillemard [205] and Osgood [206] speak of this, and describe the clever fishing, the latter as follows, referring to the streams crowded all summer with migratory salmon: —

"In fishing the bears do not get all their prey in shallow water or on bars and riffles in small streams, as is generally supposed, but often go into **Fishing.** comparatively deep water in large streams. Practically all the fishing is done at night or very early in the morning; though their habits in this respect have doubtless changed in recent decades, since they have been hunted so much. It is most interesting to watch an old she-bear with cubs. The cubs do not attempt to fish, but stay on the bank and receive contributions. The old she-bear stands upright and wades in water even up to her neck, going very slowly with the current, watching the water, and making scarcely a ripple in it. She holds her arms down at her sides with her hands spread, and when she feels a salmon coming up against her, clutches it with her claws and throws it out on the bank to the expectant cubs. Often she stands perfectly motionless for a considerable time, and when she moves it is with extreme deliberation and caution. After supplying the cubs, she puts the next fish in her mouth and goes ashore to eat it. If salmon are plentiful or easily obtained, the two sides of a fish are all that she will eat. . . . When fishing in shallow water, the bear walks slowly on all fours as silently as possible, and when a fish appears in a riffle deals it a sharp blow on the head. . . .

"In the fall, toward the end of the salmon run, when fishing becomes unprofitable, most of the bears retire to the hills, where they feed on berries and put on fat during the last few weeks preceding hibernation. The black crowberry (*Empetrum nigrum*) is eaten in great quantities, and various species of Vaccinium which abound are also taken."

How the little black bears of the Maine woods go a-fishing is related in *The American Naturalist* (Vol. XVIII, 1884): —

"I came suddenly upon a very large bear in a thick swamp, lying upon a large hollow log across a brook, fishing; and he was so much interested in his work that he did not notice me until I had approached very near him. . . . He fished in this wise: There was a large hole through the log on which he lay, and he thrust his forearm through the hole and held his open paw in the water and waited for the fish to gather around and into it, and when filled he clutched his fist and brought up a handful of fish, and sat and ate them with great gusto; then down with the paw again, and so on. The brook was fairly alive with little trout and red-sided suckers, and some black suckers. He did not eat their heads. There was quite a pile of them on the log. I suppose the oil in his paw attracted the fish and baited them even better than a fly hook, and his toe nails were his hooks, and sharp ones, too, and once grabbed the fish were sure to stay. They also catch frogs in these forest brooks."

If this seems small business for such a big beast, still more ridiculous is the fact that insects form an important part of the diet of all bears, save those of the icy regions; and those living along the shores of Hudson Bay come regularly in summer to feed upon the windrows of day-flies (ephemerids) drifted **Insect** upon the beach. The insects most sought for are **Eating.** such as dwell in colonies and have nests stored with luscious grubs or combs of honey; and all over the world Bruin's favorite summer occupation is tearing rotten logs and stumps to pieces in search of fat larvæ, and digging out ants and bees from their nests in the ground or in tree trunks — the latter an exercise of which our black bear is particularly fond.

Copyright, N. Y. Zoöl. Society.   Sanborn, Phot.

AN ALASKAN BEAR.

The outraged insects swarm over the marauder, buzz in his coat, creep into his ears, eyes, and mouth, and sting him till he rolls on the ground in a fury of pain, or blinds himself with a smear of honey and dirt in mad efforts to brush the tormentors away; but his appetite outlasts his distress, and he keeps at it till gorged with honey, and then, cloyed and bedaubed with "linked sweetness," stumbles off to some retreat where he may give himself sleepily to the delightful task of licking his fur. The most inveterate insect hunter of the tribe, probably, is the Indian sloth bear, a common name for which, indeed, is "honey bear." Baker [147] remarks that its favorite delicacy is termites, for which it will scratch a large hole in the hardest soil to the **Sloth** depth of two or three feet. "The claws of the fore- **Bear.** paws are three or four inches in length, and are useful implements for digging. It is astonishing to see the result upon soil that would require a pickax to excavate a hole.

Upon the hard sides of such pits as those made in search of white ants the claw marks are deeply imprinted, showing the labor that has been expended for a most trifling prize, as the nest when found would only yield a few mouthfuls."

To this Jerdon adds some curious facts as follows: "The power of suction in the bear, as well as of propelling wind from its mouth, is very great. It is by this means enabled to procure its common food of white ants and larvæ with ease. On arriving at an ant-hill the bear scrapes away with the fore feet until he reaches the large combs at the bottom of the galleries. He then with violent puffs dissipates the dust and crumbled particles of the nest, and sucks out the inhabitants of the comb by such forcible inhalations as to be heard at two hundred yards' distance or more."

Nevertheless in summer and autumn bears live mainly on vegetable fare, — fruit, berries, roots, bark, lichens, tender shoots, etc., according to the productions of the country. "When the nuts and berries are ripe, . . . and the corn is in the milk tender and delicious, and the wild fruits, grapes and persimmons and pawpaws, are ripe, then truly does the black bear laugh and grow fat." Even the surly grizzly, and the giants of Alaska and Tibet, feed in autumn mainly on this fattening fare — absorbing fuel to keep the fire of life burning during the coming winter's famine sleep. Osgood [206] tells of a glossy young black bear which he shot one September evening in southern Alaska whose stomach was packed full of clean crowberries.

"The feeling of satisfaction enjoyed by the possessor of this well-filled paunch was very evident. Before shooting it I had an opportunity to watch it feeding, and was amused by its exhibition of exuberant spirits. It would browse leisurely for a few minutes, then would suddenly give a bound and roll over and over down a little heather-grown glade to the bottom, and then jump up to gallop at full speed up and down and around in a circle, apparently impelled by nothing but sheer joy."

The recorded experience of men who have met bears in their native wilderness is most contradictory. Here is a powerful
Bears and Man. and well-armed beast of prey, which must be expected to act like one; yet many persons declare bears peaceful and even timid, rather than aggressive, except in defense of their young, of whose safety the mother is anxiously jealous; the cubs are so extraordinarily helpless when little, that she must care for them far more than need most other animals. Wildcats, fishers, minks, wolves, and foxes, — all search for them as tidbits. Hence the mother is justly suspicious of everything, and liable to rush upon a man unprovoked, for fear that he meditates harm to her treasures, but otherwise a bear will frequently show no hostility, or will even run away. I have known two full-grown grizzlies, surprised upon a mountain top in Colorado, to flee at break-neck speed down a rocky slope when a couple of men appeared. The ice bears of Spitzbergen are fearlessly attacked with spears by the Norwegian walrus hunters, who bring back a hundred or more of their skins annually. Many stories are told of persons who have met our black bears in the woods face to face and received no harm. The Syrian bears are noted for their gentleness; they required a special command before it occurred to them to eat up the young hoodlums who were hooting at Elijah — and *they* were "she-bears"!

On the other hand cases abound of attack as savage and resistless as it was unexpected: a notable instance is recorded of the grizzly by President Roosevelt, and others are given in an admirable survey of the question by Porter.[126] When one is aroused to fight, its boldness and strength make it exceedingly formidable, and a blow from one of its paws is of killing force. A grizzly has been known to break the neck of a bison with one such stroke. That seems to be the customary method of attack, followed by clawing and biting, for the popular notion that a bear hugs its victim to death has no facts to support it. "The bear's temper, disposition, and power of offense seem to be underrated with respect to the species at large," is the conclusion of Porter's studies.

"Whether because its appearance is less impressive than that of animals which have gathered about them most of the world's gossip, or for any other reason to which this inappreciation may be attributed, both in Europe, Asia, and America, the Ursidæ in general have undoubtedly less reputation than they seem to deserve, and less than the deeds they do and have done in all countries would apparently have brought with them as a matter of course. Poorly armed and primitive populations throughout the earth think differently, however, about them. In the folk lore of Europe and Asia this creature is conspicuous. The great hunters write of it in a respectful strain. No man who ever stood before an enraged bear thought lightly of its prowess. A host of well-known names are appended to statements concerning destructive arctoids in the Scandinavian mountains and the Pyrenees, in the Himalayas and Caucasus, the highlands of central India, and the forests and plains north and south of 'the stony girdle of the world.'

"There is every reason why this beast should be formidable wherever it has not encountered modern weapons; and that it is so its whole literature attests. Richardson's name (for the grizzly), *Ursus ferox*, translates his own experiences and those of native tribes. Colonel Pollok asserts that 'in Assam bears are far more destructive to human life than tigers.'"

The hibernation of the bear is a matter of necessity, depending upon climate, ability to get winter food, and the need of rest. In very cold and snowy countries the females "den up" early and may be snowed under for weeks. **Hiberna-tion.** They do not go into torpidity but simply lie quietly, subsisting on their accumulated fat, the slow assimilation of which sustains their own life, and enables them to nurse the babies, which are born during this winter retirement. It is thus the female ice bear passes the cold months, but the males are abroad during all the long, dark, polar night, even as far north as men have ever gone. In the case of other northern species the males also hibernate, each by itself, but are liable to come out from time to time.

Two strange little bears are very distinct from the remainder, and deserve a few words. One is the glacier bear of the St. **Glacier Bear.** Elias Alps, Alaska. It has been known only since 1895, and only one good specimen has thus far been examined. It stands only twenty-four inches high, and is of the general color of the silver fox, whitish on the belly, with the hair not long, but remarkably soft and with an underwool; the nose and cheeks are tan, the back of the very short ears and the outer faces of the limbs, black. This pattern recalls that of the Æluropus, which endures a similar climate. Nothing is known of its habits.

The other one is the little sun bear, found from Assam down to Borneo, which weighs only about sixty pounds, and is black **Sun Bear.** with a yellowish breast mark and a funny round head with a square muzzle. These little "bruangs" are merry fellows, the pets of every "zoo," and at home spend their lives mainly in trees, which they climb like cats by the aid of their long, curved, exceedingly strong claws.

The bear, so familiar yet so mysterious, so formidable yet having almost human traits, has appealed powerfully to the imagination of men in all places and ages; and among the primitive folk of both the Old World and the New has been feared, revered, and endowed with marvelous gifts which have passed into a rich folk lore. Every book regarding the native North Americans tells of the veneration with which it was treated by our Indians in all parts of the continent; the Ainu, or aborigines of Japan, still worship it;[207] and European mythology abounds in stories and legends of the heroic part it has played in the mystic affairs of the past.[208]

Associated with the bears in the "arctoid" group are the "coon-bears," — a family (Procyonidæ) of odd little plantigrades, all American save one, of which our raccoon is leader. The structural relationship is undoubtedly closest to the bears and dogs, yet many of the species much resemble Oriental civets. Such a resemblance is not surprising, since fossils from the Oligocene and Miocene rocks illustrate the evolution of these animals from primitive civetlike Eocene Carnivora. The connecting link between the raccoons and the bears is found in the panda, or coon-bear, of the eastern Himalayas and Tibet, which seems to be a fairly close cousin of the Æluropus. It is about the size of a big cat, **Panda.** but of a form all its own, having high haunches, bearlike limbs and feet, with the long claws partly retractile, a thick woolly coat, and a long, furry, ring-marked tail. The upper

parts are bright, glossy rust-red, but the triangular face is white with a red streak from each eye to the corners of the mouth, and the lower surface of the body and the legs are black. This quaint creature spends most of its time on the ground, but it can climb trees, and its

A COON-BEAR, THE PANDA.

food and habits generally are much like those of a real bear.

The remainder of the group is American. No animal, indeed, is more characteristically American than is the raccoon, nor has any of our quadrupeds been more thoroughly and lovingly treated by our writers generally.

Captain John Smith, in his report upon Virginia, mentions "a beast they call aroughcun, much like a badger, but vseth to liue on trees as Squirrels doe." The rapid Ameri- **Raccoon.** cans quickly shortened these sonorous syllables to "raccoon," and then cut even that down to "coon." If you were to dock his tail to a mere scut, and do not compare the markings on the face too closely, he is "much like a badger," as the observant Smith said; but this is an accidental likeness soon forgotten, for the flexible nose, flat-soled feet, arched hindquarters, and long-ringed tail quickly impress themselves upon a new acquaintance. It is therefore its ways rather than appearance which declare him a miniature Bruin, —"that brief summary of a bear," as John Burroughs says.

The home of a raccoon family is usually in a hollow high up in a tree, where a limb has been wrenched off by the wind, or water has rotted a hole large enough for their accommodation; but now and then a place is selected nearer the ground, as a hollow log; and Kennicott tells us that on the prairies it will shelter itself in a hole dug by some badger or skunk. Properly, however, the coon is a woodsman, and rather prefers swamps. In its chosen retreat are produced in early spring five or six young ones that by and by grow

THE AMERICAN RACCOON.

large enough to leave home and follow the parents in their nocturnal vagabondage, staying with them a year or so until they found families of their own. Hence in summer and early autumn, when coons wander a good deal, they are most often met with in family parties. It is rare to see a wild coon out of doors in daylight, however, for then he is usually rolled up asleep in some lofty crotch, where he dozes in the sunshine, rocked by the breeze. As winter comes on they restrict their roving, seek a permanent abode, and in the coldest weather hibernate completely. This, however, is only in the North, and even there they are liable to awake and stir around during warm spells, and usually emerge from their torpidity in February or early March, when they are so thin and weak as to fall an easy prey to wildcats and other foes, and often enter barns and even farmhouses in search of food, to the joy of the farmer's boys and dogs. The raccoon eats anything he can get hold of; and Kennicott has summed up the matter concisely:—

"The raccoon," he says, "is omnivorous. It eats flesh of any kind, preying upon small birds and mammals, when it can catch them, and sometimes making destructive forays into the poultry yard. It devours birds' eggs whenever within reach, procuring the eggs of woodpeckers by thrusting its paws into their holes; it also watches turtles when depositing their eggs in the sand, and, upon their departure, digs them up. This animal is fond of fish, and displays remarkable dexterity in capturing them with his fore paws. It is also a most successful frog hunter, and may frequently be tracked along the river's edge, where it has been searching for frogs, crayfish, water snails, and dead mussels. In summer, frogs often form a large portion of its food, when some species leave the water and therefore are easily caught. Insects are eaten to some extent, as are slugs and snails. It also feeds largely upon various vegetables in summer; and its particular fondness for green corn (maize) is well known to every farmer."

The coon is as clever as a monkey with his paws; and to see one sit up with his back against a log, holding something to eat between his hind feet, and daintily picking away and handing morsels to his mouth with his paws, is irresistibly comic. Give one a half loaf of bread, and he will first of all dig a deep round hole down the center of its softest interior, now and then cocking up a knowing eye to ask what you think of the method. The common name along the southern coasts of the United States for the small, narrow, tangled, wild oysters that grow so abundantly in the salt marshes and inlets, is "coon oyster," in reference to the practice of the raccoons, who come down to feed upon them at high tide. Their partiality for crayfish, also, is notorious, those living in the far Southwest subsisting almost wholly upon these subterranean creatures, which they scratch out of their tubular burrows, so that the name "crab eater" has been given to the very similar species of South and Central America. One of the **Habits.** singularities of the raccoon is its habit of dipping its food in water or washing it, to which it owes its specific name, — *lotor*, the washer. Various explanations of this have been given; but it is probable that the simplest — namely, that it seeks to cleanse the food — is the nearest the truth. Bears do much the same thing on occasion, and will soak bread and similar dry, stiff food in water whenever they can before eating it.

The prime delicacy of the world in the coon's opinion is Indian corn, when in that milky condition of sweet half-ripeness which so attracts the squirrels, the mice, the birds, and you and me, if you please; and when he has found it he strips back the husk as deftly as any "neat-handed Phyllis," and disposes of the succulent kernels with ease and rapidity. This is his occupation and delight in the still, hot August nights, and this is the time when coon hunting is most fun and best rewarded, for then the animal is so fat that a large one may weigh twenty-five pounds, and his flesh is tender, juicy, and well flavored, whereas at other times of the year it is rather poor provender, even for a stew, and sometimes as rank as that of a muskrat; nevertheless, our colored friends in the South are willing to eat it at any time.

Coon hunting is one of the truly American sports of the chase, though its devotees have found difficulty in persuading folks to take their sport seriously. It is, in truth, a comical sort of hunting, yet calls for endurance, since an old coon may run four or five miles after he has been started, zigzagging hither and yon, circling round and round trees, leaving a track calculated to make a dog dizzy, swimming streams, and running along the tops of logs and snake fences, hiding his trail with the craftiness of a fox.

The hunt is always organized late at night, and consists of a headlong scramble after a pack of curs known as "coon dogs," because good for nothing else, by the aid of flaring torches or the uncertain moon; and ends in finding the gay little rascal up a tree, whence he must be shot, or shaken down into a fierce mêlée among the dogs by some adventurous climber, or perhaps the tree itself must be felled. Only one instance is on record of a coon coming down because he was asked to, — that in which Davy Crockett made the request!

In Mexico and the southwestern United States there is a charming cousin (Bassariscus) of the raccoon, called "cacomistle" by Anglo-Mexicans, but known more commonly among

RING-TAILED BASSARISC, OR AMERICAN CIVET CAT.

us as the ring-tailed cat, or American civet cat — not inaptly if one can imagine a civet with the head of a fox.

"In nature," says Lockington, "it is a dweller in the woods, making a moss-lined nest in a hollow tree. . . . It often grows bold and enters the miner's tent, and plunders his provision bag, thus sometimes getting caught. It is **Cacomistle.** easily tamed, and becomes so familiar and entertaining that it does much to soften the asperities and relieve the monotony of the miner's life. To him it becomes a plaything, and its merry kitten ways make it almost companionable. . . . In Mexico, where it is often tamed, it repays all kindness by keeping the house clear of mice."

Far more imaginative and vivid is the picture of it given us by Mr. Beebe,[242] a part of whose account I must give myself the pleasure of quoting:—

"A ring-tailed cat squealed from the entrance of its cave somewhere up among the dense shadows on the cliff wall [among the foothills of the volcano of Colima], and presently the little animal leaped to some overhanging tree and scrambled down to level ground. . . . Shrill little squeals have often wakened us at night, and now the little black-and-white creature which is making its way so stealthily through the leaves gives utterance to this strange cry. The moonlight is bright and every detail is plain, as the animal leaves the shadows of the underbrush. Its motions are quick and catlike, its ears small and erect, surmounting a tiny face like some little gnome of the woods. Mouth and nose are pointed, eyes large and lustrous, glowing round and deep in the pale light. But what the gorgeous train of feathers is to the peacock its tail is to the ring-tailed cat. The creature stands half crouching, listening to all the night sounds, when suddenly its tail appears — no bare possumlike affair, nor even like the more fluffy appendage of the raccoon, but a great filmy mass, ringed with black and white, curling and furling gracefully over and around the little animal. Now the hairs lie close, and the tail narrows, again it expands and fluffs out larger than the entire body of the little cat.

"Here the ring-tailed cat or bassariscus — for he seems to have no generally accepted common name — comes and goes, taking bits of meat to his family somewhere up among the rocky cliffs. He is a full-grown animal, and yet his tiny face has a wistful, almost infantile expression. How interesting must be the baby ringtails! But the innocent expression of these little fellows is only skin-deep. Great is the havoc they work among the doves and other birds which roost near by. They are somewhat like the raccoons, but are much more active and catlike. Among the branches they are at home, and can run up a tree trunk like a squirrel. A strange habit is that, like the iguanas, they sometimes leap from high limbs, crashing down among the dense underbrush. . . .

"The ring-tailed bassariscus is interesting on account of its relations to the raccoons. A study of its skeleton shows that it is almost identical with certain doglike creatures which lived during the geological age known as the Oligocene, perhaps over a million years ago. These animals of ancient days were the direct ancestors of the modern raccoons. So it was a hint of the far-distant past which squealed and leaped about our tent at night."

A second larger species makes its home in the Tropics, where also dwells a relative the kinkajou, or potto as the Brazilian negroes call it, borrowing very naturally the name of an African lemur, for this animal looks **Kinkajou.** like a yellowish, woolly, round-headed, long-bodied galago. It dwells almost altogether in trees, feeds on fruit and insects,

SOUTH AMERICAN KINKAJOU.

honey, etc., and has a long, prehensile tail; its good nature and monkeylike activity make it a favorite pet.

Lastly we come to the long-nosed, pig-snouted, ring-tailed, funny and fierce little brown coatis, which root up the mold of the tropical woods in search of worms, grubs, beetles, and other edibles. These piglike man- **Coatis.** ners are enhanced by their gathering in packs, when they become foes by no means to be despised by larger animals, for their tusks are long and sharp. Lockington [75] and Belt [26] give the fullest accounts known to me, — the former of the animal in captivity, and the latter wild. Says Belt: —

"One day I came upon a pack of 'pisotis' (*Nasua fusca*), a raccoon-like animal that ascends all the small trees, searching for birds' nests and fruits. There were not less than fifty in the pack I saw, and nothing seemed likely to escape their search in the track they were traveling. . . . They are very fond of eggs; and the tame ones, which are very often kept as pets, play havoc amongst the poultry when they get loose." He mentions elsewhere the animal's fondness for iguanas, which it gets only with difficulty, as it has to climb every tree, and then, unless it can surprise them asleep, see them drop off the branch and scuttle safely away. "I once," Belt continues, "saw a pisoti hunting for iguanas among some bushes near the

THE RED COATI (*Nasua rufa*).

Lake, where they were very numerous, but during the quarter of an hour that I watched him he never caught one. . . . Master Pisoti, however, seemed to take all his disappointments with the greatest coolness, and continued the pursuit unflaggingly. Doubtless experience had taught him that, sooner or later, he would surprise a corpulent iguana fast asleep on some branch, and too late to drop from his resting place. In the forest, I always saw the pisoti hunting in large bands from which an iguana would have small chance of escape, for some were searching along the ground, whilst others ranged over the branches of the trees."

Says Mr. Beebe, speaking of a locality near Manzanillo: —

"A colony of these coatis lived among the rocks not far from our camp, and every evening they started out on their foraging expeditions. They **Manners** did not join their cousins, the raccoons and ring-tailed cats, **in Mexico.** about our tents. When they came out about dusk, they all trooped down to the water's edge and drank thirstily, then washed their faces, coon-fashion, and combed their handsome fur with their long claws. They appeared to feed upon lizards and berries, and they were also very fond of a certain kind of hard, round fruit. When four or five of them were among the branches of a small sapling, the young tree suffered severely. They hunted mice in the open spaces of the woods, and I sometimes saw several crouched here and there, waiting for the first signs of life among the leaves. With a dog they were easily treed, and they fought fiercely when cornered. When playing and leaping about each other they uttered low, harsh grunts, and we never heard any other utterance. The Mexicans delight to hunt these coati mondi, treeing them with dogs and killing them with revolvers. They work themselves up to a high pitch of excitement, shouting, as a kind of hunting cry, '*Adios, Tejon!*' — the latter name being the Mexican name of the animal.

"How perfectly the actions and general *mien* of these nocturnal creatures reflect the efficiency of their means of defense! The life of the little mice, the prey of all, is one great fear; they nibble, wash their fur, scamper about, but ever with large fearful eyes, ever with feet braced to spring to the protection of their holes. The opossums start at every sound and slink tremblingly away. The coatis make little show of defense, but when there is any avenue of escape flee quickly. The ring-tailed cats turn a moment and bare their teeth in a defiant snarl before taking to flight. The armadillos potter serenely on their way, heeding little to right or left, respectful of others' rights, but calmly confident in their tooth-and-claw-proof armor of scales. The skunk alone dares to herald his presence with flourishing tail."

MARINE CARNIVORES — Order, PINNIPEDIA

THERE would follow here, were it to be included in the present volume, a chapter on the sea bears, seals, and walruses, which constitute the marine division of the Carnivora termed *Pinnipedia,* — the fin-footed carnivores.

The members of this group have their entire organization modified to adapt them to an exclusively aquatic existence. The body approaches a fishlike form, and the four limbs are turned into more or less perfect paddles, or "flippers." The teeth are of the carnivorous type, but without a special carnassial; the eyes are always large and prominent; and external ears are lacking except in one family, — the fur seals or sea bears. They are found almost exclusively in the cold seas and in salt water.

While there is no doubt of their kinship with carnivores, the degree of it, or the history of the divergence of the ancestors of the pinnipeds toward a maritime life, is not well known. Their closest relatives on land seem to be the bears; but no particular connection between them and the pinnipeds has been made out, nor does the sea otter, in spite of sundry resemblances, seem to be among pinniped ancestors. The most acceptable opinion at present is, that this is a group of very ancient independence, descended from a creodont origin (see page 80). The most complete history of the group is Allen's "Monograph," [234] but much has been published in respect to the fur seals by the United States government.

HOOFED ANIMALS — Order, UNGULATA

THIS is the great assemblage of animals whose toes are guarded by hoofs instead of armed with claws, and which feed on plants, — the herbivores. It embraces, besides many extinct groups and species, the cattle, sheep, antelopes, giraffes, deer, camels, swine, horses, rhinoceroses, tapirs, elephants, and their kindred. They exist in every part of the habitable globe except Australasia, have furnished sustenance to the larger Carnivora, and have supplied the need of man for assistance in his labor, and with materials for food, shelter, and clothing. Without them human civilization would have been impossible.

One cannot distinguish among the earliest mammals the forerunners of the carnivorous from those of the herbivorous lines; but before the end of the Eocene period they become differentiated, and there appear forms Condyl-arthra. clearly in the line of evolution toward the ungulate type. Thence onward they fall into distinct lines of development, termed suborders, the oldest and most generalized of which is the *Condylarthra*,[210] which originated in the Cretaceous age and came to an end in the middle of the Eocene. These were animals of moderate size, imperfectly plantigrade, with five toes all around, teeth adapted both to cutting flesh and grinding plant tissues, and small, smooth brains. The best known is Phenacodus, — a slender, long-tailed creature, resembling a tapir in proportions, but smaller. The condylarths are believed to foreshadow the perissodactyls (see page 352); but their nearest representatives are a second suborder, the *Hyracoidea*, which, beginning in the earliest Eocene, has persisted until now in the African conies, rock-badgers, or hyraces.

These extraordinary little animals, ranging in size from rats to rabbits, have an outward likeness to rodents, but are really very different. The **Conies.** skull and teeth much resemble those of the rhinoceros; there are twenty-one pairs of ribs, and the short legs end in five toes, which are united by the skin, as in the elephant and rhinoceros, and are round and soft, merely protected in front by a broad nail, which does not reach the ground. Their tailless bodies are clothed with thick, uniformly dark brown hair, discolored or absent around a curious gland near the middle of the back. They live in rocky or stony places, in communities,

THE SOUTH AFRICAN ROCK BADGER (*Hyrax capensis*).

like rabbits; make their homes in holes under rocks; feed at night or in the early morning on leaves and young shoots of trees and bushes; are timid and disappear with a squeaking cry at the least alarm; and in general behave much like our pikas. The only Asiatic one, the daman, inhabits Syria and Arabia, and is the "cony" of the Bible, prohibited to the Israelites under the mistaken belief that it chewed the cud; but it is now eaten by the Arabs. Several species inhabit Abyssinia and East Africa down to Mozambique; and the Cape and Natal are the home of one, familiar to English colonists as rock badger or rock rabbit, and to the Dutch as dasse, and often tamed as a pet. Three species of Central Africa differ decidedly from the others by their arboreal habits, making their breeding nests in holes in trees.

Amblypoda (stump-toed) is the name of another primitive suborder which began as a contemporary of the Condylarthra, if, indeed, it did not develop out of it, but lasted much longer, and furnished some of the most remarkable of the great fossils disinterred from the early rocks of Wyoming. They had rather small, short feet with **Ambly-poda.** five toes, each covered at the end by a little hoof, and all, with the heel, resting in a bunch on the ground; and were large animals, some even elephantine.

The earlier forms, such as Pantolambda, were light, long-tailed, and horn-less, somewhat doglike in form, little removed from the creodonts, and probably largely beasts of prey. Later (in the Wind River formations) came the coryphodons, chiefly American, which carried a huge skull lightened by big air chambers as in our elephants, and containing a very small brain; and the canine teeth projected from the mouth in strong tusks so that the head must have been much like that of a hippopotamus. Cope[211] said they probably resembled long-tailed bears, with the important exception that in their feet they were much like the elephant, and doubtless had a shuffling and ambling gait, awkward from the inflexibility of the ankle. But in compensation for the probable lack of speed, these animals were most formidably armed with tusks more robust than those of the Carnivora, and generally more elongate, and attrition preserved rather than diminished their acuteness. The size of the (about twenty) species varied from that of a tapir to that of an ox.

These died out and were succeeded by a group of still more gigantic amblypods, the Dinocerata,[212] with limbs taller and more slender in proportion, though strong enough **Dinoce-** to support a body in some species as large as an **rata.** average elephant's; and they stood upon their toes.

These huge beasts must have had much the appearance, habits, and food of our rhinoceroses, but their low-hanging heads were far more uncouth and remarkable, since the skull was long, narrow, flat, and with almost no brain cavity. No mammal known had a brain so small and reptilian as had these. They were armed not only with long tushes hanging from the upper jaw like walrus tusks, but with three pairs of horns, — two on the snout pointing forward, two on the upper jaw bones flaring outward, and two above the eyes with a bony crest arising broadly behind them. A series of skulls exhibited in the Natural History Museum in New York shows most strikingly the evolution of these protuberances from an insignificant beginning; but whether or not they were covered with horny sheaths is not known. The various forms have been named Dinoceras, Tinoceras, Loxolophodon, Uintatherium, etc. These amblypods became extinct at the close of the Eocene, and the last ones, though greatly superior in bulk and armament, had smaller and less useful brains than had their earlier forbears. The group degenerated and ended in failure — the machine became too big and unwieldy for the engineer in charge.

Another primitive ungulate suborder, *Ancylopoda*, widespread in Miocene and earlier times, contained large beasts shaped **Ancylo-** somewhat like hyenas, and having curiously huge-**poda.** clawed feet and other features which make their true place undeterminable as yet. The most typical ones are Chalicotherium and Macrotherium.[213] The *Typotheria* and *Toxodontia* are other extinct primitive suborders somewhat approaching the Elephants (Proboscidea), and a part of that amazing early Tertiary fauna of the Argentine pampas disclosed by the labors of Lydekker, Ameghino, and Scott. Toxodon was a prominent representative genus of a group of great rhinoceroslike, marsh-loving, hoofed creatures such as the nesodons (yet some were smaller), with massive heads and high hindquarters, having in much of their structure a most curious resemblance to rodents. Some of them were armed with self-sharpening tushes like a huge boar.

None of the foregoing seem to have been successes, so to speak; that is, they were unable to change with the gradually altering conditions of climate and vegetation as time advanced, and were crowded out by the more adaptable progenitors of modern hoofed mammals.

All existing ungulates except the elephants and conies fall **Ungulate** within one of two suborders, according to the struc-**Distinctions.** ture of their feet, namely: —

I. *Artiodactyla* — even-toed, or split-hoofed ungulates.

II. *Perissodactyla* — odd-toed, or solid-hoofed ungulates.

The artiodactyls differ, then, from the perissodactyls most conspicuously in the form of the foot. Both have lost the plantigrade walk of their Tertiary ancestors, and now step on the tips of their toes. This has been gradually gained as an adaptation to the increase of dry land and the formation of grassy plains, which we know went on more and more as time advanced, especially through the last third of the Tertiary period. The short massive legs and spreading five-toed plantigrade feet, useful in sustaining an animal's weight in marshes, were slowly changed to longer, more slender limbs and a digitigrade walk, as greater speed and nimbleness were required in making their way over wide pastures and to and from watering places, or in escaping the beasts of prey which were themselves

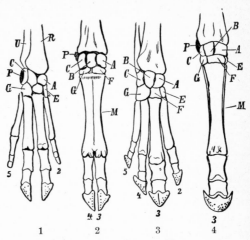

SKELETON OF FORE FEET OF UNGULATES.

1, Pig.   2, Ox.   3, Tapir.   4, Horse.

Bones: *R*, radius; *U*, ulna; *A*, scaphoid; *B*, semi-lunar; *C*, cuneiform; *D*, trapezium; *E*, trapezoid; *F*, magnum; *G*, unciform; *P*, pisiform; *G*, centrale carpi; *M*, metacarpus (metapodials). The digits are numbered.

steadily becoming swifter and more active in jumping by a similar evolution. The carnivores kept pace with them in every sense of the word. This useful alteration in limb structure, following changing habits, reached its utmost development in the two groups we are now considering, and brought about interesting alterations in the skeleton. The instep and palm bones (metapodials) were greatly lengthened, and the bonelets of the wrist and ankle (carpals and tarsals) were changed in form and rearranged. These changes proceeded from the earliest beginnings along two lines. In the first the third and fourth toes of the original five (practically the central ones, as the first, being useless, was lost almost at the start) were continually forced to bear the weight and make the push as each step was taken, and consequently grew at the expense of the others, and equally; and this formed the two-toed, cloven, or artiodactyl style of foot. The outside digits (second and fifth) of each foot, getting less and less shock and strain as the middle toes were enlarged by constant use, remained undeveloped, or even gradually lessened, until all that is left of them in most cases are the two little "false hoofs" which hang behind the pastern.

In the second line (perissodactyls) the strain came, for some unknown reason, more upon the third or central toe, and this by a similar history developed at the expense of the side toes, until in its most perfect form, the horse, nothing remains of the latter, and the whole weight rests upon the hoof-shod tip of the single central digit. At the same time, in both divisions the smaller bones (ulna and fibula) of the limbs became reduced and fused with the radius and tibia; and the clavicles disappeared as a result of the elevation and compacting of the body.

Coupled with this went on changes in the dentition, also along divergent lines.[1] Canines would be an incumbrance to grazing animals, and have been reduced or have disappeared except where serviceable as weapons. The gap they left has gradually broadened into the "diastema," or space where a horse carries its bits. In the artiodactyls, largely browsers, the incisors of the upper jaw have been practically lost, and the premolars and molars are unlike and have broad, flat crowns; while the perissodactyl (grazers) are furnished with strong, chisel-shaped biting incisors in both jaws, and all the cheek teeth are much alike, — long, deep-set, and strong, with massive, squarish crowns crossed by curving ridges of dentine, making them the perfection of grinders. The stomach is a much more complicated organ in the artiodactyls than in any other group. It must be conceded, however, that these and other present distinctions weaken or disappear when traced back toward the common ancestry of the two divisions which seem to have separated at the very dawn of mammalian history. An explanation of why there should be *two* such lines of development rather than one is that the originator of the split-hoofed line walked with that twisting motion of the feet still very noticeable in cattle.

The order Artiodactyla is divisible into two well-marked sections: —

A. *Ruminantia* — ruminants; horned animals.

B. *Suina* — non-ruminants; swine.

The former include the cud chewers — those which gather and swallow their food in haste and then at leisure gulp it up and rechew it in small quantities (cuds) and very thoroughly. This strange operation,[1] like the carrying away of food by pocket mice, monkeys, etc., enabled these comparatively defenseless animals to gather nutriment in a short time and then retreat to a safe place to prepare it for digestion. **Ruminants.** Associated with this practice is a large, complicated stomach, normally consisting of four chambers, into the first and largest of which the hastily swallowed forage is first received and well moistened, and out of which it comes

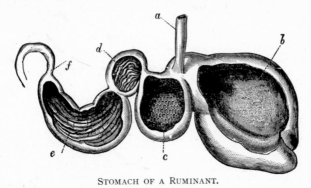

STOMACH OF A RUMINANT.

Stomach opened to show the internal structure. *a*, Œsophagus; *b*, rumen; *c*, reticulum; *d*, psalterium; *e*, abomasum; *f*, duodenum.

as "cuds." Then, when swallowed a second time, it passes on into the second or true stomach, where real digestion begins. The ruminants are also called Selenodontia, because of the crescentic outline of the hard ridges shown on the worn crowns of their molar teeth; they never have more than a single pair of incisors in the upper jaw, and usually none; their metapodials are united into a "cannon bone"; and they alone among *existing* animals wear paired horns.

"Under the term 'horns' are commonly confused two very distinct structures. . . . The word ought not, strictly, to include the bony antlers of deer or the giraffe, since these, although to a certain extent **Horns.** epidermal outgrowths, consist of true bone built up from blood deposits, and are not at all transformed cuticle or 'horn.' Nevertheless, as Beddard points out, the difference is one of degree rather than of kind.

The simplest condition is seen in the giraffe, each of whose paired horns is a straight, bony outgrowth, the os cornu, originally separate from the skull, but becoming permanently fused with it early in life, and is covered with wholly unmodified furry skin. In deer there is the same os cornu which may here be branched, and never becomes fused with the skull, but on the contrary is shed and renewed annually, and is covered with a skin modified into 'velvet,' which decays and drops off as soon as the horn core (antler) is perfected. Between these two falls possibly the extinct Sivatherium and certainly falls the modern pronghorn. . . . This is an isolated case, but connects the giraffe and deer with the Bovidæ, or proper 'hollow-horned' ruminants (Cavicornia). In this family the males of every species, and in most cases the females also, possess upon the top of the skull protuberances of bone into which air cells often extend from the frontal sinuses. These are called 'horn cores,' and form the support of the corneous sheaths that cover and often extend far beyond them. They are not present at birth for obvious reasons, but begin to grow immediately afterwards. The horn sheaths grow with them, and continue even after they have reached normal size to push out at the base as fast as they wear away at the tip. Their form and position on the head is characteristic of each group: round and lateral in the oxen; slender, retrocurved or twisted, and somewhat compressed or sharply keeled in most antelopes; heavy, cross-ridged, triangular in section and often spiral in the sheep and goats, and so on." [20]

The oxen are the most typical as well as important of the leading ruminant family Bovidæ, and differ from the other genera by their stouter build and by the fact that their horns stand out from the sides of the skull, and are simply curved and smooth. No wild oxen inhabit South America, Madagascar, or Australasia.

The foremost species, now extinct as a wild animal but perfectly traceable, is the original wild ox of Europe, the source of our farm cattle. It was much larger than any existing breed, and bore immense horns, several of which, following the custom of the primitive Germans, were mounted in silver standards and long kept in European cities as ceremonial drinking horns. One of these, preserved almost to the nineteenth century at Zabern, near Strassburg, would.

Aurochs.

hold three quarts; and other examples and records show that these horns sometimes exceeded six feet in length. Old bulls were black, but there is reason to suspect that the cows and calves may have been red. This great animal roamed throughout Europe and western Asia, and was counted among the fiercest of game in Cæsar's time, who found it called ur or

AN OX OF THE WHITE BRITISH PARK CATTLE.

auerochs; the former word was Latinized as *urus*, and the latter, when this ox had disappeared, became transferred to the bison. Even in Roman times the wild ox was growing scarce, and it died out early in the seventeenth century. Meanwhile, from prehistoric days, calves had been tamed by the peasantry, and such cattle as Europe and the Mediterranean basin generally possessed were until quite recently little better than rough descendants of this captured stock.

The so-called "wild white cattle" preserved in various British parks, and often described [215] are, according to Lydekker, [65] albino descendants of the tamed native black aurochs stock, of unknown antiquity, and are kept white (with black or reddish ears and muzzles) by weeding out the dark-colored calves which occasionally appear; but do not represent the original aurochs as well as do the Welsh breed preserved in Pembroke since prehistoric days. It is on record that anciently the Pembroke cattle were prevailingly black, but now most of them are yellowish, with the muzzle, inside of the ears, and often the fetlocks black. These park cattle are all of moderate size, elegantly shaped, with soft hair, white, black-tipped horns of moderate length, and many wild traits. From such stock have arisen all the domestic cattle of Christendom.

In India and the farther East there live four species of wild oxen nearly related to the aurochs — heavy animals with mas-

Gaur.

sive, upcurved horns, rather flattened in front, and twenty to thirty inches long, a ridgelike spine, and a very short tail. The bulls are brownish black, the cows and young paler, and both sexes have white "stockings." The hair

is soft, fine, and glossy. The gaur is the finest of the three, a big bull standing six feet high, but the cows are smaller. It inhabits all the hill jungles of India, Burma, and the Malayan Peninsula; is known to the Malays as "sladang"; and is one of the foremost game animals of the East, and the books of nearly every sportsman-author in that part

AFRICAN, OR CAPE, BUFFALO.

of the world recount exciting and perilous encounters with it, and usually, also, miscall it "bison." The biographies by Sanderson [162] and by Pollok [156] are perhaps the most satisfactory.

Reports of this animal's behavior toward the hunter show a great variety of temperament and action. Some sportsmen pronounce gaurs extremely dangerous to meet in the jungle, — others not at all so. The difference of view and experience is shown in accounts given me by two personal friends, — Casper Whitney and William T. Hornaday. The former declares sladang in the Malay Peninsula the most formidable quarry on earth. "In India, where the range of the gaur is the hilly, wooded districts, they are more apt to be found in herds of some size, and, because of the more open sections, less difficult of approach, and less dangerous to the hunter. In Malaya it is snap shooting, where the game, on being wounded, turns hunter, and, concealed, awaits the sportsman, who must approach with infinite caution, with senses always alert, and hand ever ready if he would stop or turn aside the vicious charge." It was in that region that Colonel Sayres was tossed and killed by a wounded bull gaur.

On the other hand, Mr. Hornaday tells me that in India he has shot five bulls and three cows. " Not one of them manifested the slightest disposition to charge, nor did any of their companions. Outside of the excitement of the chase, I found the actual killing of 'bison' no more dangerous than shooting Texas cattle. Of course when wounded and closely cornered they will charge."

The gayal or mithan is a smaller, milder sort, little known except as a semidomestic race kept for the sake of meat by the hill tribes of northeastern India and Assam; it does, however, occur wild in Tenasserim. A third species, **Gayal.** the banteng or tsine, occurs both wild and tame throughout Burma and down to Borneo, large herds being kept by Malays in Java and Bali. Its haunts and habits are those of the gaur, from which it differs in being slighter, less ridged along the back, and in other particulars giving it a resemblance to the aurochs. The bulls are black, but the cows are reddish brown, like the young, and both sexes are distinguished by a large white patch on the hindquarters. As in the case of the other species, domestic races interbreed and also cross successfully with the Indian humped cattle. This latter curious animal, characterized by the fatty hump over the fore shoulders, a convex forehead, large, drooping ears, an enormous dewlap, and sloping haunches, is now known only by domestic races, and no one can say what was its true form as a wild species or where was its original home.

"While the largest individuals," says Lydekker, who knew them well, "stand as high as a buffalo, the smallest are but little taller than a calf of a month old. The most common color is a light ashy gray, which may shade off into cream color, or even milk-white; but various tints of red or brown are often met with, and occasionally black individuals are seen. In disposition these cattle are always gentle, and the larger varieties are employed in India for drawing native carriages. The voice of the humped cattle is more of a grunt than a low; and these animals differ from European cattle in habits, insomuch as they but seldom seek the shade, and never stand knee-deep in water."

In a most entertaining chapter of the elder Kipling's book, "Beast and Man in India," [11] we get a graphic picture of the cow as the servant and friend of the Hindoo, and the venerated symbol of the most precious cult in his religion.

" The peculiar sanctity of the animal may be a degradation of a poetical Aryan idea, and the cow — originally used as a symbol of the clouds attendant on the sun god — may have succeeded by a process of materialization to honors for which she was not intended, but she is now firmly enthroned in the Hindoo pantheon. . . .

Sanctity of Cow in India.

"Though there is a bewildering variety of local breeds, some broad differences may be easily learned. The backward slope of the horns of the large and small breeds of Mysore cattle, — perhaps the most popular type in use, — the royal bearing of the splendid white and fawn oxen of Guzerat, and transport and artillery cattle bred in the government farms, at once strike the eye. These are the aristocrats of the race, but they have appetites proportioned to their size, and are too costly for the ordinary cultivator. . . . On the wide alluvial plains, where the people are thickly planted, a small, slender, and colorless cow seems to be the usual poor man's animal. The well-to-do keep breeds with foreign names and of stouter build. On the great basin of volcanic trap or basalt, which includes much of western India, the cattle are more square in shape, large in bone, and varied in color.

" The richer pastures and cold winters of Kashmir and the hill country near develop a sturdy, square-headed, short-legged race, with a coarse coat like that of the English cow. In the Himalaya, where the grass is deficient in nourishing power, there are breeds of tiny, neatly formed animals, with coats that look like black or brown cotton velvet. These pasture on the mountain side, climbing almost as cleverly as goats, and their grazing paths, trodden for centuries, have covered leagues of steep slope with a scale-work pattern of wonderful regularity when seen from afar; . . . but the beast at its best is a true Hindoo of the plains."

Much relating to bull and cow worship may be found in Gubernatis's "Zoölogical Mythology." [208]

The humped cattle are also used in China, Madagascar, and eastern-central Africa; and the ordinary Galla or "sunga" ox of Abyssinia is a big variety with enormous horns, which a German authority, Professor Rütimeyer, thought closely allied to the banteng. Fossil great-horned species of gigantic proportions occur in the recent deposits of both Europe and India.

The forests of Celebes contain an extraordinary little wild cow (sapi-utan), the anoa, not much bigger than a goat, with a soft brown coat and straight triangular horns pointing backward. It is of no service except as food. A somewhat larger relative, or perhaps a hybrid between it and something else, is the tamarao of the Philippine Islands.

Anoa and Tamarao.

This interesting little animal was first brought to scientific notice by an American collector, J. B. Steere, in Mindoro, who gave an illustrated account of the matter in *The American Naturalist* for 1891. A bull is about the size of a small Jersey cow, but lower and heavier, with a swollen appearance about both body and limbs. "It was lead-black in color, with lighter markings on head, legs, and under parts, with thin, short hair, a little switchlike tail, like a swine, and nearly straight, sharp, black horns, which ran upward and backward, spreading but little more than the width of the head, and being in line at the tip with the nose and eye. This narrowness and backward set of the horns gave the animal a peculiar look,

THE ANOA.

but must be especially fitted for crowding its way through the wild vines and canebrakes. . . . The skin was of immense thickness, and was entirely covered with gore marks of many battles." The cows are about as large as the bulls, and calves are chestnut in color. "We found them," says Steere, "chiefly living in canebrakes, upon the young shoots of which they were feeding. At night they would gather in some numbers along the open beaches of the river. During the morning they would feed solitarily, or lie in the mud and water of the small streams, and later in the day would take refuge under certain trees, whose branches drooped to the ground, forming an almost impenetrable shelter."

This introduces us to the true buffaloes, — a section of tropical cattle, usually heavily built, with massive, flattened, wrinkled **Indian** horns rising from the forehead, and the hair so thin **Buffalo.** that in old animals the bluish black skin is left almost naked. The typical buffalo is that native to India and Ceylon, where it formerly roved in herds, which, quickly forming into a compact bunch, heads and horns out, defied attack from even the lion or tiger. Bulls often exceed five feet in height, are bulky, extremely strong and yet quick, and carry rough horns, sweeping back circularly, which may measure twelve feet around the curve. Such a veteran herd master spends his days wallowing in marshy jungles, his broad, splayed hoofs sustaining him in the muddy soil, and his hairless back, coated with clay, proof against insects; but evenings and mornings he leads his band out to feed in lush prairies where the grass is tall enough to hide them.

Sportsmen agree that no game animal is more dangerous than a bull buffalo, for it is not only likely to attack one unprovoked, but nothing but death will stop its rush. "A buffalo," declares Baker,[147] "if not killed, will assuredly destroy its adversary. There is no creature in existence that is so determined to stamp out the life of its opponents, and the intensity of fury is unsurpassed when a wounded bull buffalo rushes forward upon the last desperate charge." The bloody history of both East Indian and African sport is filled with practical evidence of the truth of this statement. Pugnacity and revenge seem the animal's ruling impulses, and tremendous fights constantly take place between rival bulls and with other animals. Blanford says instances are known of elephants being knocked down, and of tigers caught, tossed, and then trampled. The half-wild herd bulls are nearly as vicious as those of the jungle; and a favorite sport of Indian princes was to pit two in the bull-ring or against a captive tiger or bear. Nevertheless, this buffalo has long been domesticated, first on the Indian plains in prehistoric times, and is greatly esteemed for qualities in which the humped cattle are deficient. Oriental husbandry needs both; but while the buffalo is made use of, it gets none of the affectionate respect

INDIAN BULL BUFFALOES — THE FIGHT.

245

with which the sleek and handsome cow is regarded. In the religious my-thology of that imaginative population it figures in gloomy and forbidding episodes.

This animal is highly valued throughout the East wherever rice is cul-tivated, and the Philippine carabao is a small variety of it. Egypt re-ceived it very long ago, and will spread it southward, since it is adapted to the hot lowlands now being brought under cultivation in the Sudan, and likes coarse aquatic vegetation better than dry-land forage; hence it has long thriven and proved useful in the Niger Valley. It was introduced into Italy for labor in the northern marsh districts several hundred years ago, and serves well in Spain, Turkey, and elsewhere in the West.

Africa has native buffaloes of much the same character in two species, neither of which has been found domesticable. Both **African Buffaloes.** are growing rare even in remote districts, chiefly through the ravages of rinderpest. The South African buffalo is nearly equal in size and appearance to the Indian one, but its horns are somewhat shorter and their bases nearly meet in a broad, flattened "buckler" over the forehead. These buffaloes, too, frequent marshes and rivers, wading about and eating aquatic plants. Their sense of smell is remarkably keen, and they are further warned of the approach of a dis-turber by the buffalo birds or ox peckers, a kind of starling that remain near them with untiring vigilance. Similarly in the East, cattle are attended both by starlings and small herons, which perch on their backs and hunt for ticks and other parasites. The African buffalo, like his Indian brother, has the distinction of being regarded as perhaps the most danger-ous brute a sportsman can meet in that land of dangerous beasts, and the literature of African hunting makes good this reputation. Only rarely will even the lion attack one single-handed, and then seldom succeeds.

The West African species is smaller, has shorter and less massive horns, and is ruddy brown in color.

Strangest of the ox tribe is the yak of Tibet and the high Himalaya. In its wild state, on the lofty plateaus, it is a huge and graceful animal capable of fighting off the packs of wolves that in winter haunt its trail by means of its spreading, smooth, and sharp horns. It has a massive form with short legs and goatlike feet. The shoulders are some- **Yak.** what humped, and the head is carried low. On both body and head the hair is short, but from the chin, throat, and lower parts of the sides, it grows very long, forming a shining fringe or valance, which serves as a mat under the animal when it lies down upon the snow or icy rocks, and a warm blanket beneath which to curl its legs — a striking adaptation to the climate in which it lives. The color in summer is dark brown, growing grizzled with age, and lighter in winter. The tail is sometimes six feet long, thick and silky; and these tails are in demand as ornaments and for the fly whisks so necessary in the East, often fancifully mounted on antelope-horn handles.

Wild yaks range throughout the loftier regions of central Asia, keeping near the snow line in the mountains, and pasturing on the tough wiry grass which grows luxuriantly in the elevated valleys. Vast numbers still inhabit the Tibetan solitudes, sometimes gathered into herds of thousands. Père Huc, who was the first to describe the wild yak, says the name is Tibetan and imitative of the animal's cry — "very much like the grunt of a pig, but louder and more prolonged." Few are the men who have added the head of this noble ox to their hunting trophies, for it is on the almost unreachable flanks and plateaus of the Pamir that yak hunting must be followed.

Tame yaks have long been used throughout central Asia, and many breeds of various sizes and colors are known. Strong and surefooted, it is a beast of burden where none other can exist, and invaluable for mountain traveling, but trying for Europeans, since its pace rocks its rider to and fro as if on ship in a cross sea. "The going was awful," writes one miserable traveler, "stony and very steep; but the yak never made a mistake, though it puffed and blew and grunted a great deal. Its gait is very slow, nor can it be urged faster, nor kept from stopping as often as it pleases to eat snow, of which it consumes surprising quantities." Wilson's "Abode of Snow" is full of yak riding; and General Macintyre groans over many a bone-racking experience. Huc tells us that he saw whole droves with loads on their backs sliding down frozen slopes on their haunches. The flesh, he says, is excellent, the milk of the cow delicious, and the butter made from it above all praise; but "the cows are so difficult to milk that it is impossible to keep them still; and not a drop is to be had from them without giving them their calves to lick during the operation." From the hides clothing, tent covers, and harness are made; and from the hair is twisted a rope of remarkable strength and elasticity.

From this animal we pass readily to the bisons, the last of the wild cattle. These are the forest oxen of Europe and the "buffalo" of our plains.

The word "bison" has been greatly misused. It is an English corruption of *wisent*, the proper German name of the big, humped, shaggy-browed oxen which people came carelessly to call "aurochs," after the true aurochs had disappeared; but when the English went to India, and met there a formidable wild ox (the gaur), they called it "bison," while, with heedless inconsistency, they dubbed a true bison, when they found it in America, the "buffalo."

Bisons differ from other oxen mainly in having over the withers a hump formed by spines rising from the backbone to **Bison.** give attachment to the great muscles needed to hold up the head, and this gives a droop to the hindquarters; they also have fourteen instead of thirteen ribs. The forehead is convex and protected by a thick mop of hair, the service of which seems to be to act as a cushion in the tremendous pushing matches which the bulls wage with each other, in fencing for a chance to make play with their short and powerful horns, against which the masses of long hair on the shoulders are a still further guard. The more peaceable cows are far less shaggy and of smaller size. This description applies in the main to both European and American bisons, which are probably mere local races descended from an identical stock. The color of both is dark red brown, much faded in late summer.

Three fossil species were recognized by Dr. J. A. Allen in his classic monograph.[217] One (*Bison priscus*) is a very large, long-horned species, widely distributed in the Pleistocene formations of Europe. Another closely similar fossil (*Bison antiquus*) is found in northern America, and the two were perhaps local races of a then circumpolar species, direct ancestor of the modern forms. The third is *Bison latifrons*, a more ancient type of gigantic size, with horns that must have spread ten or twelve feet. Additional fossil species have since been described.

The wisent (or "zubr," as it is known to Slavic-speaking men) was once widely distributed over Europe and neighboring parts of Asia, except on the Russian steppes, but was gradually exterminated, until long ago all that remained were small herds in the Lithuanian forests and in the Caucasus, which were protected on imperial estates, and now number less than one thousand individuals. It is a wild, shy, pugnacious, forest-keeping animal, living mainly on leaves and twigs, not gathering in large companies, nor capable of useful domestication, nor have crosses between it and other cattle yielded encouraging results. A fine pair were living in the New York Zoölogical Park in 1905.

Wisent.

The American bison or buffalo is perhaps on the average not so tall, but more robust and shaggy than the wisent; its life, however, was in great contrast to that of its European relative. Our bison belonged to plains and prairies; and although some penetrated the forests east to the heights of the Alleghanies, and roamed in the West throughout the wooded Rockies, the great body were grazers, and kept to the plains — the bunch-grass country — from Great Slave Lake southward to the Texas coast and the northern interior of Mexico, and as far west as eastern Utah and Nevada.

American Bison.

In this open country, where family bands could sight one another, and were naturally attracted together, and where wolves forced them to combine for common security, gregarious habits foreign to their sylvan ancestors were inevitably formed; and latterly enormous herds congregated during the spring and fall when climate and pasturage compelled annual migratory movements, particularly in the north. Ordinarily, however, these vast assemblages were much scattered, and the bands composing them had a habit of keeping each by itself, and moving in single file, so that in the early days the plains were marked by innumerable paths worn by their feet, especially distinct where leading to and from watering places or fords, or

GRAPHIC HISTORY OF THE DISAPPEARANCE OF THE AMERICAN BISON.

over mountain passes; and the early "pathfinders" of the Rockies had nothing to do but follow them. The speed and agility of these heavy beasts (an old bull would weigh a ton) were astonishing; [219] they also swam well, and the present writer [94] has seen scores of them crossing the upper Missouri by swimming. Another interesting feature of this animal was its harmlessness. It never, or rarely, charged, and hunters on foot or on horseback entered the herds, and approached solitary and even wounded bulls, with no more than ordinary precautions, since, despite the pawing and snorting, little serious action would follow.

This behavior, so much in contrast to that of other kinds of wild bulls, is explained, of course, by their gregarious instincts, leading them to gather in a bunch for safety against danger, but also by the fact that there were on the American plains no such powerful beasts of prey as menace African and Asiatic cattle. Hence individual defensive action was not bred in our bisons as it was in the Old World oxen.

This enormous national asset of beef cattle, upon which the Indian population of the West almost wholly depended for food and clothing, has been swept away within a century. A careful investigation in 1904 discovered about twelve hundred then living in the parks of the world, while a few are protected, though at large, in northwestern Colorado and in Yellowstone Park, and perhaps four hundred still exist in the rough, wooded country west of Great Slave Lake. A full history of the decline and destruction of this fine animal has been written by William T. Hornaday.[218]

Next follow the sheep and goats, with little in structure to separate them from the oxen, though it is easy enough to recognize the three apart. Sheep have massive-looking horns, usually triangular in section, rough, cross-wrinkled, and tending to coil beside the head into a "ram's horn" spiral. Distinctive features are a small gland in each foot between the hoofs; and the ewes having but two teats. The rams are devoid of any strong odor, and have no beard. "As regards the character of their molar teeth, the sheep resemble gazelles,

Cop. N. Y. Zoöl. Soc.   Sanborn, Phot.
OORIAL OR SHA.

and may trace back their descent to extinct antelopes more

or less allied to that group." They are younger than the oxen, geologically. Sheep are naturally mountain dwellers, their round, firm hoofs, their warm winter undercoats, cultivated in domestic races into a heavy fleece, their ability to exist on scant herbage, and their keen senses are all adaptations to an alpine life and cold climate. Hence we find no wild sheep except on mountain ranges, and, in fact, only on those forming the "backbone" of central Europe and Asia and extending along the western side of North America. There are high mountains elsewhere, but the sheep seem never to have crossed the intervening forested lowlands.

The species longest and best known is the mouflon of Corsica and Sardinia, still an object of the chase in the mountains **Mouflon.** of those islands, but frequently found by the shepherds with their flocks, and probably one of the sources of European domestic sheep.

As to the originals of this perhaps most valuable and least educated of the animals reclaimed from nature, we are in the dark; it is probable that, like dogs, they came from the taming of local species of various regions, and have modified by mixture as well as by breeding. The oldest definitely known is the "peat sheep" of the early Swiss lake dwellers, which was a small-horned breed, apparently represented at the present day by the sheep of Graubinden, Germany; but at a somewhat later time the Copper-age people of France and the British Isles had a big-horned sheep with a strong infusion of mouflon blood. "The variations of external characters seen in the different domestic breeds are very great. They are chiefly manifested in the form and number of the horns, which may be increased from the normal two to four or even eight, or may be altogether absent in the female alone, or in both sexes; in the form and length of the ears, which often hang pendant by the side of the head; in the peculiar elevation or arching of the nasal bones in some Eastern races; in the length of the tail and the development of great masses of fat at each side of its root, or in the tail itself; and in the color and quality of the fleece."

Asia Minor and Persia have a mouflon similar to the Corsican one but larger; and a diminutive variety inhabits Cyprus, or formerly did so. India's only wild sheep is the oorial ("sha" in Ladak), a tall, rather lean reddish gray species, found from the Punjab to eastern Persia and from northern Tibet to Beluchistan, and this great variety of habitat has produced an equal variety of size and form. It will interbreed with domestic sheep, and has no doubt entered largely into the parentage of the Asiatic flocks.

Although every sportsman who visits the Himalaya has a shot at oorial, which are active and wary, awakening the echoes with shrill alarm whistles when the hunter fancies they have no idea of his approach, a more creditable game is the great guljar, or Marco Polo's sheep, of the Pamirs. In summer it roams in the grassy valleys fifteen thousand to eighteen thousand feet above the sea, cropping the young herbage springing at the edge of the melting snow fields, but in winter must retreat to lower levels. Old rams are nearly white, and carry circling horns which may measure sixty inches around the outside curve.

Polo's Sheep.

What it means to hunt these and other mountain sheep and goats may be learned by reading the books of Himalayan sportsmen. An experience by Captain R. P. Cobbold in 1897 may serve as an example. He had climbed on yaks with Kirghiz companions to treeless valleys on the Pamir about thirteen thousand in altitude, where at that season (late October) the mercury fell at night below zero; and before dawn, one morning, he began a heart-breaking tramp over steep ridges in search of the game. When it became light enough to see anything, certain animals were discovered through field glasses on the opposite hillsides.

"After half an hour's stiffish uphill work, we got to the plateau where the creatures had been feeding, but they had gone. Looking up, I saw they were ibex, and some fine heads among them; but I did not want ibex, as I had shot them before, so I did not bother about them; they went up into some rocky cliffs, playing and butting each other, and kicking down stones. . . . We descended halfway, and then had a look around from behind some rocks on to the hillside and the Pamir below. It was getting pretty good light now, and I made out two white ponies about two hundred yards off; at least, that is what they looked like to me. I thought it rather odd that the Kirghiz should leave their ponies to wander so high up, so I called

Mirza Bai's attention to them, when he immediately dropped like a stone, and, dragging me down, whispered, 'Guljar, sahib.' I got the rifle ready; but they had our wind, and scampered off.

"We continued watching the two large poli, which were half a mile or so distant. They kept turning their heads up towards the rocks behind which we were, and the appearance their long, curving horns gave them was most weird. After a bit, they fed down into the bed of the ravine, and

GULJAR OR POLO'S SHEEP.

then, as we were hidden by its banks from sight, down we went, as hard as we could go. Carefully we crept up, I walking in moccasins; but when we looked over they were gone. We went up the ravine a little way, and then saw them going slowly up the nullah about two hundred yards off. It was bare and stony going, and no cover; so it was useless following them. I and Mirza Bai then took counsel as to what was best to be done, not that either of us could understand the other, as I cannot understand Turki, nor he Hindustani. However, by means of signs, I made him understand that we must climb up to the top of the ridge, and follow it along to the head of the nullah and then down, and hope to find some projecting cliffs to give us cover. It was tiring work, all shingle, which kept on slipping and giving to one's feet; and then, when we got to what had looked like the top from below, we found that there was lots more still to climb. This happened over and over again. At last, however, we got to the real top of the ridge and followed it along to the head of the nullah, every now and then carefully looking down to see if the poli were still there. At the head of the nullah there was a nasty descent; but some projecting cliffs gave us cover and we got down all right, and proceeded cautiously toward the spot where we had last seen the guljar lying. It was impossible to walk anything like quietly, as the nullah was a mass of broken rock and shingle, which kept clattering down however carefully one stepped.

"I noticed that the wind had changed and was now blowing up the nullah towards us; and I wondered if the Kirghiz, who had been left near the entrance of the nullah, had had the sense to move further away, or if the guljar would get his wind. Sure enough, they had, as I saw them coming up the nullah towards us in a rare hurry. We squatted among the stones, and I saw that with any luck they must pass not more than a hundred yards away. I got the Mannlicher ready, and covered the whiter animal of the two. They came on at a gallop; but as the ascent began to tell on their heavy bodies they stopped opposite me for a moment. I dropped the big beast dead; the other one made off for the opposite side of the nullah; I missed him the second shot, and then putting up the 200-yards sight, dropped him dead with the third shot. Mirza Bai was in a frantic state of delight, and, seizing my hand, kissed it vigorously, murmuring, 'Atcha, sahib!' and many endearing epithets which I did not understand." — *Innermost Asia* (New York, 1900).

Inhabiting all these high ranges from Turkestan to Mongolia, is another magnificent sheep, the argali, ammon or nyan, which offers so many variations that it figures in books under many local and scientific names; but all varieties seem to blend, and it is not at all certain that it even differs specifically from the guljar.

Argali.

Last of the typical sheep are the various "bighorns," if indeed more than one species locally diversified by climate and other circumstances can be counted; these are the Rocky Mountain, Alaskan, and Kamchatkan sheep. Our bighorn, which until about 1884 was considered as only a single species (*Ovis montana*), is the one long familiar to us throughout the Rocky Mountain region, from the head of the Rio Grande to central British Columbia, but not in California or Oregon. From central California southward into the lower peninsula is found Nelson's sheep; and in the northerly sierras of Mexico a Mexican species. Now to the northward of the bighorn range occur three kinds of mountain sheep,

Bighorn.

regarded by Merriam, Hornaday,[222] and other American naturalists as distinct species, as follows : —

ROCKY MOUNTAIN BIGHORN.

(1) *Stone's,* — somewhat smaller than the bighorn; light colored when young, dark in maturity, with a nearly black dorsal stripe, and wide-spreading horns grooved along the side; it makes its home on the snowy ranges between the heads of the Stikeen and the Yukon.   (2) *Fannin's* or "saddle-

back,"— white except the back and sides, where the color is faintly brownish
gray, "giving the appearance of a white animal covered by a gray blanket";
it inhabits the Rocky Mountains between the Yukon and the Mackenzie.

(3) *Alaskan White* or *Dall's*, — a little
smaller than the bighorn, "everywhere
milk-white, both in winter and in summer, and from birth to old age"; it
seems to be a tenant of all the
mountain ranges north of the sixtieth
parallel, from the Rocky Mountains
to the Alaskan and arctic coasts. Its
horns are rather lighter both in weight
and color than those of the others, and
most resemble those of the Kamchatkan sheep (just across
Bering Strait) which is described as "brown and neck
rather grayer than the rest of the body."

H· OF S.

The hunting of these sheep, nowadays, at least, taxes a man's
wind and endurance, his sure-footedness, skill in stalking, and
ability to shoot straight,[219] beyond that of any other game; but
twenty-five years ago it was not so difficult to get near them.
In 1874, and again in 1877, I watched at ease many bands
among the high valleys and cliffs of Colorado and Wyoming —
fifty in a flock sometimes.

The blue sheep, bharal or nahura of Tibet, represents
another type, having horns nearly smooth, and curved more
like an S than in a coil; and the fur is smooth, **Bharal**
close, and strikingly marked about the face and **and Aoudad.**
front. Still more intermediate between sheep and goats stands
the familiar North African pale brown aoudad, as the Moors
call it (it has many other names), which, like the bharal, has
horns curving backward from the middle of the occiput, and
about twenty-four inches long. Its most striking peculiarity,
however, is the fringe of very long whitish hair on the throat,
chest, and about the fore legs.

These odd animals are common in the Atlas, where they range over
the more precipitous regions of its arid southern slopes from the Atlantic

s

to Tunis, keeping within sight of the desert; and Buxton,[223] who has told us much that was novel in regard to the animals of the Sahara and Atlas regions, speaks feelingly of their remarkable skill in hiding among the fantastically worn and brushy rocks of those mountains. All mountain sheep and goats know how to stand absolutely motionless and unnoticeable, or to lie quietly beside a rock with which their dun hue perfectly blends. One or more of a band is likely to choose some high place commanding a wide outlook, and so is prepared to catch sight of anything alarming in the neighborhood; but the "posting of sentinels," so frequently stated of these animals, probably amounts to no more than this habitual watchfulness by wakeful ones.

Goats. Goats differ from the sheep in such small particulars as the absence of hoof glands, the rank odor and beard of the rams, and in the shape of the horns, which typically are high, sweeping, and triangular, and are likely to be knobbed on the front. Standing about as high as the average wild sheep, say three feet at the shoulder, the goats are rather lighter in weight, more active climbers, and are likely to be found in more precipitous parts of the mountain system to which they, like the sheep, are confined, for no true goat now occurs naturally outside of Europe and Asia, except along the Egyptian shore of the Red Sea. Geologically, they have been traced back to the Pliocene, when an ibex wandered over the chilly plains of central Europe; but since the Glacial period they have remained upon alpine heights, separating into various closely related species by the influence of isolation. Goats are further peculiar in being mostly browsers, cropping the leaves and twigs of brush, sprouts, and aromatic plants; hence flocks of tame goats not only keep the woods where they run free from undergrowth, but ruin any attempt to reforest areas once cut over.

Turs. Nearest to the sheep, and with the bharal and aoudad uniting the two groups, are the brownish turs of the Caucasus, whose massive black horns are comparatively smooth and cylindrical, and extend outward and backward like those of the bharal. Very similar are the goats of the moun-

258

tains of Spain, though the horns of the rams are more angulated, rough, and twisting. As with most game, the old bucks are solitary most of the year, and stay on the high, cold peaks, but in the late autumn they seek the company of the does, and then large flocks often gather. The does are likely to winter in the lower and more sheltered valleys, and the kids (two, as a rule, as elsewhere in this family) are born in April. All are so extremely alert, and so agile in climbing and hiding, that, although constantly hunted since prehistoric times, goats are numerous all over the Iberian peninsula.

Between this and the ibexes comes the common wild goat of Persia, which occurs on all the highlands from Crete to the barren hills of Cutch, and is the original of domestic breeds. Its coat in winter is brownish gray, in summer more reddish, with the buttocks and under parts nearly white; while the older bucks have the forehead, chin,

Bezoar Goat.

beard, throat, front of the legs, a stripe along the spine, the tail, and a band on the flanks dark brown. The horns of the old bucks measure forty to fifty inches along the curve, rise close together from the top of the skull, and sweep backward in an even curve, with the front edge forming a strong keel marked by irregular promi-

RAM OF PERSIAN, OR BEZOAR, GOAT.

nences; the horns of the female are much smaller and smoother.

This goat, from whose stomach are taken the best bezoars ("pasan"), formerly so highly valued in medicine, and which was the one familiar to the classical and biblical authors, and supplied much of the repulsive mythology with which its race is connected,[208] is a favorite game animal in its region, especially on the Elburz range.[224]

"The relations of the goat to mankind," remarks Shaler, "are in certain ways peculiar. The creature has long been subjugated, probably **Domestic** having come into the human family before the dawn of his-**Goat.** tory. It has been almost as widely disseminated among barbarian and civilized peoples alike as the sheep. It readily cleaves to the household and exhibits much more intelligence than the other members of our flocks and herds. It yields good milk, the flesh is edible, though in the old animals not savory, and the hair can be made to vary in a larger measure than any of our animals which are shorn. Yet this creature has never obtained the place in relation to man to which it seems entitled. Only here and there is it kept in considerable numbers or made the basis of extensive industries. The reason for this seems to be that these animals cannot readily be kept in flocks in the manner of sheep. . . . There seems reason to believe, also, that they cannot easily be made to vary in other characteristics except their hairy covering at the will of the breeder, and so varieties cannot be formed. . . . The present rapid variations in the physical characteristics of our sheep, which are induced by the breeder's skill, make it evident that we are far from having attained the maximum profit from these creatures. The goats also give promise, when selective work is carefully done upon them, of giving much more than they now afford to the uses of mankind; but from neither of these forms is there reason to hope . . . for any considerable gain in the intellectual qualities."[225]

This brings us to the ibexes, which are simply large wild goats with horns that stand nearly straight up in a scimiter-**Ibex.** like curve, and have heavy ridges across the front. The ibex proper, the bouquetin of the French and steinbok of the Germans, once roamed throughout the Alps, but now remains only as a few preserved specimens in the Piedmont valleys. Two other species inhabit Abyssinia and the rough heights of Syria; but the finest ibex is the Himalayan, standing forty inches tall, and having horns sometimes fifty inches long. These dwell upon the heights of all central Asia, and maintain themselves in goodly numbers in spite of wild dogs, leopards, hunters, and avalanches. The same mountains are the home of the markhor, — a light-colored goat which dwells among the gigantic peaks of the "roof of the world" on the northern border of Kashmir, and is believed to be the parent, at least in part, of the valuable Angora goat.

"It is the finest of all wild goats," exclaims Hornaday, in an article in *Scribner's Magazine* for September, 1905, describing heads and horns of game in his own very notable collection of such trophies in New York, "and in every respect a very picturesque creature. **Markhor.** Its jet-black horns rise jauntily from the forehead, then sweep backward and outward, twisting as they go, until they make a complete turn, or even two turns, and attain a length of from forty-eight to sixty inches. Under its neck hangs an astonishing mane of creamy yellow hair a foot long, and the body coat also is long and shaggy.

"To some persons, doubtless, a pair of markhor horns are merely a pair of odd-looking, screwlike horns, and nothing more. To others they call up pictures of snowy peaks, wet and soggy clouds drifting by, tremendous chasms, rock walls going down thousands of feet, shaggy-headed, wild-looking natives with chocolate-colored skins, and tiny villages

Copyright, N. Y. Zoöl. Society.   Sanborn, Phot.

A YOUNG MARKHOR RAM.

of mud huts perched like sea birds' nests on frightful ledges. And then one thinks of the journey down, drop after drop, to hill, forest, and plain; the bazaar on the frontier, the bazaar 'down country'; through a dozen hands and half a dozen languages, until at last they reach a white sahib thousands of miles away."

Beyond these monarchs of the land in the sky stand the goat-antelopes, so called because they unite in some degree the two

Goat-antelopes.

groups represented in the name. They are small, robust, active animals with rather long and woolly coats, short, inconspicuous, upright horns, no beards, and goat-like haunts and habits. Examples are the shaggy brown tahrs of the mountains of India and Arabia; the ungraceful, pug-

Copyright, N. Y. Zoöl. Society.   Sanborn, Phot.

ONE OF THE SHAGGY TAHRS.

nacious serows, several species of which are scattered over the highlands of southeastern Asia, including Japan; and the similar, but far rarer, takin of eastern Tibet, a heavily built animal with figure and horns not unlike those of a musk ox; indeed, this may be more than an accidental resemblance, for in Beddard's opinion it is the nearest relative to that strange arctic animal, and its head is as much a prize to the collector of trophies. In this group also fall the chamois of Europe and the Rocky Mountain white goat.

It is often an irritating incident of reading old books to run against the phrase, "too well known to be described," in respect to something the reader would like particularly well to learn; but I must ask for once to retreat behind it, and refer the reader to the encyclopedias, or, better, to such authors as Baillie-Grohman [227] for a history of the chamois. This will be more excusable, perhaps, if I add that the chamois (gemse, izard, or atchi), once numerous on high mountains from Spain to Greece and Persia, is now extinct as a wild animal west of Transylvania, except on a few baronial estates.

Our western American pure white mountain goat is one of the most peculiar and to us the most interesting of the group — a "white buffalo" the Indians styled it, when they reported it in British Columbia to Alexander Macken- **White Goat.** zie on his approach to the Pacific coast in 1793; this is the oldest mention of it I have been able to find, and the next is the vague account furnished by the writers of the Lewis and Clark Expedition. In place of a formal description of this mountain antelope (for he is no more a goat than is his "nearest of kin," the chamois), let me quote a portrait sketch by Owen Wister,[219] who paints from life: —

"He's white, all white, and shaggy, and twice as large as any goat you ever saw. His white hair hangs long all over him, like a Spitz dog's or an Angora cat's; . . . and against its shaggy white mass the blackness of his hoofs, and horns, and nose looks particularly black. His legs are thick, his neck is thick, everything about him is thick, saving only his thin black horns. They're generally about six [often more than nine] inches long, they spread very slightly, and they curve slightly backward. At their base they are a little rough, but as they rise they cylindrically smooth and taper to an ugly point. His hoofs are heavy, broad, and blunt. . . . The female is lighter built than the male, and with horns more slender — a trifle. And (to return to the question of diet) we visited the pasture where the herd of (thirty-five) had been, and found no sign of grass growing or grass eaten; there was no grass on that mountain. The only edible substance was a moss, tufted, stiff, and dry to the touch. . . . I also learned that the goat is safe from predatory animals. With his impenetrable hide and his disembowelling horns, he is left by the wolves and mountain lions respectfully alone."

The pelage of this goat is the softest and finest worn by any American hoofed mammal excepting the musk ox; but the hairs are coarser and stiffer along the spinal column. The wool was formerly formed into a sort of felted yarn by the Indians by teasing it and then rolling it under the palm on the bare thigh.

The hunting of this animal requires climbing to the topmost heights of the most alpine of American mountains, unless one goes to Alaska, where the altitudes but scarcely the difficulties

ROCKY MOUNTAIN WHITE GOATS AT HOME.

will be less. Its home is in the far Northwest, where the climate is damp and the snowfall abundant. Nowadays it is not to be found south of northwestern Montana. In British Columbia it is widely distributed from the eastern slope of the Rockies to Pacific tidewater; and it is abundant throughout southeastern Alaska. It is a singular fact that sheep and goats rarely live in the same range, or when they do never apparently on the same mountain.

Hunting the white goat, says George Bird Grinnell, editor of *Forest and Stream* and of the Boone and Crockett Club's excellent publications, is man's work, and "calls for the best qualities of the mountaineer." When **Goat Hunting.** the goats have once been found, however, it is usually easy to secure them, for they are gentle and unsuspicious.

"The most charming, innocent creatures that I met in the Cascade Mountains were the white goats," writes Frederick Irland. "What do you think of a wild animal which, after he knows you are on his track, will stop and turn back, to peer around the corner and see what you are? These stately animals, with their long white aprons, coal-black [1] eyes, and sharp little horns, really seem to me too unsophisticated to shoot." "Although the goat is nearly related to the chamois," to quote again from Mr. Grinnell's narrative of a climb after these animals (*Scribner's Magazine*, Vol. XV), "it has little of the activity of that nimble species. The bighorn is the runner and jumper of the western mountains, while the goat is the plodder. He gets over the ground and climbs the loftiest peaks 'by main strength and awkwardness.' The bighorn rushes away along the mountain side at a headlong pace, the alarmed goat starts straight for the mountain top at a rate which seems slow, often no more than a walk, but which is so steady and continuous that it soon carries the animal out of the way of danger.

"The goat is marvelously sure-footed, and from the day of its birth is practiced in climbing over the rocks, but it must not be imagined that it never falls from the insecure perches which it frequents. Such falls are not uncommon, but seem rarely to result in serious injury. Kids which have been captured when very young and kept in captivity have been observed to play at rolling down steep banks, repeating the tumble over and over again, as if practicing for the falls which they might be obliged to take later in life."

The musk ox, as already intimated, arranges itself better in this company than elsewhere, since it is now plain that it is not a connecting link between the oxen and sheep, **Musk Ox.** but must stand quite by itself, with the takin as its nearest apparent relative. The musk oxen are arctic in the

---

[1] The eyes are black only in kids; in adult goats they are straw-yellow. — E. I.

strictest sense of the word, for Peary found them upon the northernmost shores of Grantland and Greenland, and none wander even in midwinter farther south than the Arctic Circle; they are not found west of Cape Bathhurst, nor east of Fox Channel and Baffin Bay, nor on the west coast of Greenland, although frequenting the east coast south to about N. Lat. 70°. None now occurs anywhere in the Old World, but in Pleistocene

Copyright, N. Y. Zoöl. Society.   Sanborn, Phot.
GREENLAND MUSK OX AND CALF.

times these animals inhabited Asia and Europe down to the east-and-west mountain axis, and were hunted by the men of the early Stone Age; [83] and at a somewhat earlier time musk oxen, of extinct genera as well as species, roamed over this continent, as far south as Kansas. These singular animals have little resemblance to other ruminants except in the bisonlike head. "I gaze upon each living musk ox in captivity with a feeling of wonder, as if it were a creature from another world," exclaims Hornaday,[95] who took a particular interest in them from the fact that in 1902 he had under his charge at the New York "Zoo" a female captured by Eskimo near Lady Franklin Bay, and brought around to San Francisco by a whaler; and also a calf brought from Fort Conger (Lat. 81°), Greenland (see illustration); neither lived out the year, nor have specimens brought to Europe long survived.

MUSK OX OF THE BARREN GROUNDS.

"In it," says Hornaday again, "one sees an oblong mass of very long and wavy brown hair, four and a half feet high by six and a half feet long, supported on very short and postlike legs, that are half hidden by the sweeping pelage of the body. The three-inch tail is so very small and short it is quite invisible. There is a blunt and hairy muzzle, round and shining eyes, but the ears are almost invisible. The whole top of the head is covered by a pair of horns enormously flattened at the base, and meeting each other in the center-line of the body. From the meeting point they sweep downward over the edge of the cranium, close to the cheeks, but finally recurve upward before coming to a point, like the waxed mustache of a boulevardier. . . . The outer hair is a foot or more in length, and often touches the snow when the animal walks."

The name is due to a musky odor, useful in enabling the animals to find one another and keep together during the winter darkness and storms of their terrible home, which is perceptible to human nostrils at a considerable distance, but does not taint the flesh if a carcass is quickly and properly disemboweled; and the meat is excellent.

Musk oxen go about in bands feeding upon anything vegetable they can find. How they get enough in winter is a mystery. They probably paw down through the snow; and Schwatka concluded they used their horns as snow-shovels, as the reindeer do. Their one natural enemy is wolves, and against these they have learned that their only safety is in standing firmly in a bunch with the young in the center, and the rams forming a fighting front all around. The same tactics are used when the Eskimo and their wolfish dogs attack a herd.

Lieutenant Frederick Schwatka witnessed such an assault, and speaks of the musk oxen as presenting a most formidable appearance, with their rumps firmly wedged together, a complete circle of swaying horns presented to the front, with great bloodshot eyeballs glaring like red-hot shot amidst the escaping steam from their panting nostrils, and pawing and plunging at the circle of furious dogs that encompassed them. This habit of quickly coming to bay makes it easier for men to get near them; and the natives often stab them to death with spear or knife. The conditions seem much harder on the Barren

Grounds, however, than near the arctic coast. The sport of hunting the musk ox, as depicted by Whitney,[219] Pike, Russell, and others, appears to lie more in the satisfaction of having overcome tremendous hardships than in the actual killing, which resembles butchery. Without dogs it would be practically impossible to get near them, at any rate in the Barren Grounds.

The antelopes remain to be treated in the broad family Bovidæ, of which the cattle form one section, the sheep and **Antelope Tribe.** goats a second, the musk ox a third, and the Antilopinæ a fourth. This group is the oldest and most generalized of the family, dating from the Miocene, the fragments recovered indicating at first small, gazellelike animals, and later large ones with stout, somewhat twisted horns. In those days they were widely diffused over southern Europe and Asia, but seem never to have reached America, for *our* "antelope" belongs to another family. It is still one of the problems of zoölogy to account for their disappearance from Europe. Their introduction into Africa appears to have been comparatively recent, but once established there they diversified and multiplied in a manner unparalleled elsewhere, the total number of kinds of African antelopes now exceeding ninety.

"It is exceedingly difficult," writes Beddard,[87] "to separate the antelopes from the sheep, oxen, and goats;" and paleontologists believe the latter are offshoots from an early antelopelike stock.[244]   Mr. Beddard continues: "The term 'antelope' is rather of popular than of zoölogical significance. . . . It is perhaps with the goats that the antelopes have the nearest affinities." The foremost authorities on the group, Messrs. Thomas and Sclater, whose "Book of Antelopes," [228] in four quarto volumes with magnificent colored plates, is a model of what a monograph of a group of animals ought to be, arrange the thirty-five recognized genera in the following order: —

First come the big bovine elands, the koodoos, nilgais, and "harnessed" bush bucks. The eland is the greatest of African antelopes, six feet in height, and weighing fifteen hundred pounds; and the straight, upstanding, closely twisted horns, present in both sexes, may measure twenty-eight **Elands and** inches long. The form is oxlike, enhanced by a **Koodoos.** small hump, great dewlap, and long tail; and the proper color is bright fawn, but often the thinness of the hair gives the old bulls a bluish cast. Formerly numerous all over eastern and southern Africa, the excellence of its flesh and hide and the ease with which this heavy and comparatively slow animal could be killed, together with the epidemic of rinderpest which swept over central Africa a few years ago, have practically exterminated this noble species, which soon will be visible only in captivity. It breeds well in confinement, and there seems no reason why it should not be led slowly to increase into a valuable domestic. The Derbian eland is a rare and handsome West African form.

AN ELAND BUCK.

The related koodoos are a genus of large, handsome African antelopes with spirally twisted horns (on the male alone), whose skins are variegated by irregular white stripes down the sides, and by a V-mark below the forehead. Still more pleasingly marked are the bush bucks, of which several species are scattered over all Africa south of the Sahara, varying in size from that of a goat to that of a pony, and having richly colored coats ornamented with irregular white stripes, while their horns are wavy rather than spiral. All this group avoid the open plains and extensive herding, and wander alone or in small parties in rough, bushy country, where they browse as well as graze. Schillings[269] has much to say of them, and especially of the protective value of their striped coats.

"The prettiest creature of the jungles is the harnessed antelope (*A. scripta*). This is never found in herds, but generally in pairs, or three or **Harnessed** four together. It is seldom met with in open plains, but is **Bush Buck.** an inhabitant of the bush, and will lie tolerably close, starting up with a frantic rush when suddenly disturbed. A fine buck will weigh about ninety pounds. The male is dark brown, ornamented with snow-white stripes, six or seven of which descend from the back upon either

A HARNESSED BUSH BUCK.

flank and the hindquarters; a few white marks are upon the shoulders, and white spots upon the thighs; a long white line from the shoulder extends in a continuation below the transverse marks upon the flanks, and terminates near the junction of the hind leg. This resembles a white trace, hence the name 'harnessed antelope.'" [147]

Of the bush bucks, however, the most rare and noteworthy is the inyala or Angas's antelope, whose home is in the fever-

ANGAS'S HARNESSED ANTELOPE; OR, INYALA

haunted coast jungles of Portuguese East Africa. The accompanying colored plate will give an idea of the peculiar form
and coloring of the buck, whose fine lyrate horns and
mantling fringes give him a very distinguished ap-   Inyala.
pearance. The female is rich rufous red, with a black line
along the spine, and many narrow white stripes down the sides
and haunches; she is hornless. Although long known, it is
only since 1896 that we have gained much knowledge of its
habits or obtained specimens, the latter chiefly through the
efforts of F. C. Selous. Everywhere this antelope spends its
life in the densest, miasmatic thickets; and in much of its
range the natives refuse to eat its flesh. The trials the inyala
hunter must undergo may be judged by the difficulty Selous
met with in securing his first one.

"We now commenced to creep very cautiously through the thick thorny
bush, making our way for the most part through tunnels made by hippo-
potami during their night excursions in search of food. We had usually
to walk bent nearly double — often having to creep on our hands and
knees; and, as the day was now very hot and steamy, we were soon
bathed in perspiration.

"We had been creeping about the bush in the uncomfortable manner
I have described for about an hour, when we suddenly came upon a little
circular opening some fifty or sixty yards in diameter. As we approached
the edge of this open space, advancing very cautiously in a stooping attitude down a hippopotamus path, my guide suddenly dropped to the ground.
As he did so, I got a clear view past him, and saw standing amongst the
grass and bush, . . . a great black shaggy form, which, indistinctly as I
could see it in the deep shadow of the bush, I knew was an inyala ram —
the first that my eyes had ever looked upon in the flesh."

That this hunting may be dangerous sport, as well as risky to one's
health appears from a memorandum of another hunter: "Living, the bush
buck is dangerous enough; when wounded, one I shot through the heart
at eighty yards charged me like a flash of lightning, falling dead ten yards
from my feet; and another, shot by an acquaintance of mine, also through
the heart, drove his bayonetlike horns into the stomach of a native, killing
him on the spot."

By such perils and pains are the treasures of our museums collected!

Relatives of the inyala are the shy marsh-hunting sitatungas, whose feet are furnished with hoofs of relatively enormous length, which spread

far apart at every step, enabling their owner to walk upon marshy ground without sinking deeply, or at all. With this modification goes great flexibility of the ankle joints, which yield to the weight of the body sufficiently to allow the false hoofs and the smooth, tough, horny skin at the back of the pasterns to rest upon the soil and thus further broaden the supporting surface; but these "slimpsy" ankles and elongated toes give the animal a very awkward and comparatively slow gait when it is compelled to walk on hard ground.

HOOF OF SITATUNGA.

To this section, although a native of India, belong the oddly cowlike nilgais, which, where not much disturbed, become so fearless as to mingle with the village cattle herd. They prefer a dry, hilly, thinly wooded country, and where it is open **Nilgai.** may sometimes be run down on horseback and speared; otherwise they are not much hunted, for the short little horns are a poor trophy. The general color is dark gray with a black mane and some faint white markings about the head. In some parts of India these animals commit great havoc by nightly depredations on the crops, but the Hindoos will seldom destroy them on account of their resemblance to the sacred cow—an unexpected phase of "protective mimicry"! A common name in India is "blue cow."

Another section of the group embraces very large antelopes of Africa, having long, stout, ringed horns in both sexes, such **Oryx.** as the sable and roan, the gemsbok and allied species. Among these are some of the most conspicuous and familiar antelopes of the arid plains south and east of the Mediterranean. Thus the addax, beatrix, beisa, and other large, pale, dark-legged species of the Sahara, Arabia, and

Syria, known broadly as "oryx," are represented on the Egyptian monuments; and their long, straight, powerful horns, sweeping back almost to the haunches, may, when seen in profile, look as if only one were there, and so have anciently suggested the fabled unicorn. All are handsomely marked in sharply contrasted patterns of dark and light colors, and some of the most striking, as the gemsbok, inhabit South Africa, or did formerly. The most admirable of all antelopes, perhaps, is one of these, the sable, the discovery of which by Captain Cornwallis Harris in 1838 was the beginning of an admiring enthusiasm among sportsmen, increasing as its subject becomes rarer and more remote. "It were vain," declares Harris,[230] "to at-

Copyright, N. Y. Zoöl. Society.   Sanborn, Phot.

THE ROAN ANTELOPE.

tempt a description of the sensation I experienced when thus after three days of toilsome tacking and feverish anxiety, . . . I at length found myself in actual possession of so brilliant an addition to the riches of natural history. . . . We thought we could never have looked at or admired it sufficiently." A few years later Gordon Cumming repeated these joys.

"Cantering along through the forest," he records,[142] "I came suddenly in full view of one of the loveliest animals which graces this fair creation.

This was an old buck of the sable antelope, the rarest and most beautiful animal in Africa. It is large and powerful, partaking considerably of the nature of the ibex. Its back and sides are of glossy black, beautifully contrasting with the belly, which is white as driven snow. The horns are upward of three feet in length, and bend strongly back with a bold sweep, reaching nearly to the haunches. . . . The one which was now before me was the first I had seen, and I shall never forget the sensations I experienced on beholding a sight so thrilling to the sportsman's eye."

In that admirable work of the artist John Millais, "A Breath from the Veldt,"[232] which is replete with charming sketches of South African scenes and animals, many pages are given to this beautiful creature.

Sable Antelope.

"There is about the whole animal," this artist assures us, "that indescribable charm which is so intensely African and associated with the wild life. . . . Apart from its satinlike hide, sweeping horns, erect mane, and great strength, the sable antelope presents an appearance of fearlessness and nobility that is very striking, to say the least of it. Though the koodoo surpasses his rival in elegance and general appearance when dead, he is but a skulker, and makes but a poor show beside the sable on the veldt. . . . Like the koodoo the horns of the sable are its chief glory, and the noble manner in which the head is carried by the buck when on the move is a splendid thing to see. I could hardly imagine a finer subject for an animal painter."

All these antelopes have an equine form and gait, but this one as he stands on the open plain where they love to pasture, a few together (mostly chestnut cows), with neck arched, mane flying, and chin drawn down, personifies a mettlesome, coal-black steed. Schulz[152] says the animal *must* take this attitude, in consequence of the length, curve, and sharpness of the horns, whose points would otherwise severely lacerate the back when the buck was in rapid motion; the horns are used with nervous quickness and force as weapons, wielded with undaunted courage even when attacked by lions. "More than once have natives related to us," Schulz notes, "that they have found the remains of a lion and sable lying side by side with the lion transfixed by the sharp horns of its prey." It is a satisfaction to be able to record that many scattered herds of this stately species still exist in eastern Africa between the Transvaal and German East Africa; and as it is readily tamed, and seems able to breed in captivity, the world is not likely soon to lose its handsome presence.

In the company of the sable and roan antelopes come the koodoos, which like most of the larger antelopes are wonderful jumpers. F. J. Jackson, in his "Big Game Shooting in Africa," tells how he measured a jump by one of these antelopes to satisfy himself of its length.

"She had been chased by a hyena," he says, "along a narrow footpath in a dense bush. In the middle of the path was a thick green bush about five feet high, round which the path took a turn and then went straight on again. The kudu had taken a flying leap over this bush, and the distance between the spoor of her hindfeet, where she took off, and the edge of the bush, was fifteen feet. The diameter of the bush was six feet, and the distance from the edge of the bush on the other side to where she landed — *i.e.* to the spoor-marks of her hindfeet — another ten feet, in all thirty-one feet. The hyena had given up the chase some thirty yards farther on."

Following these large antelopes come the small, delicate, active gazelles, which have furnished to Oriental poetry a type of gentle grace, and especially of beauty in the eye; it is therefore disconcerting to be informed **Gazelles.** by a matter-of-fact naturalist that "the beauty of its eyes is not to be compared with that of some other ruminating animals, the whole face being far too sheeplike!" He referred to the common dorcas gazelle of Egypt and Syria, a fair type of the whole group, which is believed to contain twenty or twenty-five species, scattered from Morocco to India. It stands about twenty-four inches high and weighs sixty pounds.

"Born in the scorching sun, nursed in the burning sand of the treeless and shadowless wilderness, the gazelle is among the antelope tribe as the Arab horse is among its brethren, — the high-bred and superlative beauty of the race. The skin is as sleek as satin, of a color difficult to describe, as it varies between the lightest mauve and yellowish brown; the belly is snow-white; the legs from the knee downwards also white, and as fine as though carved from ivory; the hoof, beautifully shaped, tapers to a sharp point. The head of the buck is ornamented by gracefully curved, annulated horns, perfectly black, and generally from nine to twelve inches long on the bend; the eye is the well-known perfection — the full, large, soft, and jet-black eye of the gazelle."

These gazelles are numerous in twos and threes all over Egypt, Arabia, and Syria, and in the summer become comparatively tame in the oases. Young ones are frequently caught (and make delightful pets) as they come to the springs to drink in

DORCAS GAZELLES.

very hot weather; then also they feed on juicy plants and scrub, and visit the crops at night. At other times they will lie absolutely quiet while a man or a caravan passes not far away; and doubtless hundreds so resting are not seen at all, or are mistaken for a heap of stones. Like all gazelles, too, they will stand motionless for some time when they first see a person approaching, so that a man moving very quietly may often walk within easy rifle range before they take to that swift, ground-skimming gait graphically spoken of as "flight." A more sportsmanlike way of getting them than by shooting is to course them with greyhounds, or falcons, or both. Ordinary dogs they regard with contempt, and are caught by jackals only by the cleverness of these hounds of the desert in working in relays which head off and turn the game until it is exhausted. Even a pack of the best greyhounds often fail.

Egyptian Arabs frequently catch them in a form of trap which is widely employed against all the small antelopes and some other game, and which is made wholly, except the short rope, from the date palm. It consists of a ring, of plaited leaf fibers, about three inches in diameter, through which are pushed date thorns, which converge toward the centers where they slightly overlap. A hole is then dug in a likely place, and the ring set over it, capped by the noose at one end of the rope, which at the other end is tied to a heavy buried stick. The whole is then sprinkled with sand and left. Should a gazelle put its foot through the ring, it will be held by the in-pointing thorns, its struggles will tighten the noose around its leg, and the attached stick will so impede flight that next morning it can easily be tracked and overtaken. This trap in some shape is used for the capture of all sorts of animals throughout all northern Africa.[55]

Nearly allied to this gazelle are several others in Africa and Asia whose habits are similar, yet in regard to each of which many peculiar and entertaining facts are on record. **Blackbuck.** A familiar Indian one is the blackbuck (Hindoo, *sasin*) in which the bucks are blackish brown down to the middle of the sides and chest, and down the outside of the legs, sharply contrasted with pure white below and inside the slender limbs. Its dandified manner of walking and holding its head haughtily high, the long horns lying gracefully along the satiny back, give it a most fetching air of self-satisfied pride. Does and young bucks are fawn-colored and white.

This beautiful and agile gazelle is one of the game animals of all the open plains of India, and requires quick shooting to bring it to bag. Cumming records a queer incident in this connection. "One of our party," he says, "fired at a buck antelope and struck it on the side of the horn about three inches above the head. The effect of the shot was to wrench off the horn from the spiral bone which it covered. In fact, it was simply *unscrewed*, and by the force of the shot was sent spinning several feet into the air." This blackbuck is the special object of sport with the cheeta.

The desolate plateaus of Tibet and Mongolia sustain flocks of several species of antelope, one of which, the chiru (Tibetan; Mongolian, *orongo*), is notable not only for its long, dense coat of crisp, pinkish fawn hair, but for its enlarged puffy nose, due, perhaps, to the need of breathing more co-

Chiru. piously the thin air of its lofty home than is required at lower levels. Remarkable, also, are the markings which distinguish the male, — a sooty black muzzle and a narrow black stripe down the front of each leg; and still more the straight, sharply ringed, strikingly erect horns, which are perhaps unsurpassed among antelopes as effective weapons. They measure twenty-three to twenty-six inches in length or height, and are in demand among the people of Tibet not only for their practical excellence as handles, etc., but for miraculous virtues, — in fact, the whole animal is "sacred" in the opinion of the llamas and is not eaten. Few book writers have seen the chiru, one of the fullest accounts being that by Kinloch.[160]

"In the mornings and evenings," he tells us, "it frequents the grassy margins of glacial streams, which frequently flow between steep banks gradually scarped out by the floods of centuries and now remote from the ordinary water's edge. The ravines have for the most part been cut through gently sloping valleys; and on ascending their steep sides, slightly undulating plains will be found to stretch away until they merge in the easy slopes of the rounded hills which bound the valley. To these plains the antelope betake themselves during the day, and there they excavate hollows deep enough to conceal their bodies, from which, themselves unperceived, they can detect any threatening danger at a great distance."

Far more ugly in countenance, by reason of the swollen shape of the nose, is the somewhat larger saiga (Russian, *säi-*

Saiga. *gak;* Kirghiz, *kiik*), formerly numerous throughout southern Russia and still roaming in small herds over the steppes east and west of the Caspian Sea, and migrating with the seasons. Their habits are much the same as those of our pronghorn. In Pleistocene times this and another species of saiga abounded in all parts of Europe, and was hunted by the primitive sportsman, who found its flesh, as do modern hunters, unusually good.

The lovely South African springbok is almost a gazelle, and has been the delight of every visitor to the veldt since the days of Captain Harris, — one of the earliest and best of naturalists to tramp over South Africa, and to pic- **Springbok.** ture for us with both pen and brush the teeming life of its plains a century ago. The colored drawings in his doubly valuable book [230] give a vivid idea of the throngs and the diversity of antelopes then to be seen, at favorable times, graz- ing on the pastures of the Orange River Valley, where now so few creatures are visible save branded flocks and herds.

LODER'S GAZELLE OF THE SAHARA DESERT.

Nevertheless some still remain, and among them none is more certain than the periodical visitations of springboks.

"In the old days," Bryden [231] tells us, "trek bokken (springbok migra- tions) were a source of the greatest alarm and danger to the colonist, quite as much, in fact, as the locust flights. Countless thousands of these ante- lopes, impelled by drought and the loss of their more secluded pastures, migrated from their true nursery and headquarters, in the country formerly known as Great Bushmanland, into more fertile districts in the interior of the colony. The immense numbers of the antelopes literally swept everything before them, and farmers frequently lost whole flocks in consequence. Our host described the approach of the trek bokken I speak of; enveloped in clouds of dust the herds came on. At one time the sight was positively alarming, for the springbok on these occasions cannot retreat from sheer press of numbers, and one has to be careful to keep out of their way. As the leading antelopes feed and become satiated, they fall back and allow those in the rear to come to the front; but for this provision of instinctive nature the rear guard would be starved to death, for those in front, of course, leave not a particle of nutriment as they pass. During these migrations the farmers shoot as much venison as they desire, and prepare immense quantities of biltong (salted and sun-dried flesh), of which the springbok furnishes the best quality."

Gordon Cumming [142] graphically describes a similar sight; and Millais [232] shows in delightful sketches their graceful manner of leaping and running. Turning to Bryden's book again: —

"When we had got within three quarters of a mile, the antelopes became disturbed and began those extraordinary saltatory accomplishments ('pronken,' the Boers term them) from which they take their name. One of the herd, followed by several others, would spring sheer and straight from its four feet, with arched back, ten or twelve feet into the air, as if made of india rubber; this leap would be repeated half a dozen times or more, and then the animals would settle to a canter, and thence into a gallop. While these marvelous bounds are being executed, the springboks erect the curious mass of long snow-white hair, which extends from about the middle of the back as far as the tail, imparting a most singular effect. When the animal is not excited or alarmed, this hackle or ruff lies closely to the back, and is almost enveloped in the loose fawn-colored skin which closes over it."

Next to present themselves is a group of large deerlike, reddish, water-loving African antelopes, called waterbucks, **Water-** and also reedbucks, because found mainly in marshes, **bucks.** where their splay feet keep them from sinking in the mire. The big shaggy waterbuck proper is familiar in menageries; and in its native land is as likely to be found on rocky hills as wading among aquatic weeds, but most of its relatives are smaller and more strictly swamp dwellers. Oddly enough the nearest allies of these marsh lovers are quite their opposites in habits, — the rheboks, steinboks, and klip-springers, small, short-horned, shy creatures, with the agility of a diminutive chamois. They will scale with ease a cliff that looks impossible to any- thing but a bird, and will leap from point to point among rocks hardly large enough for a mouse to perch upon. "It seems extraordinary," Drummond exclaims, "how their delicate limbs escape injury when they take bound after bound like an india-rubber ball in places that a cat would shudder at." The steinboks, of which several species are scattered through-out Africa south of the Sahara, are less acrobatic and feed in flocks on the veldt, mingled with springboks. Among them are the smallest of all ruminants, the bright chestnut-and-white "royal" antelope of the Guinea coast, which is only twelve inches tall; but the exquisite beni Israel, seen bound-ing along the arid, volcanic rocks and sands of the eastern coast of the Red Sea, and beloved of the Arabs and Abyssin-ians, is not much larger.

Some of the species of the next group, the duikerboks (*i.e.* diving goats as the Boers named them, because they plunge headlong into the chaparral when alarmed), are also tiny, — the mouse-colored bluebucks, swarming in the Natal jungles, stand-ing only thirteen inches high; but most of the duikers are larger.

"They abound in forested and bushy districts, moving about in small parties, leaping among the rocks, and dodging into and through the thickets with surprising agility, while their plain colors render them practically invisible when quiet. All have very convex foreheads, and very large eyes and ears between which, in both sexes, rise two little spike horns and a median tuft of stiff hairs. All these antelopes feed largely on berries and small fruits, and their flesh has an excellent flavor. The typical species, known in the North as 'deloo,' is very common in southwest Africa, and is often tamed as a pet."

To this group belong also the larger wood antelopes and zebra antelope of West Africa, which dwell in steaming forests, and hence are richly colored. The zebra antelope, in fact, is unique among ruminants in having "eight or **Zebra** nine black transverse bands crossing the back and **Antelope.** loins, and gradually narrowing to a point on the flanks, the ground color being golden brown." Lastly, there must be mentioned another singular form, the four-horned antelope or chousinga of India, of which the bucks usually have two pairs of horns. This curiosity is small, sand-colored, lurks in bushes and tall grass, and behaves more like a hare than an antelope. The books of sportsmen abound in stories of these pygmies among game, but it is distressing to read of shooting such charming little creatures.

The last of the antelope section contains the hartbeests and gnus, — a class of large, powerful, African antelopes **Hart-** with somewhat cattlelike characteristics. The **beests.** hartbeests vary from three feet two inches to four feet in height at the fore shoulder, from which the back slopes decidedly toward the haunches; this, with their thin necks, long narrow heads, and queerly bent, spreading, and rugged horns, give them an ungraceful figure. The color is always some tint of red; and Willoughby, who found them in thousands in Somaliland, says it is highly protective, for he was often mistaken in thinking one lying on the ground to be only an ant-hill. Another observer, Mr. Gedge, noted the same thing in British East Africa about 1892.

"Coke's hartbeest is usually seen in company with other game, and the sight of these vast mixed herds, which include zebras, and Grant's and Thomson's gazelles, is one not easily forgotten. Like all hartbeests, it is very wary and difficult to approach, its senses of sight and smell being extremely keen. During the time that the herd is grazing there are usually one or two sentinels posted on the nearest elevations to give warning of the approach of danger. The white-ant hills with which the entire country abounds are usually selected for this purpose, and are patronized to such an extent that I have seen as many as eight or ten occupying the summit of one of these hills, which looked as if it could support only a third of that number. The reddish color and general contour of these mounds bear in many cases so close a resemblance to the antelopes themselves, particularly when grazing, that I have frequently been deceived." [228]

Every one speaks of the deceptive gait of these animals, which appear to go at a moderate rate until one tries to overtake them, especially on rough ground. Captain Swayne, whose "Field Notes" (Proceedings Zoölogical Society, London, 1892) contain so much that is novel and important in regard to the fauna of Somaliland, remarks: —

"There is not always much game to be got at in the Haud; but a year ago, coming on to ground which had not yet been visited by Europeans, I found one of these plains covered with herds of (Swayne's) hartbeests, there being perhaps a dozen herds in sight, each containing three or four hundred individuals. Hundreds of bulls were scattered singly on the outskirts, and in spaces between the herds, grazing, fighting, or lying down. . . . In the midday haze on the plains they look like a troop of lions. The pace of the hartbeest is an ungraceful, lumbering canter, but this species is really the swiftest and most enduring of the Somaliland antelopes. . . . From their living so much in open grass plains, the hartbeests must subsist entirely on grass, for there is nothing else to eat; and they must be able to exist for several days without water. Hartbeests are the favorite food of lions."

Among the better known are the tetel of the North (also Syria and Arabia); Coke's, Swayne's, Jackson's, and Hunter's of the East Coast region; the korigun of the Sudan and Senegal; the black-marked caama of South Africa, the one to which the name was first applied; the sassaby, konzi, and violet-hued, strikingly face-blazed blesbok and bontebok; but several of these no longer exist save in the remotest wilds.

Associated with them are the grotesque South African gnus, or wildebeests, which seem a composite or caricature of the whole hoofed-and-horned tribe. "The body and legs are antelopelike, but the head is so massive and broad as to resemble that of an ox. The muzzle is naked, the eyes small, with a gland beneath each, whence sprout long, stiff hairs, and the horns, which in old age form a helmet over the forehead, are broad, black, and shaped like an African buffalo's, to which must be added the bovinelike circumstance not present elsewhere among antelopes, that the horn cores are honeycombed with cavities." There were two species,

Gnus.

the white-tailed of the Cape region, which was deep brown, with a long, white, horselike tail and mane, and a fringe of long hair on the chest and chin; and, second, the blue or brindled gnu, of duller hue, and with tail and mane black and no hair hanging between the fore legs. The latter lived north of the Zambezi, and not being able, because of its depend-

WHITE-TAILED GNU.

ence upon water, to flee to the deserts in which several of its more enduring allies have been able to find refuge, has been nearly exterminated, as have also the blesboks, bonteboks, and other relatives once numerous.

The information in the writings of African sportsmen and naturalists as to the haunts and habits of antelopes is almost endless, and it is only as a sample of the excellent reading these books offer that the following is quoted from Gordon Cumming, who shot and wrote when the fair plains of the Karoo were more alive with game than even now are they with herds and flocks.

"Blesboks differ from springboks in the determined and invariable manner in which they scour the plains, right in the wind's eye, and also in **Blesbok Herds.** the manner in which they carry their noses along the ground. Throughout the greater part of the year they are very wary and difficult of approach, but more especially when the does have young ones. At that season, when one herd is disturbed, and takes away up the wind, every other herd in view follows them; and the alarm extending for miles and miles down the wind, to endless herds beyond the vision of the hunter, a continued stream of blesboks may often be seen scouring up wind for upward of an hour, and covering the landscape as far as the eye can see. The springboks, which in equal numbers frequent the same ground, do not, in general, adopt the same decided course as the blesboks, but take away in every direction across the plains, sometimes with flying bounds, beautifully exhibiting the long, snowy-white hair with which their backs are adorned, and at others walking slowly and carelessly out of the hunter's way, scarcely deigning to look at him, with an air of perfect independence, as if aware of their own matchless speed.

"The blesbok is one of the finest antelopes in the world, and is allowed to be the swiftest buck in Africa. He, nevertheless, attains very high condition, and at this period was exceedingly fat. I was surprised and delighted with the exquisite manner in which his beautiful colors are blended together. Nothing can exceed the beauty of this animal. Like most other African antelopes, his skin emitted a most delicious and powerful perfume of flowers and sweet-smelling herbs. A secretion issues from between his hoofs which has likewise a pleasing perfume.

"The black wildebeests, which also thickly cover the entire length and breadth of the blesbok country, in herds averaging from twenty to fifty, have no regular course, like the blesboks. Unless driven by a large field of hunters, they do not leave their ground, although disturbed. Wheeling about in endless circles, and performing the most extraordinary variety of intricate evolutions, the shaggy herds of these eccentric and fierce-looking animals are forever capering and gamboling round the hunter on every side. While he is riding hard to obtain a family shot of a herd in front of him, other herds are charging down wind on his right and left, and, having described a number of circular movements, they take up positions upon the very ground across which the hunter rode only a few minutes before.

"Singly, and in small troops of four or five individuals, the old bull wildebeests may be seen stationed at intervals throughout the plains, standing motionless during a whole forenoon, coolly watching with a philosophic eye the movements of the other game, eternally uttering a loud snorting noise, and also a short, sharp cry which is peculiar to them. When the hunter approaches these old bulls, they commence whisking their long white tails in a most eccentric manner; then springing suddenly into the air, they begin prancing and capering, and pursue each other in circles at their utmost speed. Suddenly they all pull up together to overhaul the intruder, when two of the bulls will often commence fighting in the most violent manner, dropping on their knees at every shock; then quickly wheeling about they kick up their heels, whirl their tails with a fantastic flourish, and scour across the plain enveloped in a cloud of dust." [142]

The "antelope" of the North American plains stands in a family (Antilocapridæ) by itself, on account of the singular structure of its horns, which make the name prong-horn far more appropriate. Its nearest relative among us is the white goat; but it has no false hoofs, and is unlike any other sheathed-horned creature in that its horns are branched, in the way their covering is acquired, and most of all

Pronghorn.

PRONGHORN
Growing horns, showing the hardening at the tips.

in the fact that they are periodically shed and renewed. All together it is the most singular of ruminants.

The skull is surmounted by two spike-like horn cores, rising over, not behind, the great eye orbit and leaning outward. These are covered with a skin and coat of bristly hairs which agglutinate at the tip and change into a sheath of horn, the change proceeding toward the base until the bony cores are sheathed with horns which stand about a foot in height, are curved inward, so as often to be truly lyrate, and have one prong (occasionally more) on the front edge. Every winter these horns are pushed off by a new hairy growth beneath them, comparable to the "velvet" of deer's antlers, which in turn hardens into another pair of true horns. It was not until about 1865 that the fact of the shedding of the horns, which had been long before asserted by Indians and plainsmen, was admitted by "the faculty"; Audubon declared he had "proved to the contrary." To Dr. Caton [216] belongs the credit of tracing the full process. The affinity of the pronghorn to the deer, suggested by this fact, becomes more apparent when it is recalled that in the Miocene era there lived in our West a group of small, graceful plains runners called now deer-antelopes, because, with the general structure of antelopes, they bore on their heads branching antlers of the American type, *i.e.* round, equally forking, and without a brow tine; but these antlers rose from right

Merycodus.

above the eyes, not from a point well behind them, as in deer. A complete skeleton of one of them (Merycodus), mounted in the Museum in New York, is about as big as a gazelle and has four-branched antlers. From one of these deer-antelopes descended, it is believed, our pronghorn, the antler having degenerated into a deciduous horn, and the pedicel become elevated into a permanent bony core.

This singular and beautiful animal half a century ago ranged in enormous plenty over all the plains and valleys of the far West, avoiding mountain slopes and arid deserts, from the North Saskatchewan to central Mexico; but now only scattered remnants survive, and the species is likely soon to become extinct outside of

CURIOUSLY DEFORMED HORNS.

governmental reservations, because it will rarely bear young in captivity. I feel that it is a duty to repeat the warning uttered by the experienced Mr. Hornaday: —

"Let him who may hereafter be tempted, either lawfully or unlawfully, to raise a death-dealing rifle against one of these beautiful prairie rovers, remember two things before he pulls the trigger: In this land of plenty, no man really needs this creature's paltry pounds of flesh; and if his two-cent bullet flies true to the mark, it will destroy an animal more wonderful than the rarest orchid that ever bloomed. . . . Surely this animal is worth perpetual protection at our hands, rather than needless, cruel, and inexcusable slaughter. It cannot be perpetuated by breeding in captivity; *and unless preserved in a wild state, it will become extinct.*"

The pronghorn buck stands about thirty-eight inches high at the shoulder, and is a varying yellowish brown above, darker on the face, but dull white on chin and cheeks, in two crescentic patches across the throat, on the under surfaces, and in a broad heart-shaped patch around the brown scut of a tail.

This whiteness of the stern belongs in a greater or less degree to nearly all the ruminants, and to some other kinds of animals that associate in flocks; and is regarded by naturalists as a "recognition mark" by which members of a herd are able to see and follow their leader and each other. At such times, or when one of the troop suspects danger, the white area is increased, or is made more showy by a "cocking" of the tail displaying its white under side, as do rabbits, hares, goats, and conspicuously **Signifi-** our Virginia deer; or by the erection and expansion of the **cance of** hairs on the patch, which are longer than elsewhere in such **White** **Stern.** animals. This last arrangement is characteristic of the roe, the sika deer, and of our prongbuck. Ernest Thompson Seton has described it picturesquely as a "great double disk or chrysanthemum of white that shines afar like a patch of snow"; but he gives it an exaggerated importance.

PRONGHORN BUCKS AND DOES.

In summer the hair of the pronghorn is smooth and flexible, but as winter approaches it lengthens; each hair becomes thick, its interior becomes white and spongy, it loses its flexibility, and at last becomes brittle, so that its point is easily rubbed off. This deerlike coat forms a close and warm covering for the animal, but renders the skin useless as fur, nor does it make serviceable leather. The flesh, however, is delicious.

The life of our antelope is very simple. It is the genius of the dry, gravelly, bunch-grass plains, where it finds in the sun-cured nutritious herbage relieved each spring by a juicy new growth all the sustenance it craves. Wooded spaces it naturally avoids, not only because it has no appetite for leaves and twigs, but because thickets shelter wolves **Habits.** and wildcats; yet now and then a solitary buck will make a grove his hermitage, or a heavy doe retire to some bushy glade to be delivered of her fawn. Of late, however, under the changed conditions in its home, the pronghorn seeks cover more than formerly. It has no goatlike fondness for rocks, and rarely climbs the rough slopes of even the foothills.

The young, usually two, are dropped in May or early June, when the mothers have stolen away separately to secret places, and the bucks are wandering alone or in small gay parties by themselves; and these fawns are not spotted, but plain dun miniatures of the mother, and for the first few days lie motionless whatever happens, trusting to be overlooked; but soon they get upon their legs and begin to accompany the doe. From the start they show an instinctive intelligence in meeting the dangers that beset them, clinging, as if bound by a short tether, to the heels of the mother when, as so often happens, a coyote does its best to get past the valiant doe's defense of lowered horns (which are short, sharp, and unforked) and striking feet, to seize the tender youngling. I have told at length elsewhere [36] of such a battle which I once witnessed on the Wyoming plains. Rattlesnakes are another ever present peril, but these the antelope, if not first fatally struck, cuts to pieces by stamping upon them with quickly repeated bounds, all four hoofs alighting together on the reptile's coils. A pronghorn's javelin-like fore feet are its best weapon, though the bucks — furious in their rivalry when forming their harems — push one another about with their forked horns. Nowhere is to be read a more discerning, intimate, and delightful account of the prongbuck than in President Roosevelt's chapter on it in "The Deer Family" [233]; and on this point he notes: —

"All the deer are fond of skulking; the whitetail preëminently so. The prongbuck, on the contrary, never endeavors to elude observation. Its sole aim is to be able to see its enemies, and it cares nothing whatever about its enemies seeing it. Its coloring is very conspicuous, and is rendered still more so by its habit of erecting the white hair on its rump. It has a very erect carriage, and when it thinks itself in danger it always endeavors to get on some crest or low hill from which it can look all about. The great bulging eyes, situated at the base of the horns, scan the horizon far and near like twin telescopes. They pick out an object at such a distance that it would entirely escape the notice of a deer. When suspicious, they have a habit of barking, uttering a sound something like ' kau,' and repeating it again and again, as they walk up and down, endeavoring to find out if danger lurks in the unusual object. They are extremely curious, and in the old days it was often possible to lure them toward the hunter by waving a red handkerchief to and fro on a stick, or even by lying on one's back and kicking the legs."

Yet in summer, when small scattered parties dot the plains — or used to — a band would lie down during the midday hours in some open valley and rest in negligent ease. More **Curiosity and Intelligence.** than once have I ridden quietly over a ridge and thrown such a resting band into a momentary paralysis. Surprised, yet hardly knowing what to fear, they would spring to their feet then, suddenly panic-stricken, start off in high, stiff "buck jumps," making no progress, and the picture of wild terror. An instant later, however, gathering its faculties, the band would skim away in flight, then, if not followed, halt a few hundred yards off to look back. ·This curiosity is a strong trait, and often brings antelopes close to camp, or into a band of horses or mules; and their liability to panic leads them now and then to run right into danger. Audubon pictures their contradictory behavior excellently in that long account of the animal as he saw it on the upper Missouri in 1843, which so enriches his great work on American quadrupeds.

This disposition is a mark of the high intelligence of the animal, whose wits have been sharpened by generations of life in the midst of danger. Judge Caton [216] came to have a very high idea of their brain power after keeping them in his park. "When taken young," he says, "it soon acquires the attachment of a child for the human species, and when captured adult in a short time becomes so tame that it will take food from the hand and follow one by the hour, walking through the grounds. . . . One that was in the constant habit of following me soon became disgusted with the elk which chased him, so that whenever he saw me going toward the gate which opened into the elk park, he would place himself in front of me and try to push me back." Hornaday warns us, however, from his experience in zoölogical gardens, that as the bucks grow older they become dangerously rough in their play.

The speed of the pronghorn is scarcely surpassed by that of any antelope, but it is unable to sustain a swift pace for many miles, so that a pack of coyotes working together **Speed.** will tire it out, and a good hound, from which at first it will glide away with ease, will finally overtake it; nor does it seem able to leap over an obstacle more than a yard or so high, which accounts for the great influence the cattlemen's wire fences have had on its disappearance. This animal, indeed, seems to have a superstitious fear of iron, and the early railroads across the plains permanently divided the herds north and south of them. Like all plains runners the pronghorns gathered toward winter into herds, and those of the North migrated southward to where the snow lay thinner over the pasturage, and streams remained unfrozen; but thousands starved during severe winters. Nowhere were they originally more abundant than upon the high, dry plains of the Arkansas Valley, western Texas, and thence out to California.

The history of sport in the West abounds in stories of how the pronghorn is shot and coursed with hounds. The present writer will never forget some rides of that nature near Cheyenne, when his mettlesome gray seemed more bird than pony, as it raced over sage bush and gopher hole, up hill and down, after the fleeing quarry. It was great fun for us, and usually did no harm to the antelope. No better pictures of antelope hunting in every form can be found than those by Mr. Roosevelt in the books already commended to the reader.

Another familiar animal, standing with the pronghorn in a "betwixt and between" position as to antelopes and deer, is the **Giraffes.** giraffe. In most of its characteristics it is deerlike, but neither sex has antlers, while both bear on their forehead skull projections covered with hairy skin as in the pronghorn; but this skin never hardens into horn. It appears

Copyright, N. Y. Zoölogical Society. Sanborn, Phot.

NORTH AFRICAN GIRAFFES IN THE NEW YORK ZOÖLOGICAL PARK, 1906.

probable, however, that in the Sivatherium, a gigantic predecessor of the giraffe, fossil in the Pliocene formations of India, the horns were sheathed, and, moreover, were forked as in the prongbuck. The ancestral giraffes had shorter necks and legs more nearly of equal length than have their descendants.

The modern giraffe (family Giraffidæ) is the tallest of all animals, not only in carrying its head in some cases eighteen or nineteen feet above the ground, but in the height of its fore legs; and the short, deep-chested body slopes on the back rapidly down to drooping hindquarters and a cowlike tail. The extraordinary neck, which has been obtained by the lengthening out of the vertebræ, not by increasing their number (7), serves the animal well by lifting its head high above the thickets and grass of the bushy country in which it most often dwells — a living conning tower. As it looks and listens for the ever possible enemy, it browses the crown of one or another of the mimosas whose tablelike tops seem arranged for the purpose, or show how often their twigs have been nibbled away, year after year. It is curious to watch the long, flexible lips and tongue curling around the leaves and tearing them off to be munched between the lower front teeth and the horny pad in the upper jaw; but still more comical is it to see the beast pick a fallen leaf or tuft of grass, for his neck, despite its length, is not long enough for that, so that he has to straddle out his legs by jerks, like a photographer adjusting the height of his camera on its tripod, until he can reach the ground or get his mouth down to the surface of water to take a drink; but that is a luxury the modern Kalahari exiles, at least, must go without for months together. The giraffe's eyes are very large, dark, and liquid, and the expression of its face infantile and gentle; but keepers at the "Zoo" say that it is sometimes viciously ill-tempered, and can deliver terrific kicks with both fore and hind feet, which are shod with heavy hoofs.

The horns on the head play no part as weapons even in the battles of jealousy between the bulls; and probably are relics of structures more useful in the short-necked ancestral giraffes. With his present build, the animal could hardly make any play with weapons of that sort if he had them; he would be more likely to break his own neck than harm his antagonist. But antlers on the giraffes would be fine things for the perching birds! The present "horns" consist of a pair six inches or so high between the ears; and in addition to them, in old male giraffes, there rises from the forehead a third

horn, which is hardly more than a rounded boss in the southern species, but in the northern one may be a distinct horn three to five inches high. A third variety, discovered lately by Sir Harry Johnston, at Mt. Elgon, in Uganda (see Proc. Zoöl. Soc., London, 1901, p. 476), has two small additional horns behind the principal pair. The two hinder knobs are real outgrowths of the skull, but the others originate as separate bony pieces which, after growing for a time as distinct bones, join tightly to the skull.

FIVE-HORNED GIRAFFE.

The northern species is the one with which the world is most familiar by sight, as captives have almost invariably been brought from the Upper Nile region, where the animal still roves in small bands, and the young are occasionally captured. The giraffes about which *hunters* have mostly written, on the other hand, are those of South Africa, originally scattered everywhere outside the dense forests, but now restricted to the Kalahari deserts and the remote interior, whither they are constantly pursued by hide hunters, and within a few years, probably, will become extinct. Their habits everywhere are very simple. They feed morning and evening, rest in the heat of the day, and at night visit the drinking place. It is at this hour that they are most exposed to attack from their worst enemy—lions; but these stalk and seize them in daylight, too.

Andersson[149] relates an incident of his experience near Lake Ngami, where a noble bull fought heroically against two lions while three others looked on. In the late spring a single young one is born, and is able to trot by the side of its dam within three days. Selous once saw a giraffe defending her newly born calf against two leopards which had pounced upon it as it lay in the grass; and with such effect, by striking with her fore feet, that she drove the leopards off. Once alarmed, the giraffe takes to its heels and gets over the ground in a queer camel-like gallop, which it requires a good horse to keep up with, so that the chase of the camelopard has always been among the most exciting and enjoyable of the African hunter's experiences. Every sportsman's book abounds in such reminiscences, and one of the perils involved is that of being stunned by one of the flying stones hurled back from beneath the hoofs of the fast-striding quarry.

The coloration of giraffes is very striking and unlike any other animal pattern. The familiar northern kind may be described as a chestnut-colored animal, marked by a network of fine tawny lines. In the South African **Coloration.** one, on the contrary, large patches of brown or chestnut are irregularly distributed over a paler tawny ground color, while the under parts, shins, and feet are whitish. There is, however, great variation among them in both tint and pattern.

As we gaze at this always interesting animal in a menagerie, it seems as though nothing in the world could be more conspicuous, yet sportsmen have always complained of the difficulty of seeing this game in its native wilds. Not only is it that "the dappled hide of the giraffe blends harmoniously with the splashes of light and shade formed by the sun glinting through the foliage of the trees," but several writers speak of even the sharp-eyed natives mistaking its long and motionless neck and legs for weather-beaten tree trunks, which to their astonishment suddenly became very much alive. Some of Schillings's photographs show this well.

Until a very few years ago it was supposed that the family contained no other living members than the giraffes; but in the closing years of the last century Sir Harry Johnston found the negroes of the Semliki Valley, on the Uganda border of the Congo Free State, using for belts and other equipments the skin of an animal which he saw was unknown to science; but he was then unable to penetrate the forests where, the Pygmies told him, the animal lived. Later the Belgian officers of that district secured for him a skin and skull which after a time reached London and were set up in the British Museum. Sir Harry learned that its native name on the Semliki was okapi or "o'api," as the Pygmies pronounced it; and Professor E. Ray **Okapi.** Lankester named for it a new giraffine genus, and called this animal *Ocapia johnstoni*. A popular account of it was presently prepared by Sir Harry Johnston (with a colored drawing which, by permission, has served as the material for our plate) for *McClure's Magazine* (New York, September, 1901); and Beddard included a description in his "Mammalia" [37] as follows:—

"The animal is of about the size of a sable antelope and the back and sides are of a rich brown color; it is only the fore and hind limbs which are striped, the striping being longitudinal, *i.e.* parallel with the long axis of the body. The head is giraffelike, but there are no external horns; wisps of curled hairs seem to represent the vestiges of the horns of other giraffes. The tail is rather short, and the neck is rather thick and short. The skull is clearly giraffine. The basicranial axis is straight, and the fontanelle in the lachrymal region is very large."

More lately the examination of additional specimens enables Professor Lankester to decide that the first one received and above described (whence the drawing was made) was an immature female; and it is now known that the male has a pair of short, backward-sloping, giraffelike horns. In the details of its skull the okapi is extremely close to the extinct Samotherium. "It is probable," he asserts,[187] "that there are two species, a smaller and a larger, living both in the forests of the Congo."

As to its range and habits, Sir Harry learned that it was found on both sides of the Uganda border, in the heart of the densest forest, where it moved about in pairs and was said to feed wholly

THE OKAPI

on leaves and twigs. In the German periodical *Globus*, of Dec. 22, 1905, there appeared some additional notes furnished by an explorer, Dr. J. David, of the district west of Lake Albert Edward. From this account it appears that the okapi dwells in the most dense parts of the primeval forest, where there is an undergrowth of solid-leaved, swamp-loving plants and climbers which form a thick and confused mass of vegetation. The leaves of these plants are blackish green, grow more or less horizontally, and are glistening with moisture. The effect of the light falling upon them is to produce along the midrib of each a number of short, white streaks of light, which contrast most strongly with the shadows cast by the leaves themselves, and with the general gloom of the forest. On the other hand, the thick layer of fallen leaves on the ground and the bulk of the stems of the forest are bluish brown and russet, so that the whole effect is precisely similar to the russet head and body, and the striped thighs and limbs, of the okapi, which could not be seen thirty yards. Dr. David recalls that the German explorer Junker recorded in his "Travels" (*Reisen in Afrika*, 1875–1886; Vienna, 1880–1891) that in 1878 or 1879, in the Nepo district, he saw a portion of the skin of this animal which he mistook for something else; and he notes that it was called by Nepo people "makapi." Dr. David adds that by the Arabianized slaves about Lake Albert Edward the animal is known as "kenge." There may be two species.

An interesting incident of the rediscovery of the okapi is its identification by archæologists with certain Egyptian antiquities not heretofore understood.

The ideas at the base of their religious mythology led the dwellers along the Nile three thousand years or more ago to depict many of their gods and demigods with animal heads, symbolic of their origin and **The God** traits. Among these a prominent one is Set, brother (and **Set.** murderer) of the great god Osiris. After a rebellious career, he was expelled from civilized Lower Egypt, and was reduced to the mean rank of god of the desert, but later he was restored to high regard. The large quadruped, described in the hieroglyphics as "red," by whose whole figure Set is represented in the earliest monuments, although later merely its head was used, or such a head surmounting a human figure, has been a puzzle to students. The nearest they could come to it was to guess it to be the wild ass, whence have arisen certain baseless myths connected with

OKAPI HEAD OF SET.

Set. The resemblance of the Set heads to the okapi is, however, so apparent, that it was at once accepted as the solution of the puzzle, although no evidence exists that this animal ever was a resident of any part of the Egypt of historical antiquity.

Sir Harry Johnston at first thought he had found a living specimen of the Helladotherium, a fossil predecessor of the giraffe occurring in the Pikermi (Miocene) beds of Greece, which had a neck much shorter than modern giraffes and limbs more equal in length. Later fossil species, as Samotherium, in which the male was horned, and others, show that the present giraffine long neck has been very slowly acquired. Out of the direct genealogy, but within the family, is the extraordinary animal Sivatherium, found fossil in the Siwalik Hills of India, which had two pairs of horns, — the larger on the crown of the head palmated and with a few short prongs, and a shorter pair just above the eyes. This doubly armed creature (see illustration on page 6) was nearly as big as an elephant.

The Antlered Deer — Cervidae

It is most comforting to meet, now and then, a group of animals so sharply marked by one or more characteristics as to be easily bounded and described. Such a well-defined family is that of the deer, — the Cervidæ. It is enough simply to say that a deer is an animal which bears antlers. How antlers compare with other horns has already been pointed out ; how they are formed is pleasantly sketched by Lloyd Morgan: —

"Pause as, in autumn, you enter the Gardens by the southern gate, before the splendid wapiti, often misnamed the elk by American hunters. Is there a more noble and beautiful animal in the Zoo? See how the antlers branch and rebranch and once more branch again! How proudly he carries them! What terrible weapons they are with their sharp bony points! How he clashes them against the bars of his inclosure! But come again in spring or early summer when the antlers are growing. How different they look! How careful he is not to bring them in contact with the bars against which he will clash them in the autumn! **Formation of Antlers.** They are covered over with a dark skin provided with short, fine, close-set hair, and technically termed the velvet. If you could lay your hand upon this velvet, . . . you would feel that it is hot with the nutrient life blood that is coursing beneath it. It is, too, exceedingly sensitive and tender. An army of tens of thousands of busy living cells are at work beneath that velvet surface building the bony antlers, preparing for the battles of autumn. Each minute cell knows its work and does it for the general good. It takes up from the nutrient blood the special materials it requires; out of them it elaborates the crude bone stuff, at first soft as wax, but erelong to become as hard as stone; and then, having done its work, having added its special morsel to the fabric of the antler, it remains embedded and immured, buried beneath the bone products of its successors or descendants. No hive of bees is busier or more replete with active life than the antler of a stag as it grows beneath the soft warm velvet. And thus are built up in the course of a few weeks those splendid 'beams,' with their 'tynes' and 'snags.'

"When the antler has reached its full size, a circular ridge makes its appearance at a short distance from the base. This is the 'burr,' which divides the antler into a short 'pedicel' next the skull, and the beam with its branches above. The circulation in the blood vessels of the beam now begins to languish, and the velvet dies and peels off, leaving the hard, dead, bony substance exposed. Then is the time for fighting, when the stags challenge each other to single combat, while the hinds stand timidly by. But when the period of battle is over, and the wars and loves of the year are past, the bone beneath the burr begins to be eaten away and absorbed, and, the base of attachment being thus weakened, the beautiful antlers are shed; the scarred surface skins over and heals, and only the hair-covered pedicel of the antler is left."

Copyright, N. Y. Zoölogical Society.

Sanborn, Phot.

STAGES OF ADVANCING GROWTH OF ANTLERS ON A WAPITI STAG.

Of what purpose and value is this elaborate headgear, which costs annually half the time and strength of the animal, only to be thrown away? In the case of the reindeer-cari- **Use of** bou genus the answer seems easy: Weapons of **Antlers.** defense against wolves and shovels to toss aside the snow that covers pasturage in winter; but here both bucks and does wear them. In all other deer, antlers are produced on the heads of the males alone, if at all, and in the case of those whose heads are finally adorned with mightily spreading horns, this perfection is reached only after several years. Furthermore, for half of each year all deer are hornless, and at the very season when the does are bearing and attending their young, when the company and protection of a well-armed mate would seem to be of most service to them. Finally, as a matter of fact, the buck trusts more to the striking power of his fore feet than to his antlers in warding off such enemies as he cannot run away from. It appears, then, that the antlers serve their owners mainly in fighting with rival bucks for the possession of does; and it is in the gregarious, polygamous kinds that these weapons are most fully developed. Antlers are acquired gradually with increasing age,[244] starting with the single "spike" of **Antler** the yearling, and proceeding by an added tine each **History.** year until the pattern is completed, seven seasons thus being required for the European red deer or the wapiti to perfect its head and become a "full stag"; the language of venery has a special name for each stage of progress.

The variations in the antlers of different groups arise from the suppression of parts; or from their exaggeration, as the prolonged brow tines of the reindeer; or from the flattening of a beam or uniting of the tines into a "palmated" condition, as in fallow deer, moose, etc. Extraordinary duplications and malformations frequently occur, mainly as the result of injury to the velvet in the growing stage; but no points extra to the proper pattern are named or counted, except as curiosities.

A very interesting parallel is found by comparing the slow acquirement of a full head by a young buck with the history of the family as exhibited in paleontology. The oldest fossil types are Miocene, and were small creatures somewhat akin to the modern muntjacs, but totally hornless. Not until the middle of the Miocene has a deer (Dicroceras) been found with horns, and they are bifid, and stand upon a long pedicel — also muntjac-like. Later came true deer with branching horns which culminated in a European species with twelve points on each antler — the celebrated "giant stag" of the Irish peat bogs and similar places, whose palmated antlers spread ten to twelve feet from tip to tip; it was, in fact, a huge fallow deer.

Some sixty living species of deer are known, mostly American and Asiatic. Africa (except the Barbary coast, which is European zoölogically) has none, nor has Australia. All are much alike in having short brittle hair inclined to lengthen about the neck and shoulders into a mane, especially noticeable in the polygamous, contentious stags, for which it serves as a buckler against a rival's horns; short, well-feathered, and often erectile tails; tall, mobile, and expressive ears; big dark eyes, below which open great tear ducts; and canines in the upper jaw, in some species becoming formidable tusks. In color all are some tint of golden or reddish brown, deepening in some Oriental species to almost black, and elsewhere often showing a much darker tone in places, as in the dull chestnut mane of our wapiti. There is usually more or less white on the lower surfaces, and pale color about the stern, most conspicuous in such kinds as form herds in an open country; but no very striking ornamentation of the face appears. Several species, however, as the fallow, the axis, and the sikas, are spotted with white.

These spottings have been the text of much speculation on the relation between an animal's coloration and its safety from enemies. The idea in **Coloration.** this case is that the slight spottings increase the deer's chance of remaining unseen as it stands beneath the trees. "One could not help noticing," remarks one writer, after watching the dappled fallow deer in an English park, "how remarkably their mottled skins, angular outlines, and branching horns fitted them for concealment in the glades of the forest." The conclusion is that the dappled coat harmonizes beneficially with the splashes of sunlight and shade beneath forest trees in summer. Lydekker [65] points out a supporting fact in the circumstance that spotted deer become self-colored in winter, when there are no leaves to cast checkered shadows. "Accordingly, the fallow deer exchanges its dappled summer livery for a uniform coat of fawn, more in harmony with the somber color prevalent in nature generally during the northern winter. A precisely similar change takes place in the Japanese deer and its relative, the Peking deer of Manchuria, both of which have bright chestnut coats dappled with large white spots in summer, while in winter they are clothed in somber brown." The Indian axis, which spends its life in herds on the margins of rippling streams with their banks overgrown by lofty trees, or in the grassy glades that open out amid the exquisite foliage of bamboo clumps, does not make any such seasonal exchange of coat, nor does the Philippine axis, but both retain the dappled livery throughout the year; this, Dr. Lydekker says, is because they dwell in the tropics, where the trees do not become bare. But the East Indian hog deer does not conform to this alleged rule.

It would at once occur to sportsmen that the sambar was neither spotted nor changeable; but Dr. Lydekker explains that that species dwells mainly in thick woods, is chiefly nocturnal, and does not need a dappled hide for concealment. Nor has it escaped the same competent naturalist that many deer, as well as most other hairy animals of northern countries, semiannually put on a winter coat paler than their summer dress; and he regards this as in the same category, — that is, as a protective arrangement. But various larger influences seem to me to induce this tendency in almost all animals, especially ruminants, to whiten in cold climates. Why, for instance, are the roe and red deer of the Old World, and our whitetail (cases particularly referred to), wearing in summer uniform red coats when their haunts and habits are practically the same as are said to make a white-spotted dress so advantageous for the fallow deer and the chital? Our common deer dwells in the edges of the woods, in open glades and along brushy river margins, as well as in denser forest, yet is not spotted, though its fawns are, as is the case with the young of most uniformly colored animals; it has long been believed that this last fact indicates that primitively all these animals were spotted, and that most species have outgrown the condition; but why should they do so if it were so advantageous? It is apparent that more study is required in this direction.

The most irregular of the deer, and one which some naturalists would place in a separate family nearer the Bovidæ (it has, for instance, a gall bladder, possessed by bovine **Musk Deer.** ruminants but not by cervine), is the musk deer of the highlands of central Asia, from Kashmir to Cochin China.

This is the source of true musk, the product of a large gland beneath the skin of the hinder part of the abdomen of the male, connected with

sexual functions. When fresh, musk looks like moist gingerbread, and forms the basis of many manufactured perfumes; hence the "pods," as the excised glands are called, bring a high price in market, and the deer, despite their almost inaccessible homes and great wariness, are growing scarce. The musk deer is a strange, old-fashioned, solitary little creature, the size of a half-grown kid, and having very large ears, almost no tail, and no horns, but wearing a pair of keen weapons in the long upper canines which hang well down below the lower jaw. The four toes of the feet are almost equal, and the hoofs so free that they can fairly grasp any projection, so that it is not surprising to be told that the animal is a marvel of agility and sure-footedness. The long, pithy, and brittle hair is dull gray-brown, but fawns are spotted at first.

MUSK DEER.

Other quaint little Eastern deer are the reddish water deer of the reed beds along the Yangtse River, which are singular **Muntjacs.** in producing five or six young at a time; and the small, blackish, Chinese "tufted deer," peculiar in having a pencil of stiff hairs standing upright on the top of the head, and half hiding the long pedicels tipped with minute stubs of horns. A little in advance of them come the muntjacs, four species of chestnut-red deer, twenty to twenty-two inches high, creeping about the Oriental jungles, and wearing roughened, once-forked antlers, mounted upon very tall pedicels. It is not upon their tiny horns, but upon dagger play with their tusks, that all these kinds of diminutive deer rely for protection against wolves and wildcats. Although the Indian muntjac ("kakar" or barking deer) is numerous wherever wooded hills abound, and its loud, resonant, continuous barking often resounds morning and evening close to settlements, it is rarely seen, for it does not feed openly by daylight, nor gather into migratory herds. The muntjacs come nearest of existing deer to the early family type shown in fossils; and their closest living relatives are the roe deer [93] of Europe, which are a little bigger, and have some-

A ROEBUCK.

what more complicated antlers, but resemble them in habits as closely as the different circumstances permit. The roe is still found wild in Scotland and in many parts of Europe, — in fact, thousands come to market annually from the region east of the Alps; and it furnishes one of the principal game animals of that continent.[227]

The typical deer constitute the genus Cervus, and as a rule are of large size and display widely branching antlers. The smallest one is the diminutive hog deer or para, exceedingly common on the low, wet plains of northern India and Burma,[147] where it lurks alone in the grass and thickets, and looks and acts like a pig. Kinloch mentions that they are often chased on horseback and speared by boar hunters. "I have heard," he writes, "of their deliberately charging a horse; and with their sharp horns they can inflict a very severe wound." Next them stands the group of Asiatic, semitropical swamp deer, one of which, the bara-singha, is prominent among the game of India. Siam has

Hog Deer and Swamp Deer.

another species (Schomburgk's) and the lower Malay Peninsula and Hainan a third (the thamin).   They are mainly grazers,. and are to be looked for in large herds on favorable grass lands where they will pasture all day if not much disturbed.

There comes in here a Chinese deer which is as remarkable in its history as in its physical peculiarities, — the "mi-lou" of
Mi-lou. the Peking Chinese, to whom it has been known from a remote period as an inhabitant of the vast imperial hunting park south of that city.   Here herds roamed about, and furnished sport for the Court; but the deer was not

Père David's, or Peking Park, Deer, or Mi-lou.
The hinder prong of the antler normally forks into one or more short branches.

known wild, nor did it become known to Europeans until after 1865.   In 1894 the Hun River overflowed and breached the walls of the park, allowing the herds to escape into the country, where every animal seems to have been killed by famine-stricken peasants.   Thus this species of deer, preserved for centuries only in the Peking park, must now be revived from stock carried to the other side of the world out of scientific curiosity.

Even this resource may fail, for the only specimens now (1907) known to exist are a herd of thirty-seven at Woburn Abbey, England, the seat of the Duke of Bedford. These are hardy, and breed, yet are closely in-bred, and the duke fears that they will not suffice to revive the race. No female has been alive in any menagerie since 1900, so far as I can learn.

Père David's deer, as it is called after its scientific discoverer, is of medium size, with a round, donkeylike body, robust limbs, and a tail that hangs to the hocks. The color is pale fawn gray, little altered by the changing seasons. The antlers are heavy and of the forked type, the hinder main prong reaching far backward before itself forking; altogether, they are unique in pattern, and an additional singularity is the fact that in England, at least, the bucks shed and renew their antlers twice a year.

Copyright, N. Y. Zoöl. Soc.   Sanborn, Phot.

ONE OF THE AXIS GROUP.

Sambar. Related to the swamp deer by the roughened and simple form of the antlers is the sambar, — the ordinary woodland stag of all southeastern Asia, various varieties carrying the race clear to the Philippines. It wanders about in small parties or alone, feeds usually at night, and mainly on grass and certain wild fruits, but also browses much. A good sambar stag will weigh five hundred to six hundred pounds, and his antlers will form a triangle of forty-five inches along each heavy rough beam and across from tip to tip; a peculiarity is that the shedding sometimes occurs only once in two or three years. In northern India they are shot, but in Ceylon, according to Baker,[147] the custom is to chase them with hounds, and, when the quarry has been brought to bay, to spear it.

JAPANESE SIKA: ADULT BUCK AND SPOTTED FAUN.

Photographed by the Duchess of Bedford, in the Park of Woburn Abbey, Bedford-shire, England.

Very different in coloring, but otherwise closely related, are some Eastern deer, — the usually unspotted, 4-pointed, Japanese and Chinese sikas, and the pretty chital, or axis deer, of whose special characteristics I have already spoken. It is comical to watch a band of these latter deer in fly time, — every white tail whirling on its axis.

Europe and western Asia have a spotted deer of similar size, but with very different " heads," — the fallow deer, familiar to **Fallow** all who have strolled through English parks or visited **Deer.** any first-rate " zoo." Here we come upon the " palmated " type of antler, that is, one in which the beam flattens out toward its extremity like the palm of the hand, the terminal tines sticking out like fingers. Good fallow antlers may meas-

EUROPEAN FALLOW DEER

ure twenty-five or more inches along the curve, and are not completed until the buck is six years old. In color this deer is yellowish dun or "fallow," with whitish spots on the sides and white under parts; the buttocks and under side of the rather long tail are white, and the latter is hoisted in moments of alarm after the manner of our whitetail. The coat becomes grayish in winter, and a variety of great antiquity in Epping Forest, England, is dark brown, only faintly spotted.

The fallow deer is a native of both shores of the Mediterranean, and is still found wild in Sardinia and the Grecian islands. Thence it was long ago half domesticated throughout Europe, and was taken to the British Isles probably by the Roman colonists. "Fallow deer are gregarious to a great extent," we are told by Bell, "associating in large herds, the bucks apart from the does, except in the pairing season and early winter, when the sexes consort in company. Most persons must be familiar with their boldness and the confident manner in which they will approach mankind where they are well accustomed to his presence; importuning the stranger who picnics in Greenwich Park for a biscuit or an apple, which is seldom refused. . . . The fallow deer feeds on herbage; it has been noted that it is especially fond of horse-chestnuts, which the bucks knock down from the branches with their antlers, and the tree is consequently frequently planted in deer parks. Fallow deer venison is usually considered much superior to that of the red deer, being generally much fatter, but the latter is considered by some to have the finest flavor. The skin of both the buck and doe is well known as affording a soft and durable leather. The antlers, like those of other species, are manufactured into the handles of knives and other cutlers' instruments, and the shavings and refuse have always been employed in the manufacture of ammonia, whence the name 'hartshorn.'"

This brings us to the foremost exemplars of all this noble and graceful family, — the red deer of the Old World and the wapiti of the New.

The red deer, hart or stag, has been renowned for centuries as the noblest object of the chase in Europe, where it once ranged throughout the continent and far into Asia, **Red Deer.** and although long ago exterminated as a wild creature in thickly settled regions, it is preserved in all parts of

Europe as an object of the chase or an ornament to the rural landscape. To us it is inseparably connected with pictures of life in the Scottish Highlands, where tracts of rough hill land, called "deer forests," are left vacant mainly to furnish sanctuary for the herds and sport in deer stalking for the proprietor. This manly, exhilarating, and ancient form of the chase is celebrated in a fair library of books,[237] and in many a painting and piece of sculpture. Wild red deer still also range the Devonshire moors, but there they are chased on horseback, with hounds, at the proper season, by privileged persons, — an imitation of which is the running of a stag practically tame, which occurs from time to time at Windsor, near London; and when the hounds overtake the animal (which frequently refuses to run at all) it is caught by keepers, before they can harm it, and carried home in a cart! In our forefathers' days the chase of the stag was no such farce, of course; and stag hounds were something more than the show dogs to which they have now degenerated. In Hungary and South Russia wild deer are got by "driving," with the aid of a circle of beaters.

A fine specimen of the British red deer will nowadays stand about four feet tall at the shoulders (the hinds are much smaller), and in summer is bright reddish brown, the head and legs being somewhat grayer, and the buttock patch yellowish; the fawns are at first white-spotted. In winter the coat is longer and grayer. A fine Scotch stag will weigh nearly 300 pounds; but a century ago stags were to be obtained weighing 400 pounds, the modern depreciation in size and noticeably in the length and spread of the antlers being the result of a continual effort to kill the biggest and handsomest stags for the sake of their heads as trophies. The deer of the Carpathian and Balkan mountains are uniformly largest, and, with the maral, represent the central, ancestral stock of the tribe.

Asia possesses several closely allied forms of red deer, usually esteemed distinct species, but Lydekker[236] questions whether it would not be better to consider all as local races. One, the maral, inhabits the Caspian provinces of Persia; another is the hangul of Chinese Turkestan, Kashmir, and the western Himalaya, which figures largely in the hunting stories of Kinloch, Macintyre, and other Himalayan sportsmen; a fourth is the still

Copyright, N. Y. Zoölogical Society.

Sanborn, Phot.

STAG AND HIND OF THE MARAL OR PERSIAN RED DEER.

heavier shou of southwestern Tibet, sometimes five feet in height and carrying antlers of 55 inches. All these are much larger than the European red deer, yet all are exceeded by the great stags of the Thian-Shan range and eastward, which are said to stand six feet in height; they vary only in minor particulars from our wapiti. The color, habits, etc., of all the foregoing are essentially the same, and it is fair to suppose that the whole group — including our wapiti — is descended from a common ancestor, and is practically one species, perhaps originally of south-central Asia.

None of all these stags is more stately than the American wapiti, — the "elk" of all western men, — which once abounded from the Adirondacks and southern Alleghanies to California and the borders of Alaska. Everywhere of old it was in plenty and easy to kill, and the pioneers swiftly destroyed it as civilization was pushed westward, until its mighty herds have vanished almost as completely as those of the bison. It seemed to make no particular choice of country, but thrived anywhere and everywhere, climbing the wooded heights of the Appalachians (where the very last one was killed near Ridgway, Pennsylvania, in 1869), loafing in the warm, well-watered valleys of the Mississippi basin, herding on the sun-baked plains, or scrambling up and down the roughest of western sierras. Equally broad in its appetite, those that browsed or ate mast and fruits in the eastern woods did no better than those which grazed on the bunch-grass plateaus from the Rio Grande to Peace River; and, undaunted by winter, would keep fat where other deer or cattle might starve.

Wapiti.

"Their principal food," says Perry,[129] speaking of the West, "consists of grasses, mosses, and lichens. In times of continued storms they browse and keep fat for weeks on the boughs and bark of maple, alder, willow, and cottonwood trees; but, if the snow is not too deep, they paw the ground bare, in order to procure grass, lichens, and mosses. In the spring they follow the receding snows until they reach the higher mountain valleys. Here the grass, nipped weekly by frosts, is sweet and just to their taste. No sight could be more interesting to the hunter naturalist than to watch a herd of elk feeding in one of these secluded mountain valleys. If there be a stream running through the valley, bordered by a sand bar, the entire band makes this their sleeping place; and the bands always assume the same position in sleeping, — the calves, cows, and yearlings in the center, and the bucks around the outer edge of the circle, so that in case of a night attack by wolves or panthers the strongest will meet the first onset of the foe. . . . In winter they gather in large bands and are constantly on the move; while they may not travel out of a small valley yet they are in motion seeking food. At this time they develop very hoglike characteristics for so grand an animal. With them it is the universal rush of the strong against

Copyright, N.Y. Zoölogical Society. Sanborn, Phot.
ALTAI WAPITI STAG, IN WINTER.

the weak; and if the tiny calf of the band paws up a tender morsel of lichen, the grandest bull in the circle does not hesitate to drive her away and appropriate it himself. The feeding ground of a band of elk in winter often resembles a farmyard, the snow being trodden down and packed as hard as ice, and the trees, if aspen, birch, or willow, have most of the bark eaten off. All the smaller branches within reach are eaten, the animals often standing on their hind legs in order to reach the highest."

This hardihood and cheerful omnivorous disposition make the wapiti a very easy deer to keep and rear in a park, since they breed in captivity without difficulty; and it is probable that they will remain for many years numerous in and

about the Yellowstone Park, in Jackson's Hole, and along the
Canadian Rockies, under legal protection.   One or two fawns
Domestic   are born at a time, in late spring, in some secluded
Habits.   thicket in a plains country, but mountain mothers
like to go up near timber line for their accouchement.   The
little one is brightly reddish and spotted with white, and for a
few days simply lies close and quiet, giving forth no scent, and
not stirring save at its mother's signal.   The doe will defend it
bravely against ordinary enemies, but not against a man.   I
have picked one up and carried it to camp, and had the dam
follow me like an old family cow; she got her calf again in a
few moments, but took pains to hide it quickly in a new place.
No one has sketched the life of the wapiti, and the methods and
joy of its chase, so completely and delightfully as have Roosevelt and Van Dyke, — the former for the northern plains, and
the latter as he knew the animal in California, — and I wish to
quote briefly from Mr. Roosevelt [233] : —

"In its life habits the wapiti differs somewhat from its smaller relatives.
It is far more gregarious, and is highly polygamous.   During the spring,
while the bulls are growing their great antlers, and while the cows have
very young calves, both bulls and cows live alone, each individual for itself.
At such time each seeks the most secluded situation, often going very high
up in the mountains. . . .

"As the horns begin to harden the bulls thrash the velvet off against
quaking asp, or ash, or even young spruce, splintering and battering the
"Elk"   bushes and small trees.   The cows and calves begin to as-
Hunting.   semble; the bulls seek them.   But the bulls do not run the
cows as among the smaller deer the bucks run the does.   The time of the
beginning of the rut varies in different places, but it usually takes place in
September, about a month earlier than that of the deer in the same locality.
The necks of the bulls swell and they challenge incessantly, for unlike the
smaller deer they are very noisy.   Their love and war calls, when heard at
a little distance, amid the mountains, have a most musical sound.   Frontiersmen usually speak of their call as 'whistling,' which is not a very appropriate term.   The call may be given in a treble or in a bass, but usually
consists of two or three bars, first rising and then falling, followed by a

succession of grunts. The grunts can only be heard when close up. There can be no grander or more attractive chorus than the challenging of a number of wapiti bulls when two great herds happen to approach one another under the moonlight or in the early dawn. The pealing notes echo through the dark valleys as if from silver bugles, and the air is filled with the wild music. Where little molested the wapiti challenge all day long.

"They can be easiest hunted during the rut, the hunter placing them, and working up to them, by the sound alone. The bulls are excessively truculent and pugnacious. Each big one gathers a herd of cows about him and drives all possible rivals away from his immediate neighborhood, although sometimes spike bulls are allowed to remain with the herd. Where wapiti are very abundant, however, many of these herds may join together and become partially welded into a mass that may contain thousands of animals.

"The bulls fight desperately with one another. The two combatants come together with a resounding clash of antlers, and then push and strain with their mouths open. The skin on their neck and shoulders is so thick and tough that the great prongs cannot get through or do more than inflict bruises. The only danger comes when the beaten party turns to flee. The victor pursues at full speed. Usually the beaten one gets off; but if by any accident he is caught where he cannot escape, he is very apt to be gored in the flank and killed. Mr. Baillie-Grohman [227] has given a very interesting description of one such fatal duel of which he was an eyewitness on a moonlight night in the mountains."

The accepted order of classification by structural likeness requires us to turn next to the moose, — our representative of the Old World elk, whose name should have followed it here instead of being misapplied to the wapiti; but unfortunately pioneers are rarely men of learning or discrimination in natural history, and the first suggestion that comes into their heads is likely to fasten itself on the local speech. By good luck, however, the Indian name for our elk in New England, *musu* (in western Cree, *mooswa*), said to signify "wood eater," was easily remembered, and so we have the excellent term "moose" for this greatest of the deer tribe.

In the prehistoric period the elk or moose ranged as far south in Europe as the great mountain barrier, and in America to southern New York and

Ohio. It still occurs sparingly in certain large forests of Lithuania and
central Russia; and on this continent from Maine to western Alaska,
wherever unfrequented forests remain. It is stated that about thirty-five
hundred were shot in Maine alone between 1895 and 1905, yet it still is
numerous in the northern counties, as also in the Maritime Provinces,
under the enforcement of wise game laws.

MOOSE RUSHING TO MEET A CHALLENGER

The moose is a huge, immensely strong and ungainly animal,
blackish brown with pale legs and belly, and with a neck so
short that it can graze only by kneeling. A very
Moose. large bull may stand six and a half to seven feet
high at the withers, which, with the neck, are clothed in a thick
mantle of long, coarse, stiff hair; and from the throat hangs

a long hairy strip of dewlap skin (the "bell"), which in old age draws up into a sort of pouch. The long and narrow head ends in an overhanging, flexible muzzle, which can be curled around a twig like a proboscis. On this massive head and neck the bulls carry a wonderful pair of flattened antlers, always surprisingly wide in spread, but varying greatly in weight, and that irrespective of the relative bigness of the animal. The moose of the Kenai Peninsula, Alaska, are famous for the immensity and complication of their horns; one pair preserved in the Field Columbian Museum, Chicago, have a spread of $78\frac{1}{2}$ inches, show 34 points, measure 15 inches around the burr, and with the dry skull weight 93 pounds; but very few reach such dimensions.

The moose is everywhere an animal of the forest, especially where water is abundant. Roughness of country appears to give it no trouble in spite of its weight, for it will **Haunts and** crash through the thickest brush like an elephant. **Habits.** In the East it is exceedingly fond of wading in marshy rivers and ponds in summer, even neck-deep, regaling itself on the aquatic herbage, or going completely under water to pull up and enjoy the bulbous lily roots; but of ordinary grass it eats very little. It is a capital swimmer, not fearing to cross rivers or arms of the sea miles in width. Its principal diet consists of leaves and twigs, preferably the fresh foliage of small hardwood trees and willow brush, with some balsam and juniper, which it pulls off by curling about the twigs the lips and tongue; and often it will bend a young tree over by straddling it with its fore legs, and so browse all the top at ease. In the Rocky Mountains the food and general habits differ from this in many particulars.

"In the North and West," says A. J. Stone, in a thoroughly original account [233] of the creature, "they do not yard up in winter, and consequently do not live much on the bark of trees in that season; do not feed to any extent on lily pads; do not run so much in the timber; and in some sections they range much higher in the mountains." Mr. Stone seems to have been decidedly in error, however, when in this account he asserted that moose may not be " called " by a bark horn, as is commonly done in eastern Canada. Many trustworthy sportsmen (the latest, Clive Phillipps-Woolley in his " Big Game Shooting ") established the fact that moose are called as successfully in Alaska and British Columbia as in Maine or New Brunswick.

In the autumn the bull moose, their new antlers strong and bright, range the woods in search of mates, bawling out invitation and challenge night and day, and often engaging in terrific combats with rivals. At this season they are in prime condition as to both venison and robe, and are most easily procured, either by being called within shot by means of a birch-bark horn imitating their cry, or by more ordinary methods. A bull moose is then a dangerous customer when cornered or wounded, for he will charge like a locomotive, and kill the hunter who cannot get away or stop him with a heavy bullet well planted. In May, or later, the mothers hide away and bear their young, which are spotted; a favorite lying-in place is an island, and the cow will stay upon it until her calf is a fortnight old. Calves brought up in captivity become pets, and even adult moose are gentle and tractable to an unusual degree, so that they have frequently been trained, both in Sweden and in Canada, to draw sledges and work like a horse.

In snowy countries, such as New Brunswick, a moose family, with perhaps a stray companion or two, will "yard up," as the hunters say, in preparation for winter.

"About the first of November moose begin to look about for winter quarters. These are usually selected with reference to the abundance of **Winter Life.** white birch, maples (white, striped, and swamp), poplar, witch-hazel, mountain ash, and the different species of firs. While moose are not gregarious, several are often found feeding together in what are called 'moose yards.' These yards are simply their feeding grounds, and are made by the animals' constant browsing about the pasture grounds, and are not the result of plan or thought. During the time of the falling of the snow they go around browsing, following each other and unconsciously making paths. Of course, this process is kept up every day, so that when the snow becomes very deep they have well-beaten roads running in every direction over quite a large territory. They have a very delicate way of eating, nibbling only a little at a time."

Mr. Stone tells us, however, that in the Northwest the snow does not pile up so deeply as along the Atlantic seaboard, and consequently the animals remain in their favorite feeding grounds in the hills until the snow either from the winds or the warmth of a coming spring sun takes on a crust which will bear the wolf — the only enemy of moose beside man. "When the snow is soft the wolf never troubles the moose, for well it knows this big deer is more than a match under such conditions; but when the wolf can run on top of the snow, the moose is at his mercy; a band of them will bring down the most powerful bull. Unlike the caribou, the moose is a heavy animal with small feet in proportion to its size, and they can never run on top of the snow. The wolves thoroughly understand this, and a band will systematically plan an attack and execute their plans with deliberation. Surrounding the moose, some will attract its attention by jumping at its head, while others cut its hamstrings. To escape this danger, northern moose leave the hills in March and April and go down into the timber of the lowland, where the snow is yet soft."

Another flat-horned deer common to both continents is the reindeer, which we in America call "caribou." It is peculiar among deer in its deeply cleft and broad hoofs, in its hairy muzzle, in the shape of its antlers, and **Reindeer.** most of all in the fact that the females are as well antlered as the males. In the region where it lives it must fight wolves so incessantly that does as defenseless as are those of other deer could hardly survive; moreover, it is believed that the horns are of essential service as snow shovels in digging after winter forage. These suppositions are supported by the fact that the fawns get their antlers very young; and a further remarkable fact is, that whereas the old males shed their horns in the late fall the young bucks and the females retain theirs until spring. The strange, slender form and the curious, downward prolongation of the brow and bez tines, often unequally, are shown in the accompanying portraits; also the fact that the horns spring

GREENLAND.

UPPER MAINE.

ALASKA.

LOCAL VARIETIES OF CARIBOU ANTLERS.

from the very top of the skull. They are immensely variable in actual and relative weight and size, amount of palmation, and number of points. As the shape and relative size of the antlers are the principal feature by which are distinguished the many so-called species recently separated by some zoölogists, we may well agree with Dr. D. G. Elliot, one of the most judicious of naturalists, that "all these deer, irrespective of habitat, are practically one species."

The reindeer is a northern animal and is growing more and more restricted to cold latitudes. In preglacial times, indeed, as we know by their abundant remains,[83] these deer visited southern Europe, probably in winter, from the north, as vast migrations of them still take place from the arctic coasts to the interior. The Roman explorers of Cæsar's time met them in Germany, and even yet they come southward to central Russia and the Kirghiz steppes. Northward they have been found everywhere except on Francis Joseph Land, thriving, in spite of the frigidity of the eightieth parallel or higher, on the lichens which cover the rocks of the mountains, and in summer finding grass in the valleys or seaweed along the shore. They thus inhabit Spitzbergen all the year round. Similarly the most northern headlands **Barren Grounds Caribou.** of America are reached in summer by the caribou, which hasten thither in spring, led by hurrying does. There they feed mainly on the marsh plants and seaweeds, drop their young in May and June, and begin a return journey as soon, and pursue it as fast, as the fawns are able to travel. The scattered family parties unite in bands and these into herds, until at last tens of thousands together — their brown summer coats changing to white as the dark tips of the old hairs break off, and new white hairs come in — are hastening southward across the desolate Barren Grounds, urged on by the furious storms of early winter. There is a continuous loud clattering of hoofs as the crowds press on, feeding mainly morning and evening; and so they go until they reach the timber south of the Dobaunt Lakes, and find shelter and food. They are not known to wander south of the Churchill River.

Half a century ago reindeer were similarly numerous but less regularly migratory all through northern Alaska,[201] but now are rare there. Vast migrations used to occur in northern

THE CARIBOU OF THE BARREN GROUNDS.

Europe, for Nilsson a century ago described the serried masses of the traveling herds on the Norway fjälls as sometimes three and a half miles in width and packed as closely as sheep. That this is not exaggeration is shown by testimony from recent explorers of the Barren Grounds, especially the Tyrrell brothers of the Geological Survey of Canada (see Report, 1896). Food for these migratory millions is furnished by the herbage, moss and lichens, and the sprouts of heather, which may be found in wind-swept places or brought to light by scraping hoofs and snow-shoveling horns.

On these periodical movements of the reindeer, the unfortunate savages who are born to live the narrowest of lives in almost arctic deserts of rocks and snow rely for their mainstay of winter subsist- **Utility** ence; many regions, indeed, could never have been habitable **of Caribou.** otherwise. "Every part of the animal is utilized in some way. The flesh, of course, is eaten, the stomach and intestines also; even the points of the antlers, when in the soft condition, are considered a delicacy. The leg bones are broken for the marrow they contain, which is eaten raw, if wood for a fire is not available, and the blood is mixed with meat and forms a rich soup. In fact, no part of the animal's body that can be masticated is rejected, even the lichens and such vegetable matters as are found in the stomach being also eaten. The skin with the hair on is used for clothing, and no garment so successfully resists the arctic cold as this, it is so light and so impervious to the wind, which always blows a gale on the Barren Grounds. When dressed it becomes very soft and pliable, and when a number of hides are sewn together they make an excellent tent for summer, large enough for a numerous family. Cut into thongs of various sizes, it makes very strong bowstrings, wherever those ancient weapons of the chase are still used, and lines for nets and cords for deer snares; when cut into strings it is called *babiche* and is used for shoe lacing; in fact, it is utilized for the many purposes that civilized peoples employ ropes and cords. A split shin bone makes a good knife, and fish hooks and spears are made from the horns, while the tendons of certain muscles make very fine and strong thread for sewing with the bone needle. . . . .

"Probably no animal is so easily approached as are these Barren Grounds caribou in the summer time, and enormous numbers are slain every year, so many, indeed, that it would seem the race must become extinct in a comparatively brief period. In their dispositions they are not unlike sheep in some particulars, especially in following a leader; and sometimes a herd will run the gantlet of a line of hunters simply because one stupid animal had gone that way and the rest are determined to follow the lead set them. So many caribou have been slaughtered on the barrens and tundras of the arctic regions, both east and west of the mountains, that in certain districts their numbers have been greatly reduced, and in some the animals have disappeared altogether." [233]

In the forested regions of Canada, from Newfoundland and Labrador to British Columbia and Alaska, wherever trees grow,

Woodland Caribou. ranges a larger and darker animal, the woodland caribou. It does not migrate with any great regularity, although the herds, sometimes large, move about a good deal, and its habits are much like those of the moose save as to food, since it eats almost everything; but in Labrador and

 Newfoundland certain lichens and mosses are the mainstay. This woodland caribou was once to be found well within the bounds of the United States, but was early killed off south of northern Maine and the Upper Lakes, and later in the more settled parts of Canada. They are now protected by law.

They mostly affect swampy places, and have little difficulty in wandering where other deer would mire because of the spread of

HOOF OF THE BAR-REN GROUNDS CARIBOU.

Showing concave tread and sharp edge.

their deeply cleft toes, and the fact that the false hoofs are large and low, sustaining a part of the weight when the foot sinks. For the same reason they travel well on snow; while the almost complete absorption of the "frog" in winter leaves the hoof hollowed out and with sharp edges, which so take hold of the crusted snow or ice that on such a surface they make their best speed — a fact especially true of the Barren Grounds caribou.[183] They move with a swinging trot which is surprisingly rapid, and will, when alarmed, run many miles before stopping. This woodland variety, exposed to many more dangers in its forests, has become an extremely wide-awake and wary animal, whose hunting taxes the powers of the sportsmen to the utmost.

The caribou has never been utilized by any of the people of arctic America, although just across Bering Strait the same animal was kept in large herds by the Chuckchis of Siberia.

The United States government has attempted to repair this deficiency by introducing large numbers of Lapp reindeer among the Alaskans, and the experiment is proving successful.

"The inhabitants of Lapland and Finland, as well as many tribes of northern Siberia, have from time immemorial kept the reindeer as a domesticated animal. The Koreki have herds of forty or fifty thousand, the Laplanders, however, have rarely more than five hundred. The latter migrate with their herds, giving them most freedom in September, when the stock is improved by the admixture of wild elements. Just before that is the usual slaughter time, as the flesh, especially of the males, acquires an unpleasant flavor at the time of the rut. The animals serve not only as food, but the hides, horns, and sinews are all converted into useful articles of clothing, or implements of various kinds. The rich, creamlike milk, obtained with some difficulty from the animals, is made during the summer months into small cheeses — an important food-article with these northern people. It is chiefly in Lapland and Norway that the reindeer is used as a draught beast, and then they are only required to pull light, boatlike sledges over the snow. In Kamchatka, however, they are saddled and ridden by the natives, a pad over the withers serving as a saddle, and a long staff acting as a substitute for the stirrup in mounting. Pack saddles, carrying from seventy-five to one hundred pounds, are also placed on the shoulders. The Tungus have very often a train of some six to twelve reindeer acting as beasts of burden." [75]

Domestic Reindeer.

LAPLAND REINDEER.

Our common American deer remain to close the list of this important family. They differ as a group from all those of the Old World in skull structure, and form three groups, the first of which includes the white-tailed and black-tailed deer of the northern continent, the second the South American brockets, and the third the Andean pudu.

The antlers of the American deer, in fact, are constructed on a plan different from those of the wapiti and Old World cervine deer (except the

Antler Types.

roe and the mi-lou) in that there is no brow tine, and the antler, instead of bearing points from a beam, forks, as growth proceeds, into more or less equal branches. The lower prong is projected forward, and the whole antlers curve forward, as is not the case in Cervus.

HEAD OF WHITE-TAILED DEER.

Along with this go correlative facts of anatomy, thus: in the Old World cervine deer and the elk-moose (Plesiometacarpalia) the *proximal* portions of the lateral (second and fifth) metacarpals persist, and the vomer, or roof bone of the nostrils, is never so ossified as to divide them into two distinct passages; in the New World deer and the reindeer-caribou (Telemetacarpalia) the *distal* extremities of the lateral metacarpals persist, and the vomer sends down a vertical plate partitioning the rear of the nasal passage. The distinction is a very deep and ancient one, for the divergence of the two types began as early as the Miocene. Previous to that, however, the elk type had been established; and still earlier, most antique of all, began the reindeer type, entirely separate from the elk line of descent. In the light of these facts, Darwin's remarks [22] have renewed interest.

Our "common" white-tailed or willow deer — the Virginia deer or "mazama" of the older books — is known every-

White-tailed Deer.

where in one or another of its numerous geographical races. Eastern specimens stand on the average about three and a half feet high in the full-grown buck, the females being less, and southern specimens much smaller than those of the northern states; but, as in the case of all deer, individuals vary greatly in all their dimensions. The smallest known are the "dwarf deer" of Arizona. The general color in summer is a bright rufous, with the lower parts white, a black mark on the chin, and the edge and under side of the plume-like, triangular tail snowy white. All the western varieties are pale, while those of the damp woods of the Gulf states are deepest in tint. The winter coat of long, coarse, crinkled hair is much grayer, and hunters speak of the animal as then "in the blue." The antlers may attain in an old buck as many as six or seven points, but after six years, when five points are attained, age is reckoned more by the size and thickness of the antlers than by the number of the points. This deer, in one or another form, is found from New Brunswick, central Ontario, and Manitoba to Florida and southern Mexico; and a whole volume would be required to detail its habits under all the varying circumstances it meets. In general, it is a deer of the woods, although in the middle West it fed far out on the prairies, and there, as is always likely to happen with grazing animals in open regions, it formerly gathered into large herds, as it never does in forested districts. Nowhere is it more at ease than in the Adirondacks, and no one knows it there better than Dr. C. Hart Merriam.[48]

"This beautiful and graceful animal," he tells us, "by far the fleetest of our Mammalia, roams over all parts of the wilderness, being found high up on the mountain sides, as well as in the lowest valleys and river bottoms. It frequents alike the densest and most impenetrable thickets, and the open beaver meadows and frontier clearings. During the summer season . . . its food consists of a great variety of herbs, grasses, marsh and aquatic plants, the leaves of many deciduous trees and shrubs, blueberries, black-berries, other fruits that grow within its reach, and largely of the nutritious beechnut. While snow covers the ground, which it commonly does about half the year, the fare is necessarily restricted; and it is forced to subsist chiefly upon the twigs and buds of low deciduous trees and shrubs, the twigs and foliage of the arbor vitæ, hemlock, and balsam, and a few mosses and lichens. In winters succeeding a good yield of nuts, the mast constitutes its staple article of diet, and is obtained by following the beech ridges and pawing up the snow beneath the trees."

The places where they spend periods of deep snowfall become a tangle of trampled paths, as in the "yards" of the moose.

In the southern states, as appears from Dr. Bachman's extensive and eloquent biography,[90] it cares less for water, though everywhere it is compelled to make its abode where water may easily be obtained.

"In winter," he informs us, "it feeds on buds of several kinds of shrubs, such as the wild rose, the hawthorn, various species of bramble, the winter-**Winter Yards.** green, the partridge berry, the deer leaf (*Hopea tinctoria*), the bush honeysuckle, and many others. In spring and summer it subsists on tender grasses, being very select in its choice and dainty in its taste. At this season it frequently leaps fences and visits the fields of the planter, taking an occasional bite at his young wheat and oats, not

Brownell, Phot.

"NURSING THE VELVET-COVERED HORNS."

overlooking the green corn, and giving a decided preference to a field planted with cow peas, which it divests of its young pods and tender leaves. . . . In autumn it finds an abundance of very choice food in the chestnuts, chinquapins, and beechnuts strewn over the ground. . . . We once observed three deer feeding on acorns, surrounded by a flock of wild turkeys, all eagerly engaged in claiming their share. The fruit of the persimmon tree, after having been ripened by the frosts of winter, falls to the ground and also becomes a favorite food of the deer. . . .

"The deer is one of the most silent of animals, and scarcely possesses any notes of recognition. The fawn has a gentle bleat that might be heard by the keen ears of its mother at the distance probably of a hundred yards. We have never heard the voice of the female beyond a mere murmur when calling for her young, except when shot, when she often bleats loudly like a calf in pain. The buck when suddenly startled sometimes utters a snort, and we have at night heard him emitting a shrill whistling sound, not unlike that of the chamois of the Alps, that could be heard at the distance of half a mile. The keen sense of smell the deer possess enables them to follow each other's tracks. We have observed them smelling on the ground, and thus following each other's trail for miles."

As in the case of other deer, the bucks and does separate in summer, the former nursing the velvet-covered horns, the doe hiding away in some secret place and dropping her two fawns (spotted) as early as April in the Carolinas, but not until a month or so later in the North. The mating season occurs in the late fall, and the manner of seeking the does is vividly portrayed by Roosevelt [233] : —

"At the beginning of the rut the does flee from the bucks, which follow them by scent at full speed. The whitetail buck rarely tries to form a herd of does, though he will sometimes gather two or three. **Fighting** The mere fact that his tactics necessitate a long and arduous **Bucks.** chase after each individual doe prevents his organizing herds as the wapiti bull does. Sometimes two or three bucks will be found strung out one behind the other, following the same doe. The bucks wage desperate battle among themselves during this season, coming together with a clash, and then pushing and straining for an hour or two at a time, with their mouths open, until the weakest gives way. As soon as one abandons the fight he flees with all possible speed, and usually escapes unscathed. While head to head, there is no opportunity for a disabling thrust; but if, in the effort to retreat, the beaten buck gets caught, he may be killed. Owing to the character of the antlers whitetail bucks are peculiarly apt to get them interlocked in such a fight, and if the efforts of the two beasts fail to disentangle them, both ultimately perish by starvation. I have several times come across a pair of skulls with interlocked antlers. The same thing occurs, though far less frequently, to the mule deer and even the wapiti."

In the far West these deer stay in the brushy river bottoms among the foothills. They are rarely seen out in the open or high up the mountain slopes; and hence many call them "willow deer." They are hunted in a variety of ways, good and bad; and the rank of this chase as a sport depends upon the country, the method, the degree of wariness in the game, and personal preference and experience.

Though the whitetail is scattered throughout the West (except California) in favorable situations, the characteristic deer **Mule Deer.** from the Plains west is the mule deer or "blacktail." It is somewhat larger than the whitetail, and has heavier antlers, bearing normally ten points. The body is heavy and squarish, the ears eight to nine inches long and thickly haired. The base of the tail and a disk around it are white,

but the end of the tail is conspicuously black, and is wagged, not set on end, when the animal runs. The coat is pale tawny in summer and dark gray in winter; forehead dusky; nose, abdomen, and inside of the legs white. The antlers have the general shape of the whitetail's and fork equally, each fork again dividing. "A striking and beautiful animal" is the verdict of

HEAD OF MULE DEER. every one who knows it in nature. To the western Indian it was a mainstay for meat and clothing.

"For me, at least," exclaims A. G. Wallihan, whose field photographing of wild deer in Colorado has been so successful, "there is a charm about the blacktail or mule deer that no other game possesses.

"Barring the bighorn, their meat is the best, their hide tans into the best buckskin, and you turn from the large elk or the agile antelope to the graceful beauty of the blacktail buck, and find there the greatest satisfaction. The head of the bighorn is a finer trophy, no doubt, and you are led to grand scenery in the pursuit of him, but it is heart-breaking work. Where you find the blacktail you will find other pleasures, for he delights in the most charming bits of country to be found. He will jump up from the tall weeds and grass among the aspens, so close as to startle you as you ride through them, or will leap into view from the shade of a deep washout far in the desert, where he finds in the feed and surroundings something to suit his taste. He is crafty also, for if he thinks he is hidden I have known him to lie in thick bush until almost kicked out after all sorts of expedients to drive him out have failed. He has, perhaps, the keenest scent and the best hearing of all the deer tribe . . . but cannot see as well as the antelope, for I have stood within ten or twenty feet of several passing bands which failed to distinguish me from a stump or rock."

Though by no means so numerous as it once was, this deer still lingers in most of the rougher parts of its range. In California it is partial to the chaparral of the coastal slope and thicketed mountain valleys. The delightful writings of John Muir abound in pictures of the life of this deer in the unvisited

THE MULE DEER OF COLORADO.

wilds of the Sierras. Throughout the plains country it is the deer of the "badlands," whose rough ravines are filled with patches of ash, buck brush, cedar, and dwarf pine; and among the Rockies it frequently resorts to elevations, "where the covering is so scanty that the animal must be perpetually on the watch, as if it were a bighorn or prongbuck." The most noticeable peculiarity about this species is its gait, giving it in western Canada the nickname "jumping deer."

"It is a most surprising thing," wrote J. Harrison Mills, "to see a deer get up on its legs — at home, I mean, and when he would prefer to be alone. **Gait.** . . . He lies with his four feet under him, and when he is ready to go, it is like Jack getting out of the box. The tremendous extensor muscles contract with all the power and facility rest and warmth have given them, and the plump body, like a well-inflated rubber ball, propelled by a vigorous kick, flies lightly into the air. The simile is borne out as it seems about to descend; light as thistle-down it nears the earth, another giant impulse from an unseen power — *crash* — and again it describes its light parabola; — *crack — bump — thud — thud — thud* — each time fainter than the last and your surprise is all that remains." [238]

Roosevelt describes the gait as "a series of stiff-legged bounds, all four feet leaving and striking the ground together"; and it shows that the animal is accustomed to the hills, where it would quickly beat the long stride of the whitetail, so swift on level ground; nevertheless the buck-jumping of the mule deer will carry it at a great speed on flat ground, too. In their general habits mule deer do not greatly differ from the whitetail; and though sometimes in winter large numbers gather together, they are not so polygamous nor so gregarious as either the wapiti or the caribou. It has been found much more difficult to keep them and cause them to breed in captivity than in the case of the others.

The Columbian blacktail is a distinct species, decidedly smaller, and with much more black on the tail, which dwells **Blacktail.** in the forested coast ranges of the Pacific coast from northern California to the borders of Alaska. It sticks to the woods, and penetrates where they are so dense that it is almost impossible to follow it; and is able and willing to climb to the alpine pastures on mountains so steep and rough as almost to defy human feet.

Mexico has a species or variety of the whitetail, which is known southward nearly to the Isthmus; and south of that, in the drier and more open parts of Ecuador and Colombia, occurs an allied species with large, flapping ears, of which the outer surface is naked. The borders of the great **Tropical** rivers that unite to form the Parana and La Plata are **Deer.** the home of the larger "guazu," or marsh deer, so called from its predilection for morasses and its fondness for wallowing in mud; its antlers are long but only twice forked. Smaller, and with still more simple antlers, are the "guazuti," or pampas deer, common all over the grassy plains of southern South America, and possessed of many interesting peculiarities, while conforming in general to the family manner of life.[53] They lie concealed during the day in the tall, feathery pampas grass, and come out to feed at night. The antlers are very straight when seen in profile, with two prongs on the front of each horn. In the Andes occur two other deer, the "guemals," of medium size,

CHILEAN DEER.

provided with tusks, and having antlers with a single fork, of which the front one is the longer and projects straight forward; one kind is numerous in southern Chile, and the other in the highlands of Peru.

In Central America the little Costa Rican deer [114] is a well-separated form with spikelike antlers, which seems to connect the foregoing group with the fine South American brockets— a section distinguished by short, unbranched antlers, naked muzzles, and other specialties. There are four kinds, the largest about twenty-seven inches high at the shoulders, and the smallest only nineteen inches, which are denizens of the forest glades of Brazil and the northern coast countries, go about only in pairs, apparently mated for life, and furnish good sport and toothsome venison. The list closes with a remarkable little deer, the "pudu" of the Chilean Andes, which is scarcely larger than a hare, is reddish brown, and has a curiously short and rounded

head with short, ovate ears, and on the male an apology for antlers in the shape of two tiny spikes rising from the forehead.

This concludes the Ruminantia termed "Pecora" (oxen,
sheep, goats, antelopes, giraffes, and deer), which agree in having horns, two functional toes (only), and the metapodials
fused into a cannon bone. There remain two other small divisions of ruminants, — the camels and the chevrotains.

The camels and llamas (or "yahmas") form a group (Tylopoda) very much older than the ruminants, and of American

Ancestry of Camels

origin. That the camel got the pads on his feet, the
water-pockets in his stomach, and other drought and
sand resisting arrangements from an ancestry that began in the
western United States a million years or so ago, is the novel and
interesting outcome of discoveries by Cope, developed still further
by Dr. Wortman and his assistants of the American Museum in
New York.[239] These scientific explorers brought to light a series
of skeletons showing that the camel race, now confined to the
desert regions of Africa and Asia, originated in North America,
and was developed there along a line of adaptive growth.

It must be remembered that in the early Tertiary there was a slow but
persistent upheaval of the Rocky Mountain region, where a vast plateau,
studded with lofty sierras, gradually freed itself from the sea. In those
sierras were many active volcanoes, whose outpourings of volcanic dust
settled and solidified into rock, forming the whole thickness of many well-
known fossiliferous formations. The basins between the mountain ranges
contained vast quiet lakes, of which Great Salt Lake is a relic, into which
dead animals would drift and their bones become fossilized; and also desert
spaces, constantly extending, where winds blew the light soil about, and
gradually buried dead animals and perhaps frequently smothered and
entombed many of those whose skeletons show so astonishingly little sign
of disturbance. In the very oldest of these rocks, at the dawn of the Eocene,
have been found what some geologists consider the primitive ancestors of
the camel, — small creatures, little known; but the upper Eocene beds
yield skeletons of whose affinity to ordinary camels there can be no doubt.
These belong to an animal named Prototylopus, which was hardly larger

than a jack rabbit, and of course very uncamel-like in general aspect. It had, for instance, four distinct and equally important toes, protected by hoofs, on the fore feet (but only two toes reached the ground on the hind feet), and the metapodials were entirely separate. The teeth were "bunodont," that is, their crowns were formed by a pavementlike arrangement of rounded tubercles, as in modern pigs, fit only for crushing soft food; short canines and upper incisors were present, and there was no diastema. The skeleton of these early forms is more llamalike than cameloid. The next advanced form is greater in size, and the lateral toes are no longer useful, but hang to the side of the foot above the ground like a deer's. In the next, from the lower part of the White River Miocene deposits of Wyoming, the size has increased to that of a coyote. Then follow a series of improvements on lines parallel with the evolution of the early horses, size increasing, the teeth becoming more suitable to grazing uses, the metapodials tending more and more to solidify, and the external appearance gradually approximating modern examples of the tribe.

At the close of the Miocene, a dispersion of the race began. Changes took place in geographical and climatic conditions which made the plateau of the western United States unfavorable for them. One branch migrated somehow into the Old World, and finding a suitable country in Africa and southern Asia, persisted and developed there into the two existing species — the single-humped Arabian and the double-humped Bactrian. Another side branch made its way into South America and found a congenial home upon its open southern plains, where it developed into the somewhat sheeplike huanaco and vicunia. Here there was firmer, stonier ground, less need for the great sustaining pad beneath the foot, and more need for speed; hence these South American forms show smaller pads and the nails are more hooflike. This gives us the explanation of the odd present geographical distribution of the camel family.

Nevertheless, the total extinction of North American camels was extremely slow, and allowed time for the development of local forms all through the Pliocene and Pleistocene, or closing epochs of the Tertiary era. One of these was a queer, aberrant form a third larger than the modern dromedary, which must have towered up like a giraffe as it grazed upon our western plains of those days. Another, that lived near the close of Pleistocene times, was so like the true camels of our day that Dr. Wortman believes it may have been their ancestor.

The camels, then, have always been creatures of the world's desert places, and all their extraordinary peculiarities, outward and inward, from their sole pads and protectively dun coats to the ample, sphincter-closed, water-storing sacs in their stomachs (rumens), are adaptations to a desert home.

We do not know when or where camels were first found wild by mankind; nor even whether the single-humped "Arabian" **Utility of** camel is a native of Arabia or Africa. Papyrus **Camels.** records show that it was well known in Egypt at least thirty-two centuries ago. So-called wild camels, small and gaunt, range the desolate sandy plateaus of northern Tibet, but it is probable that they are feral remnants of the herds of the people who built the cities there which long ago were overwhelmed by drifting sand. This animal cannot be said to have been anywhere domesticated, but only subjugated. Without its reluctant aid the crossing of deserts, and the rise of the locally mighty civilizations of the ancient Oriental world, could never have been accomplished in Asia, Arabia, or North Africa. It has been developed against its will into many forms, some swift and elegant, others strong but more ugly than the original type, yet immensely serviceable both as baggage and draught animals, and for an almost universal utility.

"A camel differs from a dromedary in nothing save blood and breed. The camel is a pack horse; the dromedary a race horse. The camel is thick-built, ungainly, jolting; the dromedary has finer hair, lighter step, is easy of pace, and more enduring of thirst. A caravan of camels is a freight train; a company of Oman 'thelul' riders is a limited express. The ordinary caravan travels six hours a day and three miles an hour, but a good dromedary can run 70 miles a day on the stretch. A tradesman from Aneyza told Doughty that he had ridden from El Kasim to Taiff and back, a distance of over 700 miles in fifteen days! Mehsan Allayda once mounted his dromedary after the Friday midday prayer at El Ely, and prayed the next Friday in the great mosque at Damascus, about 440 miles distant. . . .

"The Arabs have a saying that the camel is the greatest of all blessings given by Allah to mankind. . . . His long neck gives wide range of vision in desert marches, and enables him to reach far to the desert shrubs on either side of his pathway. The cartilaginous nature of his mouth enables him to eat hard and thorny plants — the pasture of the desert. His ears are very small, and his nostrils, large for breathing, are specially capable of closure by valvelike folds against the fearful simoon. His eyes are prominent, but protected by a heavy overhanging lid, limiting vision upward, and guarding from the direct rays of the noon sun. . . . His hump is not a fictional but a real and acknowledged reservoir of nutriment, as well as nature's packsaddle for the commerce of the ages. . . .

"The Arabian domicile is indebted to the camel for nearly all it holds. All that can be obtained from the camel is of value. Fuel, milk, excellent hair for tents, ropes, shawls, and coarser fabrics are obtained from the living animal; and flesh food, leather, bones, and other useful substances from the dead. Even the footprints of the camel, though soon obliterated, are of special value in the desert. A lighter or smaller foot would leave no tracks, but the camel's foot leaves data for the Bedouin science of *athar*, — the art of navigation for the ship of the desert. Camel tracks are gossip and science, history and philosophy to the Arab caravan. A camel march is the standard measure of distance in all Arabia, and the price of a milch camel the standard of value in the interior. . . . Camel's milk is the staple diet of thousands in Arabia, even though it be bitter because of wormwood pasturage." — ZWEMER, *Arabia, the Cradle of Islam.*

In all these centuries, however, little if anything has been gained toward sympathetic association between the beast and its master. "The want of bodily beauty is accompanied by a viciousness of temper and general stupidity of disposition which can scarcely be paralleled elsewhere among domesticated animals." Before long it will be superseded by railroads.

We are accustomed to think of this animal as belonging only to the heated sand wastes or rocky plateaus of the arid belt stretching from India to Morocco and Somaliland; but the two-humped "Bactrian" camel is a northern form as enduring of cold as is its southern fellow of heat; and the overland trade between China and Russia, across the plains of Mongolia or Turkestan, proceeds by caravans of these animals amid the snows of winter as well as through summer's dust.

"Every year toward spring," the Abbé Huc noted in Mongolia, "the camel loses its hair, and it all goes, to the last fragment, before the new

z

comes on. For about twenty days it is as naked as if it had been clean-shaven from head to tail; and then it is exceedingly sensitive to cold and rain. . . . But by degrees the hair grows again; at first it is extremely fine and beautiful, and when once more it is long and thick, the camel can brave the severest frost. It delights then in marching against the north wind, or standing on the top of a hill to be beaten by the tempest and breathe the freezing air."

In the huanaco and vicunia of South America, we have the survivors of an original cameloid stock, as has been related, —

humpless, long-eared camels of small stature, which carry their heads erect and behave more like antelopes or deer, whose place they take in the southern continent.

The huanaco occurs wherever open districts and a temperate climate coincide, from the lofty valleys of Ecuador down the whole length of the Andes, all over Patagonia, and on the rough and grassy islands south of the Straits of Magellan. In the mountains it travels in small bands, and has the same agile and wary manners as the vicunia; but on the plains it naturally gathers into herds, especially during the pairing season, at its height in August. There these animals seem to thrive as well upon the thorny and bitter herbage of lower Patagonia as upon the rich pastures of the Andean valleys or the Argentine pampas.

Copyrt., N. Y. Zoöl. Soc.   Sanborn Phot.

AN ALPACA.

"Over a large part of its habitat none but salt water is to be had, and this it drinks readily. One very curious circumstance in its history is its habit of resorting to certain places in river valleys when it feels ill, so that nearly all which die a natural death seem to do so at these spots. This has been plausibly explained [35] as due to the influence of an instinct inherited from the time when the country was much colder, and when, whenever storms or other distress afflicted the animals, they were accustomed to seek a covert in the bushes which grew only alongside the sunken streams." They furnish the principal flesh food available to the nomads of Patagonia, and also their main resource for tentage, clothing, and leather, and are persistently hunted by the cattle herders and steadily encroaching farmers, so that their former abundance is much diminished. A fully grown male huanaco stands about four feet high at the shoulder, and is covered with a thick coat of long, almost woolly hair, pale reddish in color, and longest and palest on the under parts. Domestication is possible, but now is carried no farther than here and there to make a pet of uncertain temper and fidelity. Yet in the prehistoric past, taming and artificial breeding established from this stock two truly domestic animals of the utmost importance, — the llama for work and the alpaca (properly, "el paco") for wool.

The llama became a domesticated beast of burden among the natives of Peru unknown centuries before the Spanish conquest, and still serves as the only trustworthy carrier in the higher Andes, although in certain parts it has **Llama.** been largely superseded of late by mules, horses, or railroads. It is astonishing to read of its primitive abundance, Spanish chroniclers relating that three hundred thousand were used for transportation at San Luis Potosi alone during the flourishing development of the silver mines following the Spanish seizure of the country; yet only the males carry burdens, females being kept for milk and flesh. The load seldom exceeds one hundred pounds, for if it is too heavy the animal lies down and obstinately refuses to move until it is lessened to his liking. In the rougher and more secluded parts of the Peruvian mountains large herds still exist, and long trains may be met walking docilely in single file, attended by a few Indians and making a dozen miles a day, feeding by the wayside as they march, for the animals will not graze at night, — indeed, in many ways they are extremely vexatious and unamiable, and few men other than the Andean Indians are able to manage them.

"A flock of laden llamas journeying over the tablelands," as Tschudi [241] describes it, "is a beautiful sight. They proceed at a slow and measured pace, gazing eagerly around on every side. When resting they make a peculiar humming noise, which, when proceeding from a numerous flock at a distance, is like a number of Æolian harps sounding in concert. The Indians are very fond of these animals. They adorn them by tying bows of ribbon to their ears, and hanging bells round their necks; and before loading they always fondle and caress them affectionately. If, during a journey, one of the llamas is fatigued and lies down, the arriero kneels beside the animal and addresses to it the most coaxing and endearing expressions. But notwithstanding all the care and attention bestowed on them, many llamas perish on every journey to the coast, as they are not able to bear the warm climate." Squier, in his "Peru," gives other interesting details.

A large llama stands about three feet high to the shoulder and four and a half feet to the top of the head. It may be of almost any color, but is usually brown or a mixture of yellow and black, frequently speckled, rarely quite white or black. The flesh is spongy, coarse, and not of agreeable flavor; and the animal has an extraordinary defensive habit of spitting forcibly at any person or animal offending it — ejecting not only saliva, but the contents of its stomach; and the discharge is likely to injure a man's eyes severely. The hair or wool is inferior to that of the alpaca, but is used for similar purposes; that of the female is the finer. The llama has been introduced with the alpaca into Australia, but has never become generally useful.

The paco or alpaca is a smaller variety, mostly confined to Peru and adjacent provinces of Chile, where it is bred for the sake of its fleece. In the prehistoric days, as now, the Indians herded it in great semidomesticated flocks in the loftiest valleys, where these animals have formed interesting instincts and habits of vigilance and protection against sudden storms and snowfalls.

Alpaca.

"Once a year the Indians drive their flocks to stone inclosures or huts and shear the wool, after which the flocks are again turned loose. This custom is prehistoric, and it is stated that many of the shearing huts about Lake Titicaca have stood there since long before the Spanish conquest. . . . The alpaca's coat consists of a thick growth of woolly hair, varying from black to gray or yellowish, and reaching, when unshorn, a length of some two feet. The annually shorn fleece is about eight inches in length. The fiber is small but strong, elastic, very lustrous and silky, and highly valued for weaving warm and fine cloth. The natives of the Andes have made use of it from time immemorial for their ponchos or blankets, remains of which have been found in the oldest graves of the period of the Incas; but it was not until 1836 that the wool began to be exported to Europe and the manufacture of alpaca shawls, cloth, etc., regularly began." [20]

A VICUNIA.

A different species from the huanaco and its varieties is the Andean vicunia, and it is a handsomer animal than the others. In size it is between the llama and the paco, and is distinguished by a longer, more slender neck, and the superior natural fineness of the soft, curly wool. The crown of the head, the upper part of the neck, the back and thighs, are of a peculiar reddish yellow hue locally called "color de vicuña." The lower part of the neck and inside of the limbs are bright ocher, and the abdomen white. This animal is a true mountaineer, inhabiting the heights of the Cordillera wherever pasturage can be found short of the naked summit-rocks, and is as alert and wary as mountain goats. Tschudi tells us that the male who leads the band keeps a watchful guard over his family, and on a suspicion of danger signals the alarm by a whistling sound and stamping of the foot, whereupon all take to flight.

The Indians from time immemorial have taken them by a method called "chacu." A large company go up a mountain and build a great pound formed by a rope dangling with colored rags and stretched on low posts. Then a wide space of the mountain side is "driven," and when as many vicunias as possible have been trapped within the inclosure, the men kill with their bolas all which do not muster courage enough to jump over the dreaded fence. These customs still survive, though the animals are by no means so numerous as formerly. The skins go as tribute to the church. Tschudi describes a chacu in which he took part, and adds : —

"Under the dynasty of the Incas, when every useful plant and animal was an object of veneration, the Peruvians rendered almost divine worship

AFRICAN WATER CHEVROTAIN.

to the llama and his relatives, which exclusively furnished them with wool for clothing and with flesh for food. The temples were adorned with large figures of these animals made of gold and silver, and their forms were represented in domestic utensils of stone and clay."

One small group of ruminants remains, the Tragulina or chevrotains, the living representatives of which are some pretty little hornless "deerlets," a foot or so in height, and with legs like pipestems, known by East Indian sportsmen as mouse deer. The kanchil and other Malayan species are uniformly reddish or brown, with white markings

Chevrotains.

on the chest and belly, but the one common in Ceylon and India has spotted flanks. They hide in the jungles and rocky places and serve the Malays as a type of cunning and cleverness; they will assure you even that when a kanchil or napu is chased by dogs he will spring into the air, hook his musklike tusks over a tree branch, and swing there out of reach until the dogs get tired and go away. West Africa has a handsomely spotted chevrotain addicted to marshes and rivers. The principal interest attached to these deerlets is that they are very ancient, having changed little from their far more widely distributed ancestors in the Miocene and Pliocene periods; and in their teeth, the separateness of their metapodial bones, the fact that the stomach has only three chambers, etc., they show features from which the remainder of the ruminants long ago diverged. They therefore serve as a sort of bridge by which we may pass easily to the last section of the artiodactyls, the Suina or swine and hippo, which do not chew the cud; have a complete dentition; have simple, not chambered, stomachs; the bones of the feet not united into a cannon bone; and in most cases four toes reaching the ground.

The most specialized of the pigs are our southern peccaries, the only native American swine, which approach the ruminants in having only thirty-eight teeth; in having **Peccaries.** but three toes on the hind feet (lacking the fifth), and the two central metapodials fused at the top; and in the fact that the upper tusks are directed downward. An altogether unique feature is a large gland, navel-like and skin-deep in the middle of the back, secreting a vile-smelling oil, the stench of which infects the whole neighborhood of the haunt of a band. This gland must be immediately cut out of any animal intended to be eaten, but the flesh at best is not very desirable.

Peccaries are small, thin-legged, grizzled-black pigs, with very thick, bristly necks and large, angular heads. They have wicked little eyes, razor-sharp tusks in both jaws, and no visible tail; and the young (two) are not striped. There are two kinds, — the commoner collared peccary, which is distributed from Arkansas (but is now rare north of the Rio Grande Valley) through tropical America to northern Patagonia, and has such local names as "tajacu" and "zahino"; and the more restricted white-lipped peccary, or "warree," not seen north

COLLARED PECCARIES.

of Honduras. The former is about thirty-six inches in length and has a faint, collarlike streak on the withers; the latter is larger (forty inches), is darker, and has the lips and chin white. They are so nearly allied that they will interbreed. The collared peccary goes about in small bands, which make their home in wet thickets, and sally out at night in search of food, which in Texas and Mexico seems to be mainly pecans and similar nuts, with roots, mushrooms, and other vegetables, plus such flesh and carrion as are obtainable. Near settlements they are likely to enter and greatly damage gardens and crops. When pursued they run in open ground with great fleetness; and in cover will squat and dodge like a jack-rabbit. Though peaceable enough under ordinary circumstances, when brought to bay they will fight with courage, and inflict severe wounds with the sharp tusks.[32, 68]

The warree has much the same mode of life, but after the breeding season collects into larger herds, sometimes numbering one hundred or more, and they are credited with an innate ferocity which leads them to attack any- **Warree.** thing they see, and is irresistible. This disposition has perhaps been exaggerated in popular stories. "If you meet a flock of warrees in the bush," says Salvin,[114] "and you take no notice of them, it is probable that they will take no notice of you. But if your intentions are hostile . . . you must take care to place yourself in a safe position before you carry your design into execution." They have a particular enmity toward the jaguar, and with good reason, for he regards them as an especial prey, yet must be cautious in his hunting, since the instant he has seized one the others rush to the rescue, and if he is not quick in leaping with his catch to some limb or rock out of their reach, they are likely to cut him to pieces by force of numbers and reckless valor.

Remains of larger peccaries are found as fossils in the Brazilian caverns and other American Pleistocene deposits; and earlier fossil forms of the Miocene and Pliocene of both the Old and New Worlds, such as Hyotherium, connect the peccaries with the true pigs, proving common ancestry.

The true swine (Suidæ) are confined to the Old World and are distinguished by their long, pointed heads and mobile snouts, with forty bunodont teeth, ending in an **Swine.** abrupt fleshy disk containing the nostrils and so tough that with it they can plow up the forest mold for the roots, tubers, agarics, and other goodies of which they are fond. Each foot has four toes, but the central two carry the weight, the others helping in miry places. The exemplar of the family is the wild boar, which, where it has not been exterminated, ranges throughout Europe, northern Africa, and Asia Minor;

eastward of that many other kinds have been named, some of which are doubtless descendants of introduced and once domestic stock. Thus the South Sea Islands got the black pigs found free and numerous on many of them by the first European navigators; already in New Zealand a wild race ranges the woods and affords good sport, as might our own southern razorbacks; and Nepal and Bhotan possess a half-wild pygmy race no larger than hares. The latest monographer reduces the whole list, however, to four typical species, of which three belong to certain Malayan islands, leaving all those of the mainland and far-eastern archipelagoes, from Great Britain to Japan and the Philippines, as varieties of the common wild hog (*Sus scrofa*). The brick-red, tassel-eared, playful river hogs of southern Africa are scarcely separable.

From this widespread and variable species the domestic pigs have been derived by processes of selective breeding and intermingling, such as have **Domestic** produced so many other domestic races. The closely related **Pigs.** Javanese and other Oriental hogs have also been in domestication since antiquity; but other genera of swine than Sus seem incapable of adaptation to human service. It is a curious circumstance that while the young of all kinds of pigs are light-striped, it is very rare that such markings appear in domestic piglings; but feral races, reverted to the woods for a century or so, gradually get back to it. Domestic pigs also show a noticeable concavity of the face not seen in wild ones, and their tusks never grow very long. Much benefit accrued to European hogs by crossing them with imported boars of Siamese and Chinese stock. The most extraordinary of domestic swine is probably that Japanese "masked" breed which so much interested Darwin.[69]

The intelligence of pigs is far greater than one might expect from their appearance. Hunters have a high respect for their strategy when chased and scheming and fighting for their lives. From early times trained pigs have been among the trick animals of showmen, and as pets they have been good-tempered and perfectly cleanly. Some "educated" pigs have been credited with wonderful feats of reading, counting, selecting fortune-telling cards, and the like; but too much humbug has been mixed with this to let us judge by it of the animal's real mental capability. That it is by no means dull is shown by the readiness with which in southern Europe it is trained to find truffles. This is in the direct line of natural ability; but pigs have more than once, since that famous instance first recounted in Denick's "Rural Sports" (London, 1801), been taught to act the part of a dog in bird shooting. They show surprising sagacity at this work and a great fondness for the sport; and some declare they exceed the pointer himself in "pointing."

The wild hog loves moist ground and a chance to wallow in water, but takes care to indulge in these delights where cover is handy, to which he may retreat for his noonday nap, or at the threat of danger. In the wilderness **Wild Boar.** he is by no means nocturnal, but where he is often disturbed soon learns to show himself as little as possible. This is especially true of old boars, which lead solitary lives for the most part, while the sows and young go about in "sounders" of a dozen or so individuals. Such bands are the scourge of careless cultivators from Egypt to China, since they break through the flimsy fences and root up or trample down crops, especially sugar cane, often coming miles from the hills to enjoy such a raid. In India, indeed, they like to settle down in the growing

A CHARGING BOAR.

fields, especially at the breeding season, and have developed the habit of making huts. These may be constructed among sugar-cane or millet, or in the long grass at the jungle's edge, and a Burmese "pig camp" was thus described by a *Field* correspondent in 1900 : —

"On my return from a day's sport after sambar near the small and out-of-the-way village of Kan, I came upon a number of what first appeared to me to be ant-hills, but were really grass heaps. They were in the form of thatch, made of teak leaves, kine grass, and twigs, closely interwoven so as to be impervious to rain. These so-called little 'pig huts' are two feet thick in thatch, three and a half feet high, five feet in length, oval in shape, with one small exit, and in the majority of cases partially closed. On this occasion there were about ten or fifteen in number in close proximity to each other, about twelve to fifteen feet apart."

In such huts the sows hide their litter until the sucklings are two or three weeks old, carefully closing the entrance whenever they leave them. Another correspondent reported that in Ceylon he had seen similar huts built by two pigs, usually boars, one lying down and the other plucking up grass and so forth, and piling it over its companion. "Their occupation does not seem to last more than a day or two, and then only during wet weather. I have once known a wounded pig to take refuge in a hut."

Their food is not wholly vegetable, for they seize on worms, mollusks, lizards, snakes, and anything else fleshly that falls in their way, including carrion, and so are of service as scavengers. Along the seashore they fatten on shellfish, and in Assam dig up a kind of fish which in the dry season buries itself in mud.

An old boar will stand thirty-five to forty inches tall, and may weigh two hundred and fifty pounds. He is impervious in wiry bristles, and armed with enormous canines (tusks), of which the upper pair turn up as soon as they leave the jaw, and the lower curl upward beside them; and the latter are kept as sharp as knives by grinding against the upper pair. The lower tusks may measure ten inches in curved length, but two thirds of this is rooted within the jaw. Such an animal must

Pig Sticking. always have been an object to tempt the prowess of adventurous sportsmen, and legend does not go back far enough to tell of the beginning of boar hunting with big dogs. In England,[109] and on the continent of Europe, the custom has always been to follow the hounds afoot spear in hand; and when the dogs — predecessors of our "great Danes" — brought the animal to bay, to kill it by a javelin thrust. In Ceylon, Baker daringly did the same thing with only a strong knife as his weapon. The ordinary method in India, however, is by chasing on horseback; a lot of men armed with long-handled spears going to the boar's haunts, and then setting a company of native beaters to drive piggy into the open, where the hunters ride at him pellmell and try to strike in a spear. "Pig stick-ing" is justly re-garded as the most exciting of the whole list of East-ern field sports, and is not without its dangers, for with an upward toss of his angry head he

HEAD OF WART HOG.

may inflict terrible gashes on horse or man.[158] In addition to the large part this bold and peculiarly British sport fills in all books on East Indian outdoor life, a special volume has been devoted to it alone.

The remainder of the list of the swine family need not long detain us. The wart hog is an African form notable chiefly for its grotesque countenance and peculiarities of dentition, which indicate that it has had a long-independent line of ancestry.

Wart Hog.

"This animal," writes Baker, "is superlatively ugly: the head is dis-proportioned to the size of the hog; the tusks are so enormous that they appear as though they had belonged to some such larger creature, and had merely been assumed as masquerade; there are two prominent protuber-ances upon either side of the eyes, also two pendulous warts of large and hideous growth; and when this ugly monster becomes excited, it cocks a long thin tail, with bristles upon either side, like that of an elephant. This appendage is carried straight in the air, as stiff as a stick, which gives the animal a ridiculous appearance."

Another elaborately armed form is the babirussa, or "deer hog," a big, bluish, almost hairless hog of the wet jungles **Babirussa.** of Celebes and Boru islands, whose tusks grow to an enormous length, sometimes a foot or more outside the mouth. This is due to the fact that they do not strike against one another, for the upper pair grow right up

through the upper lip, and grow continuously, unchecked by the wear of any use, till they strike the forehead and curl down again. It, like the wart hog, is aside from the typical line of swine; but it makes good pork, and is an object of local sport.

In the hippopotamus we have

THE BABIRUSSA.   a member of the swine group

very interesting to the zoölogist, as one of those curious survivals of an ancient type alongside rapidly progressive relatives. **Hippopotamus.** It is, indeed, as Schmidt [244] points out, the only living representative of the hoofed animals with tuberculate teeth which has preserved the old structure of the limbs pretty well unchanged.

"The early Tertiary ancestors of the ruminants," he remarks, "had to dwell principally in waters and on marshy ground. Their descendants adapted themselves gradually to life on dry ground, and this is connected with the advantageous reduction of the toes. The hippopotamus family has taken an opposite course; from being an animal that liked the marshy soil of the primeval forests it has become an aquatic creature, and accordingly has preserved the completeness of hand and foot, the four toes almost fully developed. . . . If by some extravagant flight of the imagination we could conceive the existence of a one-toed leviathan, the very fact of its possessing a one-toed foot would be the cause of its speedy extinction. As regards dentition also, the hippopotamus shows signs of being geologically very old."

AN ATTACK UPON A WOUNDED HIPPOPOTAMUS.

The hippos, then, are a decadent race. Their origin is unknown, but the Lower Pliocene formations of India contain fossil species, and one existed there until after the advent of Stone-age man. In the warm Preglacial period, Europe was the home of the present African form,[60,83] and until recently Madagascar had a dwarf species; a still smaller existing one little known is the Liberian variety, only six feet long.

The range of the hippopotamus has been greatly reduced by the spread of civilization in Africa. Buffon gives an account of its capture in the delta of the Nile in classic times; and De Windt says they were to be seen at Damietta in 1109 A.D., while Burckhardt mentions seeing them at Dongola in 1819. At that date they abounded in all the rivers of South Africa, but now hippos are to be got only from the rivers of the Congo basin, in those which feed the lower Zambezi, and at the sources of the upper course of the Nile.

Horses, Tapirs, and Rhinoceroses

(*The Odd-toed Ungulates — Suborder Perissodactyla*)

We now come to the horses, tapirs, rhinoceroses, and their extinct relatives which constitute the solid-hoofed Perissodactyla. The most advanced, specialized, "highest" type of this suborder is presented by the horses; and thanks to the fortunate preservation of their remains, and to the sagacity and industry of American paleontologists, we are able to trace and understand the history of their development with gratifying completeness. While some early forms were exhumed and described in France by Cuvier, early in the nineteenth century, it was not until Marsh, Leidy, Cope, Wortman and others, began to explore the Tertiary strata of our western plains, between 1860 and 1880, that anything like a historical series connecting the ancestral forms with modern ones began to appear; and it was from the plentiful fossils collected by Marsh that Huxley, in 1876,[243] made that philosophic arrangement of the facts which presented so convincing a proof of the truth of the development theory, then new and comparatively unsupported. Latterly the work of the earlier men has been carried forward by Professor Henry F. Osborn and his assistants, prominently Drs. Wortman and Matthew; and it is due to them that we are now so completely informed as to all the details of the development of the group. Dr. W. D. Matthew, especially, has done much to popularize as well as to originate knowledge on this subject, and it is from his writings that the following condensed statement is mainly derived: —

Among the Cretaceous condylarths (see page 231) there is believed to have existed a small creature, the progenitor of the equine line. None such has yet actually been discovered in the rocks; but the Lower Eocene clay **Primitive Progenitors.** near London — the basic layer of the geological series assigned to the Age of Mammals — has yielded a pro-equine skull (Hyracotherium) which might have had such feet, judging by the structure of the known remains. About the same time, possibly three million years ago, there dwelt in the eastern foothills of the Rocky Mountains little animals undoubtedly of the horse family, known as Eohippus, whose fore feet had four complete toes and the "splint" of a fifth; the hind feet three toes and the splint of another. A little later (Middle Eocene) the rocks yield two other forms (Protorohippus and Orohippus) from which the splints of Eohippus have disappeared, and the middle toe is somewhat larger than the others — a feature still more manifest in the Upper Eocene skeletons termed Epihippus. At this time Europe had a number of related but not ancestral forms which presently died out; while the true line of horse genealogy was continued in America by the Mesohippus of the Oligocene, which was as large as a sheep and had only three toes on each foot (the fifth digit now remaining only as a splint) and the middle toe so prominent that the hinder toes did not touch the ground, as in the case of the "false hoofs" of deer or cattle. The toes disappear as they are least used, so that the thumb would be the first to

EVOLUTION OF THE SINGLE-TOED EQUINE FOOT.

Diagram (after Osborn) illustrating by means of the human hand the process of gradual loss of side toes by concentration of weight and service upon the middle digit.

go, as Osborn showed the reader could illustrate for himself by placing his fingers in a footlike position.

"We may imagine," writes Osborn, "the earliest herds of horses in the Lower Eocene (Eohippus) as resembling a lot **Ancestry of** of small fox terriers in size, . . . covered with short **Horse.** hair which may have had a brownish color with lighter spots, resembling the sunbeams falling through the leaves of trees, and thus protecting the little animals from observation."

Mesohippus was succeeded in the Miocene by Parahippus, and also by Protohippus in the Upper Miocene, the latter of which was somewhat larger, showed an increasing centralization of weight on the middle toe, and had teeth a little more advanced toward the modern pattern from the early short and tubercle-crowned type. At this date, also, several other forms existed both in Europe and in North America, which proved to be aside from the direct line of evolution, and whose races soon died out. Among them was the American "forest horse" (Hypohippus), described by Osborn as ten hands high, with large lateral toes serving to keep the feet from sinking into the relatively soft ground of the warm forest sand lowlands of its day, where it sought the softer kinds of herbaceous food for which its short simple teeth sufficed. This horse lived under the favorable conditions of the Upper Miocene period, when this country had an almost tropical climate, vegetation was luxuriant, and the continent teemed with fine animals, great and small, as did Africa and India a century ago.

With it lived the "deer horse" (Neohipparion), which was "proportioned like the Virginia deer, — delicate and extremely

By permission of the American Museum of Natural History.

EOCENE FOUR-TOED HORSE (Protorohippus).

Restoration by Charles R. Knight, under direction of Professor H. F. Osborn.

fleet-footed, surpassing the most highly bred modern race horse in its speed mechanism." Nevertheless both races became extinct and left no visible progeny. Protohippus was succeeded in the Pliocene by Pliohippus, about the size of a Shetland pony, in which the side toes no longer come near the ground; and this is confidently regarded as the lineal American ancestor of the modern horse, though the fossil connection is not yet complete. These Miocene and Pliocene horses were probably striped, like zebras, while the earlier, forest-running sorts were spotted; and the preglacial horses which followed them were probably a uniform reddish brown — an effect of the cold, rainy climate of the Pleistocene period, to which, perhaps, are also due the addition of a heavy mane and tail, useful as blanket and fly brush, and the broadening of the hoofs, adapted to walking on softer ground.

Along with the disappearance of the side toes in the evolution of the horse goes a considerable increase in the proportionate length of the limbs. **Evolution of Horse.** Greater length in the lower leg and foot enlarges the length of the stride without decreasing its quickness and, therefore, gives the animal greater speed; but it puts an increased strain on the ankles and toe joints, and these must be strengthened correspondingly by converting them from ball-and-socket joints to pulley joints. Additional strength is obtained by the consolidation of the two bones of the forearm and of the leg into one. The concentration of the step on a single firmly shod toe serves likewise to increase the speed over smooth ground, although a hindrance to travel in rough or boggy places. The increase in length of limb renders it necessary for the grazing animal that the head and neck should lengthen, in order to enable the mouth to reach the ground; and comparison of modern with early types shows that all these changes have gone on as fast as required. With them has proceeded a constant lengthening of teeth and improvement of them as grinders, until now they are capable of the thorough mastication of the flinty grasses of the dry uplands upon which few other animals can subsist. The general enhancement in size shows the effect of abundant food and increasingly favorable conditions as time went on. All these changes are adaptations to a life in a region of level, open, grassy plains. At first the race was better fitted for a forest life, but it has become more and more completely adapted to compete with enemies or rivals under the conditions which prevail in the high dry plains of the interior of the great continents. This evolution went on as gradually as the evolution of the plains themselves. Says Matthew: —

"At the commencement of the Age of Mammals the western part of the North American continent was by no means as high above sea level as now. Great parts of it had but recently emerged, and the Gulf of Mexico still stretched far up the valley of the Mississippi. The climate at that time was probably very moist, warm, and tropical, **Tertiary America.** as is shown by the tropical forest trees, found fossil even as far as Greenland. Such a climate, with the low elevation of the land, would favor the growth of dense forests all over the country, and to such conditions of life the animals of the beginning of the mammalian period must have been adapted. During the Tertiary the continent was steadily rising above the ocean level, and at the same time other influences were at work to make the climate continually colder and drier. The coming on of a cold, dry climate restricted and thinned the forests and caused the appearance and extension of open, grassy plains. The ancient forest inhabitants were forced either to retreat and disappear with the forests, or to adapt themselves to the new conditions of life. The ancestors of the horse, following the latter

A RACE HORSE: EXTREME OF MODERN DEVELOPMENT OF THE EQUINE TYPE.

course, changed with the changing conditions, and the race became finally as we see it to-day, — one of the most highly specialized of animals in its adaptation to its peculiar environment. At the end of the Age of Mammals the continents stood at a higher elevation than at present, and there was a broad land connection between Asia and North America, as well as those now existing. At this time the horse became cosmopolitan, and inhabited the plains of all the great continents, excepting Australia."

"About the early or mid-Pliocene period," Osborn informs us, "there apparently occurred the long journey of the true American breed of horses into Asia and Europe, and over the newly made land bridge **Migration** of Panama or of the Antilles into South America. That the **of Primi-** true Old World horse actually came from America is inferred **tive Horses.** because of the sudden appearance in the Upper Pliocene of the Siwalik Hills of northern India, in northern Italy, and in England, of five species of the true horses (Equus), of which no ancestors have been found in either Europe or Asia. Another strong argument for their American origin is found in the simultaneous appearance in the same countries of the camel, which we positively know to have been an exclusively American-bred animal."

Whether or not enough remained to continue here the developing race, at any rate America had many horses in Pleistocene or Preglacial times. In this era the northern hemisphere, affected by the advancing glacial cold, was continually becoming cooler and more rainy, yet the climate seems to have been, at least in the earlier part, highly favorable for horses, since a larger number of species, bigger than ever before, ranged over the plains and through the woods. One species about the size of a western bronco was numerous all over the South Atlantic states; a larger one inhabited the northwestern and middle states; while on the Pacific coast might have been seen a big one, the closest of all to the existing type.

"Like the early cave horses of Europe, it had a large head, convex forehead, stout limbs, spreading hoofs, and splint bones, which represent the last of the lateral toes." Finally, there are found in Texas the skulls of a gigantic nag whose teeth indicate a bulk a third greater than that of a Belgian Percheron; while from Mexico has been obtained, on the other hand, the smallest species known.

It is certain that South America was supplied with horses from the northern continent, and that there the stock, under the influence of novel conditions, gave rise to several species, some of which survived until after the advent of man, for their relics show that in Pleistocene times they were hunted and eaten by the savages of the period when glacial ice buried the major part of North America. This arctic condition in the North is reasonably supposed to have put an end to the horses, as well as many other animals then living here; but no such climatic disaster overwhelmed South America, where the favorable conditions remained unchanged, and where, when horses were reintroduced by the Spanish colonists, they ran wild, multiplied and flourished amazingly, especially on the pampas. No adequate explanation of their previous disappearance has been made.

As to the origin of our tamed horses the most authoritative and succinct conclusions of science are expressed in the ensuing paragraphs from Professor Osborn's book.[247]

Origin of Modern Horses.

"The conquest of the horse by man marked one of the great turning points in the history of civilization. . . . In the Interglacial or Postglacial period the remains of man and the horse are first found together. The first association occurs in the middle of the Paleolithic or rough-implement period. The discovery of all the possible uses of the horse came very gradually, for there is abundant proof that man first hunted and ate, then drove, and finally rode the animal. The remarkable drawings discovered by Rivière in 1901 in the cave of La Mouthe are believed to be of Paleolithic age. The artists of La Mouthe and other caves in France left outlines partly etched, partly in ocher, of the animals of the chase, the reindeer, mammoth, bison, ibex, and horse, which have, for our purpose, the extreme merit of telling the truth. There are varieties in these drawings which Ewart interprets as indicating a variety of races.

PALEOLITHIC DRAWINGS OF HORSES.

"The prevailing drawings of the Paleolithic horse represent him as hog-maned, with no forelock to conceal the low-bred Roman nose. . . . Besides these Roman-nosed types, to which Ewart traces the modern cart horse, there are others with small heads and flat noses, which Ewart associates with the Celtic pony, and possibly with the origin of the thoroughbred. Other cave drawings, reproduced by M. Capitan, leave little doubt that the ass was known in Europe. It is also certain from abundant evidence in the caves of France that there was a larger horse toward the south perhaps, while the smaller breeds may have frequented the cold northern regions. The horse was at first simply hunted for food, and in the Solutrian period became the chief article of food, as shown by piled-up remains of thousands of skeletons, the long bones of which were split open for the marrow.

"The northern Paleolithic horse was only ten hands high, probably as a result of the dwarfing effects of the severe climate. It was too small an animal to be ridden. It was certainly not very different in appearance from the only true wild horse which now survives in the world, and was

Sanborn, Phot.

PRZEWALSKY'S HORSE.

Photographs of a pair living in the New York Zoölogical Park in 1905; the upper figures in their summer coat, the lower one in winter coat.

Copyright, N. Y. Zoöl. Society.

possibly the same stock. This is Przewalsky's horse, of the desert of Dzungaria, which was discovered by Poliakoff in 1881, and demonstrated beyond a doubt to be distinct from the wild ass of northern Asia and the Mongolian pony. As in the Paleolithic drawings this horse is unstriped. It is covered with thick hair of a dull brown or dun color, and has a woolly under covering for winter protection. One of the Przewalsky colts, now in the New York Zoölogical Park, probably gives us a living picture of the horse as he was known to Paleolithic man 30,000 years ago."

The interesting question arises: Are these Paleolithic horses, and possibly the Przewalsky horses, the forbears of our modern domesticated breeds; and are our horses of single origin, or of multiple origin, like our dogs?

Professor Osborn answers this by the statement that Ewart has lately discovered in the Faröes and outer Hebrides a small, yellow dun pony, partly striped, with short hairs on the upper part of the tail, prominent eyes, small ears, and sometimes very small callosities on the inside of the hocks. Especially distinctive is the small, graceful head of this Celtic pony, which leads Ewart to compare it with the small-sized, small-headed horse of Paleolithic man. Ewart also observed, as a second type, large yellow duns, about fourteen and three tenths hands at the withers, with big bones, large heads, and ungraceful Roman noses. "I imagine," he writes, "that the ancestors of these animals came from the south of Europe and correspond with the larger horses of the Neolithic cave-deposits." From this second coarse, thick-set breed, similar in size to a full-grown Przewalsky's horse, and to the animals which were domesticated in the Neolithic or polished-stone age of Europe, the common type of European work horse may have sprung.

So near to the horses as not to be separable as another genus are the South African zebras, which differ mainly in their brighter coloring, less bushy tail, stiff, "roached" mane, and lack of the callosities called "chestnuts" **Zebras.** on the hind legs. So recently have the three branches of the Equidæ diverged that all will interbreed, though the progeny (mules) of every sort of crossing are sterile. Interesting but not very conclusive results have been obtained by elaborate experiments in this interbreeding, specially with zebras.

Existing zebras are of two types, — a southern and a northern. The "true" zebra, now left to us only in a few captive specimens, but once numerous on the wooded mountains near the

Cape of Good Hope, is the smallest of all (twelve to twelve and a half hands high) and everywhere striped with black on a white ground, the black stripes of moderate width, yet wider than the white spaces. This species was never seen far from the mountains. On the plains, as well as among the hills of all the more open parts of Africa from Orange River to Lake Rudolph, roamed

BURCHELL'S (OR SOUTHERN) ZEBRA.

Burchell's or the plains variety of this zebra, the one now commonly seen in menageries. It presents many local variations, but in all the coat is creamy or golden yellow, and the black stripes are far broader than in the mountain zebra, which it also exceeds in size; its ears are smaller and its mane fuller. This kind, which represents the southern type, is partial to sparsely forested country, but is, or was, to be found everywhere from the seacoast to the summits of the rocky interior plateaus.[269]

Closely related to these was a third animal, extinct since about 1875, which a century ago wandered in vast herds on the open treeless veldt south of the Vaal River and west of the arid

Kalahari country. This was the quagga. It was darker than the others,—"a dark rufous brown on the neck and upper parts of the body, becoming lighter on the sides, and fading off to whitish beneath and behind; instead of being striped, too, over the whole body, it was only strongly banded on the head and neck, the dark brown stripes becoming fainter on the shoulders and dying away in spots and blotches." Its name was borrowed from the Hottentots, and when properly pronounced, sounds closely imitative of its "barking neigh," *qua-ha;* and Burchell's zebras are to-day called "qua-has" by the colonists, — a fact which leads to confusion in some books. The plain coloration toward which it was tending seems responsive to the influences of the dry open country in which it lived, — influences also affecting the Burchell's zebras of the south to make them far paler than those of the

GREVY'S (OR NORTHERN) ZEBRA.

rougher and more wooded region northward. The French paleontologist Gaudry places the quagga nearest of all living Equidæ to the Hipparion, — a graceful equine which in Pliocene times wandered in great herds over the plains of Thessaly, and whose skeletons are entombed by thousands in the marvelous bone deposits at Pikermi near Athens, Greece.

The northern type of zebra (Grevy's) is also "extravagantly striped," but after a very different pattern, for the deep-black stripes are much narrower and more numerous, the white being mere streaks; it is also the largest of its race, fourteen to fifteen hands high, and the bigness of its head and hairy ears is noticeable. Its home is the hilly, ravine-cut plateaus of

Somaliland and southward to the Mt. Kenia range, — a country arid and open or thinly wooded. Two or three allied species or varieties are designated in the books.

The gaudy striping of these animals has caused much speculation. Professor Osborn is of the opinion that it is a trait **Colora-** acquired comparatively recently, under the brilliant **tion.** sunshine-and-shadow conditions of Africa, where the zebras have taken an opposite course of development in this respect from the horses and asses. The whole family, he believes, has inherited a tendency toward stripings from American Miocene ancestors for which transversely striped hides were useful, by making them less conspicuous in the partly forested kind of country which then probably prevailed. Wild ponies and asses yet show traces of such markings as occasionally do domestic colts; for example, the striped duns of the southwestern United States. But while in the plains-dwelling horses and asses the stripings have practically disappeared, in the zebras they have become intensified, because, as he says, these animals have kept themselves mainly in situations where sparse trees cast shadows. The hunters do not say much about it, apparently never having noticed more difficulty in getting a good sight of a zebra than of any other game; but some scientific travelers have asserted that the vividly contrasted colorings of the zebras are really protective. Schillings[269] does so, and Dr. J. W. Gregory, in his fine book, "The Great Rift Valley," writes as follows: —

"The ornamentation of the zebra was also a puzzle to me till I saw them at home. The ordinary explanation of striped animals, such as the tiger, is that stripes resemble bands of light seen through tall grasses and jungle. But this is not applicable to the zebra, which lives in open plains. Watch the zebra on these, however, and the value of the coloration is apparent. At a distance of from 250 to 300 yards the stripes of the East African species (*Equus bœhmi*, similar to *E. greyvi*) cease to be visible and the animal appears of a dull gray color. . . . In dull, cloudy weather, and especially at dawn and sunset, which are the most dangerous times for game, the zebra is practically invisible at a distance of over five hundred yards.

In bright sunshine, in the middle of the day, I have seen a herd of them at a distance of over three miles; but that is not the time when their enemies prey upon them."

A German writer, Von Höhnel, who accompanied Count Teleku on his explorations east of Lake Rudolph, has recorded some almost contradictory observations: —

"In the afternoon, I, for a long time, with the help of my field glasses, watched a little herd of animals which from their size and color I took to be wild asses. As we had not met with any before, I was at some pains to get near enough to examine them carefully, but in the end I found they were only Zebra grevyi with narrow stripes. Seen with the naked eye at the distance of some 300 paces they appeared to be a uniform gray color."

He notes making a similar mistake a second time. Von Höhnel also mentions that the noise made by a Grevy's zebra when alarmed or excited is so very like that of a leopard or lion "that we were more than once deceived by it." Was this also "protective"?

This does not agree very well with Osborn's "protective" explanation, for these examples were away from shadow; nor does Gregory's testimony seem very convincing, since in the dusk no animal, however tinted, is readily discernible; and no proof is offered that a uniformly gray or dust-colored zebra would not have been even less distinct at the distance mentioned. In fact, Von Höhnel's evidence goes to show that in the glare of sunlit plains a comparatively short distance makes all colors and patterns look alike, so that the Quaker-dressed ass is no better off than his gaudy cousin; and if he had not been an ass he would have stuck to the traditions of his gay ancestors! But Gregory asserts that in full daylight he could recognize zebras three miles away. Lastly, what would it profit a zebra to be mistaken for anything else, anyhow?

We come now to the third branch of the family, the asses, which, like the zebras, lack the hinder chestnuts and the well-haired manes and tails of the horses; but they have **Asses.** a horselike plainness of coat, and special peculiarities in the excessive bigness of the ears and in the smallness and compactness of the hoofs, indicating a long career on hard, stony ground — they are a desert race. Tegetmeier [245] asserts that they are peculiar in carrying the foals twelve months instead of eleven, as do horses and zebras.

The wild asses are much alike, and are now regarded by Blanford and other special students as divisible into only two species, — one Asiatic and the other African. The Asiatic species stands

ASIATIC WILD ASS OR KIANG.

eleven to twelve hands high, has moderately sized ears and a rather long, well-haired tail, and the general hue is reddish, with a darker stripe along the spine, but none on the withers. The African asses are larger (fourteen hands high), have much larger ears, shorter mane, and the tail scantily haired. The general hue is gray, with no reddish tinge, and the muzzle, a throat patch, and the belly are white; and a dark stripe runs along the spine and down each of the withers. Both species show obscure dark bars upon the legs, but all the colorings and markings are variable in amount and form.

Of the Asiatic wild ass there appear to be three well-marked varieties, whose many local names have created no little confusion. The largest is the kiang, koulan, or dziggettai of Tibet and Mongolia, which is dark reddish in color, with a narrow black stripe from (and including) the mane along the spine to the top of the tail; it inhabits central-Asian mountains up to the snow line, and has in winter a special furry and whitish coat. The second is the ghorkhar or onager, frequenting the plains of north-western India, Afghanistan, and Beluchistan, which is smaller and paler, sometimes silvery white, and has a comparatively broad dorsal stripe. The third variety, less well marked, is that of Persia and Syria, and is the one known to the writers of the Old Testament, who use it as a type of wild-ness and freedom (Job xxxix. 6, 7, 8).

The African ass ranges throughout the open regions of northeastern Africa, from Somaliland to the Red Sea, and westward throughout the desert, where its food and habits are much like those of the ghorkhar, ex-cept that its small troops do not congregate into herds and all show an aver-sion to entering water, preferring to roll in the dust; the Somaliland variety is paler, and has excited much interest among sportsmen. Baker de-clared of the wild ass of the Nubian deserts: "The animal in its native desert is the perfection of activity and courage; there is a high-bred tone in the deportment, a high-actioned step when it trots freely over the rocks and sand with the speed of a horse. When it gallops freely over the bound-less desert, no animal is more difficult to approach; and although they are frequently captured by the Arabs, those taken are invariably the foals, which are run down by the fast dromedaries, while the mothers escape."

The habits of all these animals — asses, zebras, and horses — are much alike in the wilderness, for all now live in substan-tially the same circumstances. They go about in small bands, each dominated by a powerful stallion, which sometimes as-semble in great herds, and seem most at home on lofty, dry plateaus. Their speed is great, so that they are able to travel long distances between their pastures and the watering places which must be visited at least once a day — usually after dark. In Africa the presence of zebras is regarded by travelers as a sure indication that water is not far distant.

"The Asiatic wild ass," Lydekker informs us, "is remarkable for its fleetness and its capacity for getting over rough and stony ground at a great pace. . . . The food of these wild asses consists in the lowlands of different kinds of grasses, which are frequently dry; but in Thibet it is chiefly composed of various woody plants, which form the main vegetation of these arid regions. In the hills to the west of the Indus these animals are to be found wandering pretty well throughout the year; but in the early summer, when the grass and the water in the pools have dried up from the hot winds, the greater number, if not all, of the ghorkhars migrate to the hills for grass

NUBIAN WILD ASS.

and water. It is stated that in western India and Persia the wild asses are very shy and difficult to approach. This is, however, by no means the case with the kiang of western Thibet, which is one of the most curious and inquisitive of all animals, frequently approaching within fifty yards or less of any strange object. Indeed, these asses are often a positive nuisance to the sportsman, as they will come to him as he is engaged in a stalk, and thus alarm and drive away his quarry. In Ladak I have frequently ridden among a herd of kiangs who would gallop close around my pony in circles; and on one occasion a kiang, apparently actuated by extreme curiosity, walked straight into the middle of my camp, where the cooking was going on, much to the alarm of the Indian servants. The speed of the ghorkhar is so great that it appears to be impossible for a single horseman to ride down an adult in good condition."

The zebras of South Africa show precisely similar traits, in regions where not much molested often trotting close to a caravan until they get a scent of human beings, when they whirl and dash away in fright. Just such behavior is seen in the "wild" horses of Turkestan, Patagonia, and our southwestern plains. Their principal enemies in Asia are wolves, and in Africa and America the great cats, zebras forming at present the principal prey of the East African lions and leopards. Zebras are usually in fine, fat condition and no game flesh is better liked by the average African. Selous notes that it is dark yellow in color, and too rich to suit the stomach of a European, but if fried with bacon is not unpalatable. The early extinction of those of the South was mainly due to the Boers slaughtering them as food for their negro slaves.

The zebra has not yet furnished us with a domestic race of any particular value, in spite of occasional successes in rearing them and training them to harness. Hybrids between them and the mare are hardy and less vicious, and something valuable may yet be made of them. Much the same is true of the Asiatic ass. Its foals are frequently captured by stratagem, and are easily reared; but it seems to require exceptional wisdom and care to make them safe and tractable, or of any use in harness. Their flesh is not liked when anything else can be had, but the Persians and Afghans find it great sport to chase them with greyhounds.

From the African wild ass, however, we have derived the donkey, — one of the most valuable of our four-footed servants. It has been varied far less than the horse from the **Donkey.** original type, although it is perhaps older as a domestic animal. It was an abused and enduring slave of the farmer and peddler in Egypt long before the horse became known there; but white asses have always been regarded in the East as animals suitable for the great to ride upon (Judges iv. 10), and are still held in honor. From the Orient they have been scattered widely, but do serious service only in the warmer parts of the Old World, or under the similar conditions in Mexico. Excepting some differences in size, donkeys everywhere are practically the same. In part, as Shaler remarks, this lack of change may be due to neglect by unprogressive owners; but Shaler [225] tells us that in Spain, where a long-continued effort has been made to develop the animal for interbreeding with the horse, the result shows that the form is relatively inelastic.

"So long as pack animals were in general use, . . . the qualities of the donkey have proved, and are still found, of value. The animal can carry a relatively heavy burden, being in such tasks, for its weight, more efficient than the horse. It is less liable to stampedes. It learns a round of duty much more effectively than that creature, and can subsist by browsing on coarse herbage, where a horse would become so far weakened as to become useless. . . . In general, we may say that the donkeys belong to a vanishing state of human culture, to the time before carriage ways existed. Now that civilization goes on wheels, they seem likely to have an ever decreasing value."

While the evolution of the horse was proceeding in North America, another group of perissodactyls, from an apparently quite independent origin, the *Litopterna*, evolved in **Litopterna.** South America a race adapted to the pampas, and singularly like the horse in many ways. These animals likewise lost the lateral toes one after another, and concentrated the step on the central toe; changed the form of the joint surfaces; lengthened the limbs and the neck, and gradually increased in size. The teeth were long and complicated the pattern, but no cement formed on them, so that they were not so efficient grinders as those of horses. This group of animals, which illustrates the principle of "parallelism" or "convergence," became totally extinct in South America shortly before the migration thither of the true horses. The latest and most remarkable example is Macrauchenia, fossil parts of which were first brought by Darwin from Patagonia. This animal must have looked somewhat like a camel, for its neck is very long and camel-like in its structure. The feet are three-toed and built on the perissodactyl plan, yet with important differences; but the most remarkable singularity is to be found in the structure of the skull, where the opening for the nostrils is an egg-shaped aperture in the forehead, almost between the eyes! Of course, this was covered with flesh, and the indications are that the external nostrils were at the end of a trunk, perhaps not very long. This macrauchene was evidently a dry-land animal, for its legs were long and slender, and its feet resembled those of hepparions, in one genus reduced to a single large toe on each foot, as in the modern horse.[65]

The nearest living relatives of the horses and zebras, thundering across the windy desert the very image of bold and active liberty and grace, are the small, retiring, ungainly tapirs, hiding in the swampy forests of the Tropics. **Tapirs.** In this startling contrast our imagination is thrown back to the steaming jungles of Tertiary times, when the forerunners of the perissodactyls could hardly be distinguished by such terms as now name their branches.[60] Back to those Eocene days may be traced the family of the tapirs until it blends with the beginnings of the lophiodons and palæotheres (which presently died out), and of the more persistent Equidæ. From that time to this, through Protapirus of the Lower Miocene of Wyoming, and other later genera, the descent of the family is traceable with the certainty, but not the detail, of its equine cousins; and in all these ages it has hardly varied. Those of to-day exhibit little advance in structure of feet or teeth over their remote ancestors; and in our tapirs we still have a fair copy of the early perissodactyls. Primitively, the pro-tapirs were scattered all over the world; but as the later Tertiary conditions slowly changed from torrid to temperate outside the Tropics, this line of animals, instead of adaptively and locally changing with them, expired elsewhere than under the equator, where heat and moisture still reigned. There they continued to live and reproduce their kind until now. Hence it is no longer difficult to understand why both South America and Malaya have representatives of the family, or why the species are many, though the numbers and range of each are limited.

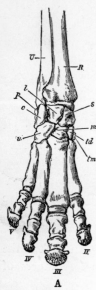

In structure, however, the tapir is nearer to the rhinoceros than to the horse, for the limbs are short and massive, and the feet have four toes in front (second, third, fourth, and fifth, the third largest), and three (second, third, and fourth) behind, each incased in a separate and proper hoof. The neck is short and thick, the skull short and high, yet the head looks long in life because of the swollen nose. The teeth are only forty-two, and are far less complicated and perfected than are those of the horse, for the food is soft and requires little grinding. The hair is short and close, forming a little stiff mane on the nape of the neck, but ornamenting no tail, since there is almost no such an appendage. The colors are dull, aiding in the concealment upon which the animal must mainly rely for safety; and it is chiefly nocturnal because defenseless.

TAPIR'S FORE FOOT.

(Compare page 235.)

The Malay tapir, the only species in the Old World, is the largest of the family, standing nearly four feet tall at the rump, where the back is most elevated,[221] and is brown black, with a grayish blanket over the back behind the shoulders, and white ears. South and Central America contain four species, differing in structural features, but all uniform brownish black and of very similar habits. A curious fact is, that two of them are more nearly allied to the Malayan tapir than to their neighbors. Young tapirs are spotted at first, as is the rule among forest-dwelling quadrupeds. Tapirs everywhere are solitary, shy, timid, and nocturnal. They have a hoglike fondness for water, and old Dampier gave us accurate information, as usual, when he wrote: [253] —

"This Creature is always found in the Woods near some large River; and feeds on a sort of long thin Grass or Moss. . . . When her Belly is full, she lies down to sleep by the Brink of the River; and at the least Noise slips into the Water: when, sinking down to the Bottom, though very deep, she walks as on the dry Ground. She cannot run fast, therefore never rambles far from the River; for there she always takes Sanctuary in case of Danger."

They are mainly browsers, for the nose and upper lip are prolonged into a fleshy proboscis precisely comparable with that of the elephant, by which they can easily seize and draw into the mouth the succulent leaves and shoots they enjoy. All sorts of plants seem acceptable, and where numerous they are likely to do much harm to the Indians' poorly fenced patches of garden or orchard. Tschudi says that this happens often in Peru. "A broad furrow marks the track along which they have passed, and the plants they encounter in their progress are trampled down or devoured. Such a visit [from a troop] is particularly fatal to the cocoa fields; for the tapirs are extremely fond of the leaves of the low-growing cocoa plant, and they often in one night destroy a cocoa field which has cost a poor Indian the hard labor of a year."

In Central America the tapir is everywhere known as "danta," and will be found in all dense forests, in Guatemala, at least, climbing high on the mountains, down which it will rush when pursued until it reaches water in which to stand at bay. This defensive trick is its means of escape from the jaguar, its foremost enemy in America, as are the tiger and other big cats in the Orient. Regular paths are made by these animals through the woods, a fact of which hunters and trappers take advantage, for in Costa Rica, particularly, the tapir is much hunted for the sake of its flesh, which is good for use fresh, and is extensively salted and dried by the backwoodsmen; while the thick hide is a favorite material for twisted whips.

Brazilian tapirs are often tamed, and are said to make amusing and affectionate pets. Shavings from the hoofs are regarded by the Orinoco Indians as very valuable in medicine; but sex must be carefully distinguished — no man must be dosed with the hoofs of any but a male tapir, and *vice versa*.

Behemoth and his Horn

The rhinoceros is another antique preserved to us as a relic of nature's early attempts to formulate a solid-hoofed type of quadruped. Its kind was once as widespread on both sides of the globe as were the tapirs, but proved immobile and succumbed in most regions to unfavorable alterations in geography and climate.

The family begins to be recognized in fossils toward the close of the Eocene, in both Europe and North America; and the Miocene genera differ **Evolution.** very little in their skeleton from the existing one. It is an interesting circumstance that some of the earliest (amynodonts) seem to have been aquatic, and in form and habits much like our hippopotamuses; while others, such as the hyracodonts, were agile, light-chested, rather long-necked and hornless, resembling a horse in build, and in the compactness of the hoofs indicating a plains-dwelling existence. These last were American. They were apparently defenseless, and soon disappeared; and probably all that saved the more direct line of ancestors was the fortunate fact that in the Old World they gradually developed weapons of defense on the nose. It is true that Diceratherium, a small American form of Miocene Age, had nose horns, but they were weak and set side by side — an arrangement which here, as elsewhere, has proved ineffective; the nose does not furnish a base strong enough for paired horns, which must be subjected to sidewise wrenches in use.

Two or three associated forms of huge middle-Tertiary mammals allied to the rhinoceros require mention. Prominent among them, and almost exclusively American so far as known, were the titanotheres, forming the family Titanotheriidæ. These in their later development exceeded in size the largest modern rhino, reaching a length of thirteen feet and standing seven and a half feet tall at the shoulders; the probable appearance of *Titanotherium robustum* is shown in the accompanying restoration. Its head was most remarkable, the skull having somewhat the shape of a

By permission of the American Museum of Natural History.

A TITANOTHERIUM BULL, COW AND CALF.

Restoration by Charles R. Knight, under direction of Professor H. F. Osborn.

saddle, with two great horn-projections in front, and others above the little eyes. Some thirty species have been recovered, together with their Eocene predecessors, Palæosyops and Telmatotherium, and one of the most interesting and valuable exhibits in the splendid paleontological collection of the Museum of Natural History in New York is Professor Osborn's series showing the gradual evolution of the peculiarities of these gigantic ungulates toward their perfected form, described by Osborn and Wortman in the *Bulletins* of the Museum for 1895 and 1896. The family seems to have reached the limit of its specialization and come to an end within the

Oligocene epoch (White River beds), since subsequent to that time no remains have been found, nor anything traceable to them.

About the same time there existed in North Africa an extraordinary relative, discovered in 1899 by Mr. Hugh Beadnell in the Fayum basin,

TITANOTHERIUM ELATUM.

Upper Egypt, and named Arsinoëtherium, after Queen Arsinoë, the wife of the wise King Ptolemy Philadelphus (B.C. 308–247), who had a palace in what was then a fertile and populous region around Lake Moeris.[187] An outline of its skull is given herewith. In bulk and appearance of body it must have resembled the titanotheres, or the huge ancient rhinoceroses (its skull alone measures three feet in length), and bore two great cores of hollow bones side by side, which in life were probably covered with sheaths of horn, besides another small pair behind them. The teeth and feet are very different in structure from those of either a titanothere or a rhinoceros, the teeth (44) forming an unbroken series, wonderfully graduated. This side branch also proved a failure, dying out and leaving no descendants.

No species of the typical genus (Rhinoceros) has been found in American rocks; but in Europe and

SKULL OF ARSINOËTHERIUM.

Asia true rhinoceroses were numerous from Miocene times until the general glaciation of the North closed the career of so many mammalian races outside of the Tropics. All the American fossil representatives of the family were two-horned, like the modern African exiles, while single-horned fossil species occur, as now, only in the Orient. A notable and interesting one is the huge and very long-horned woolly or tichorine rhinoceros, which roamed over Pleistocene Europe and Asia, and whose frozen remains, clothed in reddish wool mixed with stiff hairs, and armed with great horns, are found with those of the mammoth in the ice cliffs of the Siberian coast. A Siberian contemporary (Elasmotherium) must have much resembled it.

The world's present stock of rhinoceroses, then, are but widely scattered and varied remnants of past wealth. Two species are African and three East Indian, — the latter differing from the former in having the skin thrown into great plate-like folds; in keeping the useful incisor teeth throughout life instead of losing them in infancy as do the African; and in having but one nose horn (except the Sondaic). In all kinds the feet are round and massive, with the short toes bound together and each incased in a hooflike nail; the central (third) toe is the largest, but a sole pad sustains the weight of the body.

ELASMOTHERIUM.

The nose horns are comparable to true horns only remotely, since they are simply outgrowths of the skin based upon a thickening of the nasal bones; and are composed of a bundle of tapering whalebonelike fibers which sprout **Nose Horn.** from papillæ, like feathers, and are firmly cemented together, growing at the base as fast as they wear away at the tip.

These horns are utilized by the Africans as handles for their knives and weapons, the longer ones being formed into clubs so highly valued that only chiefs possess them; and every Boer hunter tries to own a cleaning rod for his rifle whittled from this tough material. The horn of the Asiatic species, like almost everything else in the furniture of strange animals, has been held until very recent years to have medicinal and other curious virtues, among them that it would keep sweet water in which it was laid, and that it would betray the presence of poison by falling to pieces. This latter notion has been world-wide, and is still believed by Sudanese Arabs, Chinese peasants, and similarly trustful and backward persons. The same opinion formerly prevailed in Europe in respect to ibex horns; and the consequent demand for them in the old turbulent days, as material for poison-detecting wine cups, did more than anything else to exterminate the ibex from the German and Italian Alps. The Chinese and Burmese still pay high prices for the horns, tongues, and other efficacious parts of the Eastern rhinoceros, to be ground into medicinal powders.

The Indian rhinoceros is the largest of the Asiatic species, standing five and three-quarters feet high, and ten and one-half **Oriental** feet long; its single nose horn rarely exceeds one foot **Species.** long, its skin is thick, hairless, and suggests a suit of plate armor. In life a knife blade or bullet will penetrate it easily enough, and it is sensitive to the slightest touch; but when

INDIAN RHINOCEROS.

taken off and properly dried it becomes a very suitable material for the shields with which Oriental soldiers used to be armed. It may be so prepared as to be translucent and mottled like tortoise-shell, and ornaments are made of it. Once a denizen of all northeastern India, this animal is now confined to the

Assam plain, where many a beast finds the refuge denied him elsewhere in India.

"The trees there are festooned with orchids and ferns roped together with a tangle of creepers, open glades covered with grass and undergrowth are to be seen here and there, and sluggish streams, half hidden under the leafy canopy, linger among the feathery canes and lofty peepul trees. Empty watercourses, like long white snakes, run through the green forest, forming the highways of man and beast, and in the shining sand who looks may read that elephant and rhinoceros, buffalo and bison, with deer in numerous species, daily wander there seeking their food. I need hardly say that when my duty called me to such a district I resolved to leave no stone unturned to secure a rhino. Government provided me with elephants, without which neither work nor sport, nor, indeed, locomotion of any kind, can be carried on in this wondrous corner of the earth. Imagine to yourself a vast plain covered with a Brobdingagian growth of grass fifteen to twenty feet high, in which an elephant makes no more stir than does a rabbit in a corn field at home. In this jungle there are moist hollows overgrown with reeds, and dark green islands breaking the monotony of the tawny surface of the withered grass, or a few fire-charred skeletons of lofty trees rearing themselves above it all. Suddenly one comes on a half-dried 'wallow,' where you, or rather your elephant, must walk warily, for it is in such places that you may find your rhino, either lying or feeding, should the young grass have begun to sprout; only you must be a very early bird to catch him, for when the sun arises he gets himself off to his forest, where he conceals himself for the remainder of the day."

Its habits, according to Kinloch [160] and others, are very simple — merely feeding upon the leaves, shrub twigs, and grass around it, wallowing in mud, seeking now and then a mate or meeting a companion, and from time to time fighting a tiger or leopard. Sometimes a pair will travel far at night to feast upon a field of growing grain. Young ones are easily tamed, and this species has been kept in captivity in the East since prehistoric days. Thence it was obtained by the managers of the Roman show houses for the gratification of their wonder-loving patrons; and after a dozen centuries a specimen was taken westward to amaze the people of western Europe, where it was first exhibited early in the sixteenth century. Nothing funnier can be found in the literature of natural history than the pictures, — except that by Dürer, who knew how to draw animals, — descriptions, and speculations of that century upon this beast, which writers identified with a Behemoth, the Unicorn, and what not? A sample of the cream of it may be found in old Topsell's book.[171] The animal lives well in confinement and

HAIRY-EARED VARIETY OF THE SUMATRAN RHINOCEROS.

occasionally reproduces itself, — one little one at a birth is the rule of the whole family.

The hunting of this rhinoceros is nowadays possible only by riding on an elephant, and the sport is usually tame. Its first effort is to get away, and it bolts, squealing and grunting with fright, but if wounded and stopped it will resist desperately, as will almost any other beast brought to a corner, and may charge open-mouthed, using its tushes like a boar and inflicting fearful cuts. Great scars show how severely the bulls punish each other in their jealous fights.

Smaller and lighter gray in color, and with the folds of its armor less prominent and tuberculous, the lesser or Javan rhinoceros has a much wider range, since it is found from Bengal eastward into Burma, and southward to Java and Borneo. It dwells mainly in the coastal forests, and feeds on leaves and twigs, bulbous roots grubbed out by its horn, and the like. Pollok [156] says that in Burma the swamps they frequent are quaking bogs and hence they are little molested. They are likely to come forth after dark to feed, and the natives sometimes kill them by making an ambuscade at one of the places to which they regularly go to deposit their dung, — a curious habit of all rhinoceroses, and to some extent of wild perissodactyls generally, and even of the antelopes.

Over the same country, except Java, is scattered the smallest of all living rhinoceroses, — the Sumatran or Sondaic species, which is singular in having two horns and a bristly coat of thin but long hair, forming decided fringes on the ears in some specimens. The skin is rough, granular, and blackish. The Chinese demand for its horns has nearly exterminated this species near settlements, but in the interior it still is plentiful.

Let us turn now to Africa.

"Of the rhinoceroses," wrote Gordon Cumming in

HEAD OF SQUARE-MOUTH.

1845, "there are four varieties in South Africa, distinguished by the Bechuanas by the names of the borèlé, or black rhinoceros; the keitloa, or two-horned black rhinoceros; the muchocho, or common white rhinoceros; and the kobaoba, or long-horned white rhinoceros." This was the general opinion until scientific examination showed that only two kinds were separable: the "black" or long-lipped, and the "white" or square-mouthed; but there is really no difference in their color,

African Species.

for both are bluish gray when clean. In both the skin lies smooth except about the bend of the neck, and is quite hairless; and both have two horns in both sexes, — far longer ones than are ever worn by their more peaceful and swamp-dwelling Asiatic cousins. The pair may be equal, but as a rule the front horn is decidedly longer. A horn of the common species measuring forty inches is considered long, while that of the square-mouthed sometimes reaches fifty inches; but such dimension records are glories of the past, for the square-mouthed is almost extinct, and the other species growing rare.

A century ago the square-mouth was to be met with everywhere in Africa south of the Zambezi, except in stony hills or on the waterless Kalahari Desert. It moved about in family parties and ate grass, pulling it off with the flattened lips and crushing it between the horny gums and big cheek teeth.

"When either walking, trotting, or galloping," Selous tells us, "the white rhinoceros always carried its nose close to the ground. A calf always preceded its mother, and she appeared to guide it by holding the point of the horn on the little creature's rump; and in all changes of pace, no matter how sudden, this position was always maintained. This rhinoceros was easily killed by a shot through the heart or through both lungs, but would travel very long distances, and, probably as a rule, ultimately recover from wounds in other parts of the body. . . . In disposition they were sluggish and inoffensive animals, lying asleep in the shade of trees or bushes during the heat of the day, and coming to the water to drink at night, or often before sundown in parts of the country where they had not been much molested."

The other species differs little in form or color, but markedly in the shape of the lips, which are prolonged, with the upper pointed and overhanging the other; this upper lip is extensible, and may be curled around a bunch of twigs like a finger, thus grasping and tearing loose the food instead of biting it off. This apparatus suits the feeding habits of this rhinoceros, which never grazes, but subsists wholly by browsing on the leaves and twigs of the mimosa and other local bushes. When first known it ranged throughout eastern Africa from Natal to Abyssinia, but kept away from the forested region west of the great lakes. It was everywhere fairly numerous, wandering about in family parties or singly, and scrambling up and down rough hills with astonishing agility, while its pace, when alarmed, taxed a good horse to equal. An odd difference from the other species is that when a calf runs with its mother it races by her side or heels, and not ahead, under her guiding horn.

Extremely keen of scent and hearing, one of these animals is not easily surprised; and when it catches the alarming human odor, inspired by that sudden blind and insensate fury which seems characteristic of most rhinoceroses, it will spring to its feet, prepared not only for self-defense,

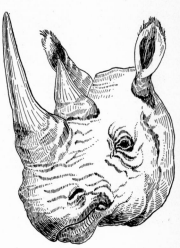

COMMON AFRICAN RHINOCEROS.

but to rush out and attack its enemy. Lowering its great head until the horn on its snout points straight forward, it charges like some armored knight with lance in rest, and overcomes what it strikes by mere weight of onslaught, then returns to trample out what shreds of life remain in its fallen foe. Often, however, an apparent charge is merely a blind rush from panic, dodging which a man is safe, for the beast flees straight away for miles. So sharp is the horn and so enormous the strength of the head and neck behind it, that a rhinoceros is able to disembowel and toss over his back any smaller animal, while he can upset and rip open even the elephant if he can get an opportunity for a flankwise attack; but elephants are extremely cautious when rhinos are about.

NEGROES OF THE UPPER NILE FOLLOWING A NOOSED RHINOCEROS AND KILLING IT WITH SPEARS.

No lion ever meddles with a full-grown kobaoba. The repu- tation for blind ferocity outlined above has been increased by almost every hunter from Harris and Andersson down. Their narratives abound in stories of unexpected attacks and dreadful accidents; yet several of the most experi- enced of modern African sportsmen assert that the **Ferocity.** danger has been exaggerated, though the latter admits that some individuals are most vicious. "In my own experience," he says, "I always found that black rhinoceroses ran off at once on getting the wind of a human being; whilst, on the other hand, if they only heard one approaching, they would come toward the noise, and I have often known them to trot up to within twenty yards of where I was standing, snorting and puff- ing loudly; but as these animals always turned round and went off eventually without charging, I came to the conclusion that they were inquisitive and very short-sighted rather than vicious." Sir Samuel Baker gives in his "Nile Tributaries" [229] a thrilling account of how those wonderfully bold and skillful hunters, the Hamran Arabs of the Abyssinian interior, chase and kill this beast by a hamstringing cut with their heavy swords, followed by a *coup de grâce* in the throat; and in another book [147] he de- scribes how the negroes along the Nile White capture Behemoth in a leg trap which is precisely like that heretofore described as used for catching gazelles, and is so weighted that he cannot get away from the spearmen.

In C. G. Schillings's "Flashlights in the Jungle" [269] will be found many reproductions of photographs of rhinoceroses taken in German East Africa, several of which represent them as sitting on their haunches in what Schillings says is a favor- ite attitude of rest and observation.

ELEPHANTS, ANCIENT AND MODERN — Order, PROBOSCIDEA

ELEPHANTS may be briefly described as large, vegetable-eating animals, whose upper lip and nose are together drawn out into a proboscis or "trunk," long enough to reach the ground. They were once cosmopolites, but now are restricted to Africa and tropical Asia.

The anatomical peculiarities of the elephants (family Elephantidæ) are largely adaptations to their colossal size, never greater than at present.

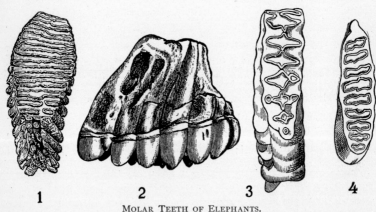

MOLAR TEETH OF ELEPHANTS.

1, Mammoth; 2, Mastodon; 3, African Elephant ("lozenge" pattern); 4, Indian Elephant. Figures 1, 3, and 4 show the pattern of the dentine ridges in the worn crown; Fig. 2 is a side view of a mastodon's molar.

To this fact is due the pillarlike straightness of the legs (mediæval writers asserted they had no joints therein), suitable to support so great a body; and the hollowness of the huge skull, whose interior is a network of bracing plates of bone, set like the struts and ties in a truss bridge, between which are air spaces communicating with the mouth and nose. Were the skull bones solid, even the muscles of that massive neck could not sustain the weight of so ponderous a head. The brain is very small, proportionately, and of a low type. The feet are short, smaller behind than before, and five-toed, each toe being united to its fellow by skin, but covered by a small separate hoof. The teeth present another striking peculiarity. There are no canines. The incisors are developed into long tusks, either with or without a coating of enamel, which in modern elephants exist only in the upper jaws, but in some ancient ones grew in both jaws. The cheek teeth are large, not easily distinguished as molars and premolars, and consist of upright plates of hard dentine, the spaces between which are filled with the softer "cement," which wears away more easily; thus the crowns of the teeth are kept rough with transverse ridges. The arrangement of the dentine plates, and the consequent pattern made by their exposed edges on the worn crown, vary with genera and species, and serve as distinguishing marks. The general anatomy shows a comparatively low organization.

The elephant is another almost solitary representative of the departed glory of a commanding race, — one of the most primitive, peculiar, and unchanging of the orders of Ungulates, the Proboscidea. A few in India and Burma, **Evolution.** saved from destruction only by human guardianship; a few more in Africa, soon to become dependent for survival upon similar protection, alone remain of a former world full of elephants. Even a short time ago, as geologists reckon time, elephants were multitudinous and, so to speak, possessed of great estates. The Indian one perhaps never passed beyond the barriers of desert or mountain north and east of it; but fossilized species closely similar, as well as others more nearly allied to the African, preceded it in the Orient or were contemporary with the youth of the species; and our African species, as well as extinct predecessors still larger in size, once wandered along both the northern and southern shores of the Mediterranean. At that time (Miocene) it is believed that dry land nearly or altogether divided that sea where it is still narrow between Italy and Tunis (the ancient "Africa"), of which land bridge Malta is a fragment yet above water; and in the rocks of Malta are found remains of adult dwarf elephants no larger than tapirs, along with the bones of the big species. At that time the British Isles, too, had elephants whose bones, when unearthed in mediæval times, gave rise to strange stories of giants and monsters among the simple folk of the Thames Valley, as one may read in the genial musings of Sir Thomas Browne, or the critical histories of Watkins [133] and Boyd-Dawkins. [83]

Back to the Miocene may be traced the history of the genus Elephas; and even the oldest species survived till after man had

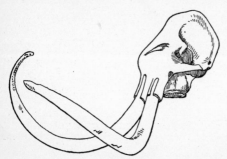

appeared, and might very likely have remained until to-day had they not been hunted to death. One, the mammoth, is world-famous, partly on account of the fact that it was world-wide in its distribution, but mainly because of the fortunate accident by which its bodies have been preserved to us entire in the ice cliffs

SKULL AND TUSKS OF THE IMPERIAL MAMMOTH.

From a photograph of the specimen on exhibition in the American Museum of Natural History, New York, showing the *inward* curve of the tusks, hitherto wrongly placed in all mounted skeletons and restorations, due to the transposition of the tusks — the right-hand one where the left-hand one should be.

of Siberia — cold-storage warehouses keeping for modern eyes many examples of the preglacial fauna.

In those days the northern parts of both the Old World and the New were more extensive in dry land and milder in climate than now. The Bering Sea region was partly or wholly out of water, and the animals of Asia for unnumbered centuries passed dry-shod into Alaska and thence spread southward. The British Isles were a part of the continent of Europe, the bed of the present German ocean was a wooded plain, and the pine woods of Siberia and Canada grew luxuriantly to the borders of the Arctic Ocean. Through those far northern forests wandered many animals fitted to endure a cold climate, for even then, of course, the winters were severe. Among these was an elephant averaging about the size of a large Indian one, which **Mam-** it much resembled, except in its remarkably small **moth.** and hairy ears and exceedingly long tusks (nine to twelve feet),[249] which had a tendency to curve upward and *inward* — not outward, as has usually been erroneously represented;— and both sexes had tusks, which is not the case in Asiatic elephants now. Furthermore, this ancient northern elephant, like the woolly rhinoceros of the same time and region, was clothed, at least in winter, with a warm yellowish brown under coat ten or twelve inches thick, and a bristlelike, darker, and longer upper coat, heaviest on the shoulders, together forming a most suitable garment for an animal in a semiarctic climate. Otherwise the mammoth varied only in minor features from those elephants now before our eyes.

The first remains of the mammoth were found in the perpetually frozen cliffs of earth and ice which border the estuary of the Lena River in 1799, and a few years later the skeleton was brought almost entire to St. Petersburg, where it may be still seen. Since that time, landslides and thawings have revealed other carcasses, from which, when lucky enough to find them, the Yakuts cut flesh to feed their dogs, and perchance got salable tusks. The offering of such a tusk disclosed to the Russians at Kolyma, in 1900, the discovery of an especially complete carcass, which in 1901 Dr. O. F. Herz was able to bring with much completeness to St. Petersburg, and to mount in the Imperial Museum. It is plain that this last animal died by miring itself in an attempt to get to or from the river. Their stomachs show that these Siberian mammoths fed on the leaves and twigs of the pine. Thousands of carcasses, however, were floated away to sea by the Siberian rivers; perhaps thousands annually, for the islands of their estuaries contain such masses of skeletons that these bone beds are regularly mined in search of fossil ivory — a recognized article of Siberian commerce, and, although yellowed by age, nearly as good as "living" ivory.

"From the earliest times fossil ivory was derived from the buried tusks of these elephants. The ancient Chinese worked in it, and even had such ideas about the edibility of the animal's flesh as makes it probable that they knew that carcasses were occasionally found on the arctic coast. This ivory was known to the Greeks, and the 'licorne' sent as a present by Haroun-al-Raschid to Charlemagne is believed to be a mammoth's tusk. Arabic writers **Fossil** of the tenth century mention it as an article of regular Rus-**Ivory.** sian trade, and ever since that time fossil ivory has come from Siberia at a rate calculated to be not less than one hundred pairs of tusks a year. Among the strange conceptions of the animal which furnished this ivory that arose among people ignorant of elephants was that of the Chinese, who said it must be a mole ('mammoth' is derived from a Tatar-Russian term, meaning earth burrower), because its remains were always found underground. This was not so illogical as the pious hypothesis held in Europe that these bones were those of St. Christopher." [20]

Naturalists cannot explain why the mammoths disappeared. They survived the Glacial period and ranged numerously as far south as the middle of Europe and the central United States, so that their extinction cannot be laid to climate. They lasted at any rate in the Old World long after the appearance of man, persisting even into his Neolithic stage, as is proved by associated remains, and prettily demonstrated by the famous sketch of the mammoth, etched on a piece of its own ivory, by a French artist whose studio was a cave in the valley of the Loire; and who showed a better skill in animal drawing than is easily commanded to-day in studios by the Seine. The primitive men, assailing the mammoth in numbers, driving it into inclosures, and entrapping it in pitfalls, could overcome it as less capable savages do modern elephants; and it is probable that in Europe, at least the waning species was finally terminated by human agency.

Contemporary with the early Miocene elephants was an Asiatic kind with peculiar teeth called Stegodon; and still farther away from the type in tooth structure was another, existing at the same time, set apart in the genus Mastodon, of which I have given an account elsewhere as follows: —

"Mastodons began to exist in the Miocene age and became extinct in the Pleistocene. They were scattered all over the globe, and more than thirty species have been distinguished by palæontologists, the latest described (1901) being a small and primitive type discovered in Egypt. This seems to confirm the prevailing opinion that the group originated in the Old World and spread to America by way of Siberia.

Mastodon.

Two or more species belong to South America (Patagonia), where no other elephant has thus far been found. It is probable that several species lived in North America, but the one best known and commonly in mind when the term is used is *Mastodon americanus*. This species seems to have ranged over all the United States and southern Canada, and to have been numerous, for its teeth and bones, in a more or less perfect condition, are repeatedly found. A dozen or more mounted skeletons are on exhibition in museums in New York, Chicago, Pittsburg, Cambridge, Albany, and elsewhere. Careful comparison and study of these and other specimens show that this mastodon at least must have had the general form and appearance of a modern elephant, with a somewhat heavier body and flatter forehead than that of the mammoth or Indian elephant; nor did its height exceed theirs on the average — if anything it was less. The tusks, too, were of similar length (nine feet, measured along the outer curve, indicating an old and large male), and they had a characteristic tendency to curl upward, sometimes almost completing a circle.

"It is probable that the animal, at any rate in the more northerly parts of its range, was warmly clothed like the mammoth, although there is not much direct evidence of it beyond the discovery, many years ago, of a large mass of woolly brown hair buried in bog in Ulster County, N.Y., in apparent connection with mastodon remains. Several of the most complete skeletons known have been obtained from that region, where animals had become mired in swampy valleys. The disappearance of this numerous and widespread species is as incomprehensible as in the case of the mammoth and the South American horse. That it existed until recent conditions were established is plain. The food remains in its stomach have been repeatedly analyzed, and found to consist of herbage, bark, and leaves of the same kinds as now grow in the place where its bones lay. . . . It is the opinion of competent judges that remnants of the herds survived the advent of mankind into North America; but the evidence is not indubitable." [20]

More anciently there existed a coördinate family, the Dinotheriidæ, the remains of whose single genus are entombed in the Tertiary strata of Europe and Asia.

Dinotherium.

The dinothere, says Beddard, occupies the most primitive position among the Proboscidea, but cannot be considered an ancestor of the elephants. It was of gigantic size, perhaps eighteen feet long, for the skull measures a yard fore and aft. The structure of the teeth resembles that of the teeth of tapirs; but from the elongated and downward-bent lower jaw grew two long incisor-tusks unlike anything else known in animal dentition. "The enormous weight of the lower jaw and tusks seems to argue that it was at least partially aquatic in habit, and that it may have used these tusks for grubbing up aquatic roots or for mooring itself to the bank."

DINOTHERIUM.

Probable outline of head; the big tusks of the lower jaw were probably used in raking up roots from the mud of rivers and lakes.

Such has been the history of the noble but decadent elephant family. Its nearest living ally, as has been said (page 232), is the quaint little cony of the order Hyracoidea. The origin of the elephants had not until recently been traced, but that they were an offshoot from the primitive condylarths could not be doubted. Professor H. F. Osborn stated in 1900 that the early ancestors of the Proboscidea would probably be found in the then unexplored Eocene formations of Africa. This prediction was realized in 1902, when Dr. Andrews examined this formation in Egypt for the British Museum, and obtained fossil evidence connecting the elephants with the primitive hoofed animals, and showing the successive stages by which the huge grinding-teeth, tusks, and trunk were gradually developed.

African Origin. A brief review of the history of the family in the light of these new facts will be useful.

The series begins in the Middle Eocene with Mœrotherium, an animal of moderate size, with a full set of tapirlike teeth, no trunk, and no tusks, but the middle incisor teeth enlarged in both jaws. In Paleomastodon of the Upper Eocene, the incisors are reduced to a pair of small tusks in each jaw, there is a short trunk, and the back grinders are becoming larger, while the fore ones are degenerating. In the Miocene Dinotherium (a side branch) the lower tusks are enlarged, while the upper ones disappear. In Trilophodon, in the direct line of descent, the upper tusks become larger, the lower ones smaller, while the grinding teeth are reduced in number but increased in size, and their cross ridges are increased in number and height. In mastodon the lower tusks are rudimentary or absent, while the upper ones are of huge size, and the length of the trunk and form of the head approaches that of the modern elephant. In the mammoth, and in the existing elephants, no trace is left of the lower tusks, the upper ones are of enormous size, and the grinders, of great size and perfection, are reduced to one, on each side of each jaw in the adult. This series exhibits a steady increase in the length of the trunk,

TRILOPHODON ANGUSTIDENS.

A primitive mastodon, found fossil in the Middle Miocene strata of the south of France. " Its ' trunk' must have rested horizontally on the lower jaw between the upper tusks — and was, in fact, not a ' trunk' at all, but an elongated upper lip — representing the middle part of the upper jaw in a soft, flexible condition. It seemed to me probable that the elephant's trunk had originated in this way; namely, by the great elongation, in the first place, of the lower jaw and upper lip and jaw, and by the subsequent shrinking of the lower jaw, and ' bull-dogging' of the bones of the face. Thus the elongated mid-part of the face — no longer supported by a long lower jaw — would gradually drop as the lower jaw grew shorter and shorter in successive ages, and at last it would hang down as a perpendicular trunk. . . . It is very difficult to form a definite idea as to how the Trilophodon made use of his tusks and horizontal ' trunk.' The upper tusks have a sharp edge along the inner face, strengthened by enamel, so that it is probable that, working against the tough skin pads of the lower jaw, they would serve for cutting vegetable matter." — LANKESTER.[187]

and the height and massiveness of the animal, and a corresponding lengthening of the trunk to enable the creature to reach the ground.

The two existing kinds of elephants illustrate the difference between the Eastern and the Western types. The Indian elephant is a creature of the dense forests and swampy grass jungles of Ceylon, eastern India, and the **Indian Elephant.** Malay region. This is the one the world has known longest and most familiarly, and from which it has derived most of the popular ideas of elephant nature. Around it has gathered a great mass of history, tradition, and fable; and it figures in the mythology and folk-lore of the East to an almost unlimited degree. Personified in one of the most ancient, respectable, and popular of Hindoo divinities, Ganésha, the wise and humorous god who is invoked at the beginning of all enterprises, whose auspicious image is placed over most Hindoo

The Elephant God.

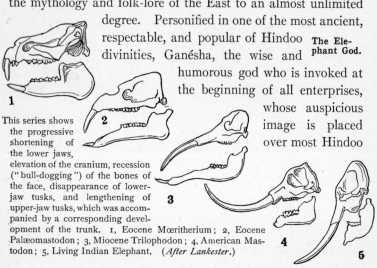

This series shows the progressive shortening of the lower jaws, elevation of the cranium, recession ("bull-dogging") of the bones of the face, disappearance of lower-jaw tusks, and lengthening of upper-jaw tusks, which was accompanied by a corresponding development of the trunk. 1, Eocene Mœritherium; 2, Eocene Palæomastodon; 3, Miocene Trilophodon; 4, American Mastodon; 5, Living Indian Elephant. (*After Lankester.*)

DEVELOPMENT OF SKULL-FORM AND TUSKS IN ELEPHANTS.

doorways, and whose mystic sign [the swastika[254]], familiarly spoken of as the "ganesh," stands on the first page of Hindoo ledgers and day books, the elephant has an immense hold on the affections of the people. "The traveller and the pilgrim look to Ganésha for protection, the merchant for fortune, the student for advancement, and the housewife for luck. . . . Although at first sight merely monstrous to Western eyes, this quaint personage grows in interest as one learns his attributes and becomes familiar with his character and person. He seems, as he sits meditatively poising his heavy head, to be the Nick Bottom of the Hindu Pantheon." The literature of the East abounds in allusion to its mystic sacredness, which culminates in the veneration paid to the albinos of Burma and Siam.

More earthly and historic are the voluminous accounts extant of the employment of elephants throughout Asia in the past, when they were the most powerful war engines of the Orient, making irresistible the armies of Persia, Assyria, Babylon, Egypt, and even of Greece and Rome, in their successive adventures toward conquest; and this aspect of their history and service, given with a wealth of curious details by Broderip [15] and by Watkins, [133] may be recommended to the reader fond of antique lore. In this martial record the African elephant has a large share, for 2500 years ago it, too, was subjugated by the people south of the Mediterranean, and those taken across the Alps by Hannibal were a natural contingent of an African army. Long before that, when Ptolemy had marched his hosts of Greeks into the Nile Valley, his Indian elephant cavalry had met Sudanese war elephants on the side of the Egyptians, and had worsted them.

The Indian elephant of to-day, while roaming in free herds through its native jungles, is nevertheless practically a subject animal, for now the British Indian rulers, and only to a less extent the allied governments of Burma and Siam, know the position and numbers of all the herds, and preserve them from wanton destruction by strictly enforced laws. This is done in order that the supply shall not be wasted, for the elephant so rarely produces young in captivity that practically its increase cannot be counted upon at all. Hence the recruits needed to meet the demand for private ownership of riding and hunting animals, or to sustain the dignity of native courts, in addition to those required for governmental service, **Capture of** must be captured from wild stock. This is done **Elephants.** usually by surrounding a band in the forest and driving it into a prepared pen or "keddah," — a corral of palisades of vast strength, — where tamed elephants, under control of their mahouts, partly force and partly persuade the frightened and furious strangers to submit to enslavement. It is aston-

Copyright, New York Zoölogical Society.

Sanborn, Photographer.

INDIAN ELEPHANT AND WEST AFRICAN DWARF ELEPHANT IN THE NEW YORK "ZOO."

ishing how soon, in most cases, they do so, becoming docile the moment the conviction forces itself into their minds that it is inevitable; or perhaps when calmness succeeds fright they do not care. Since photography has come to our aid as a means of illustration — nowhere more welcome and valuable than in natural history — magazines have abounded in picturesque descriptions of the scenes at these keddah captures; and innumerable books outside of the general zoölogies contain vivid accounts of the habits of the elephants, wild and trained, in the East, of which the foremost are those of Sanderson,[162] and Baker[147] for India, Tennent for Ceylon,[17] and Pollok for Burma.[156] In general, no essay upon the habits and character of elephants, both Asiatic and African, is more informatory and accurate than the three chapters devoted to these animals in Sir Samuel Baker's admirable "Wild Beasts and their Ways."

The African elephant is so different from its Indian cousin that some competent authorities place it in a separate genus. The bulls are taller on the average than Indian elephants, frequently ten feet at the highest part of the arched back ("Jumbo," the only one of this species ever seen in the United States until 1905, was eleven feet); but the females average smaller than in the other species. African cows have much larger tusks (which both sexes use industriously in digging up the roots that form a large part of their food in Africa), a fact injurious to the longevity of the species since man has coveted ivory, for it leads to the killing of cows as well as bulls; the molar teeth also differ in structure, and there are but three functional toes on the hind foot.

African Elephant.

More easily recognizable distinctions are the fact that the leaf-shaped ears of the African elephant are of huge size (Grogan measured one eighteen feet in circumference), lying far back on the shoulders when at rest; the profile of the face slopes more backward; and the head lacks those two bosses "which give so wise a countenance to the Indian species"; finally, the tip of the trunk has a slight triangular projection on its under as well as its upper side, — two "fingers" instead of one.

Great diversity exists, however, among African elephants, and it is not yet determinable whether the distinctions are worthy of specific rank or not. Dr. Paul Matschie,[270] one of the foremost authorities on African mammals, has separated them into four kinds, distinguished prominently by the size and shape of the ears. One of these varieties (or species) is a dwarf race, only four or five feet tall when full grown, inhabiting West Africa north of the lower Kongo. Not much is known of it, but a specimen has been living in the New York Zoölogical Park since July, 1905. It is interesting to note that it seems to resemble most the dwarf elephants (fossil) of Malta and eastward; and also that it comes from the same region as the pygmy hippopotamus.

This animal represents the last of a race with a long fossil history in Europe, and is a comparatively recent immigrant into Africa, where, when white men first began to explore the continent, it ranged everywhere outside the deserts. It had disappeared south of the Zambezi, and near the coast, except as to a few small preserved herds, before the nineteenth century closed; but throughout the vast forests and swamps between the Nile sources and the lower Kongo, this elephant still exists in countless thousands, and is little disturbed. There it is likely to remain plentiful for a long time to come, as European governments have agreed upon various laws, including a close season for females, and an export duty on the tusks, by which it is hoped to prevent rapid extermination. Indeed, in many parts elephants are a bar to the civilization of the natives, at least by means of agriculture, by destroying plantations in a way the negroes are powerless to prevent.

"The most remarkable elephant country," says Ewart Scott Grogan, in *Everybody's Magazine* for April, 1901, "is undoubtedly Toro, and all the lower slopes of the Mountains of the Moon (Ruwenzori on the maps, but known to the natives as Runzonvoro). Here the prevailing feature is undulating hills covered with elephant grass (a coarse cane brake growing to a height of twenty feet). . . . Our camp was pitched on the top of a small hill that jutted out from the main wall of the valley, and consequently we enjoyed an uninterrupted view across and up and down the river. . . . Our tents were barely pitched when we saw an enormous bull elephant emerge from the papyrus, and come gliding across the open country to reach the welcome shade of the trees in a gorge to our right. Then two more big bulls appeared, and followed majestically in his wake. They had not gone far when the wall of papyrus behind them shuddered, staggered, and collapsed, while a ceaseless stream of elephants, big and little, stately and skittish, burst upon our astonished gaze. On they came, a herd of fully two hundred, the bulls in front straggling in twos and threes, then a solid phalanx of cows, out of which from time to time little fellows not more than three feet high ran bewildered, then, steadied by the shrill trumpet of their mammas, scurried back. The mass seemed to glide over the country like an avalanche, raising a great trailing cloud of red dust that dimmed the outlines and gave the impression of some hateful tide soaking up the land. Great clumps of bushes, acres of elephant grass, loomed up in front, swayed, and were no more.

"On it swept, this wondrous mass of life, nearer and nearer, till great ivories glinted white in the red-gray wave; and yet never a sound except the screech of a circling kite, and the occasional ludicrous trumpeting of an anxious mamma. Our camp was too high, and the motion of the elephant is peculiarly noiseless. As we watched, another herd of thirty emerged from the papyrus, then another herd, and yet another one hundred strong, till the whole valley seemed to be streaked with elephants. Ye gods! it was a wonderful sight.

"The tusks of the Toro elephants are enormous; I myself secured one weighing 138½ pounds, from Kasagama, the king of Toro. Many heavier ones have gone out of the country through the Swahili traders. The heaviest that I shot myself scaled 98 pounds (dry), and others scaled 86, 85, 87, 78, 78, 69, 69, all of which would be considered unusually large in South Africa."

It may be mentioned that, according to Lankester [137] the heaviest African tusk on record is one in the British Museum, ten feet two inches long along the outer curvature, and weighing 228 pounds; a tusk of 150 pounds is considered very large.

MANATEES AND SEA COWS — Order, SIRENIA

This is a small group of aquatic animals, living along the marshy shores of both salt and fresh waters, and feeding wholly upon aquatic vegetation. Their geological history goes back to the early Tertiary, but previously is quite unknown, and their relation to other animals is obscure; the prevailing opinion is, that they represent an always aquatic line of descent from creodont sources allied to those which gave rise to the Ungulata. They are seal-like in general form, but far more clumsy, with round heads and almost hairless bodies. The hind limbs are absent, only a trace of pelvis remaining; the fore limbs are inclosed in a mittenlike webbing, and thus are modified into swimming organs, but there is no such multiplication of bones as occurs in a whale's flippers; the tail is flattened and either whalelike (forked) or paddle-form. The teats are two, and are borne on the chest.

Of the extinct forms the best known is the great rhytina, which in the eighteenth century was found by Russian navigators densely populating islands on the Siberian coast of Bering Sea. The naturalist Steller[203] was with one of the first expeditions and published an elaborate memoir on **Rhytina.** the animal. It was much like the dugong in form, 20 to 30 feet long, weighed 600 to 800 pounds, and its flesh was like beef. It lived in herds feeding on seaweed, and could neither defend itself nor escape from the seal hunters, who slaughtered it by wholesale for ship provisions. All were killed by 1767, and we should know almost nothing of the creature had not Stejneger made a special trip to Bering and Copper islands in 1883 to collect its bones and any information accessible.[251]

A more truly fossil sirenian is Halitherium, which seems to have been almost universally distributed during the Miocene period.

MANATEE.

Dugong is the Malay name of the sea cow of the Old World, found in the Red Sea, among the East Indies, and on Australian coasts. It is thus marine in its nature, but is inclined to gather near the shore in herds, which formerly sometimes numbered hundreds, and browses on the algæ which grow on submarine rocks in shallow places. The mother's affectionate care of her offspring, which she nurses embraced to her bosom as she stands upright in the water, is proverbial in the East; and it has long been believed that it furnished the original model of our mermaids; but the mermaid was a popular notion in the Orient long before Westerners knew anything about the dugong. These animals, although formerly much hunted for the sake of their oil-blubber, are still extremely numerous in the vast grassy bays of the Queensland coast; but elsewhere dugongs are now rare. Prominent distinguishing features of the dugongs are the sudden downward bending of the overhanging upper jaw in the male, and its two strong incisor tusks.

Dugong.

Tropical America has a sirenian quite different both in structure and habits. Instead of being almost black it is dark gray, and its skin is finely wrinkled and sparsely haired, especially about the head; the tail is not forked but rounded, and the flippers may bear small finger nails. Another remarkable fact is that instead of a few teeth as in the dugong, or none at all as in the rhytina, the manatee has many, which apparently go on increasing indefinitely during life. As many as twenty molar teeth have been counted in one half of the jaw, and they may get still more numerous. "This large number of grinding teeth is obviously suggestive of the whales, with which the Sirenia are believed by some to be allied. It is at least a remarkable coincidence that these two aquatic groups of mammals should both have assumed the same indefinite tooth formula. . . . The animal is assisted in feeding by a curious

Manatee.

mechanism of the upper lip; this is split in two, and the two halves, which are furnished with strong bristles, can play upon each other like the points of a pair of forceps."

Manatees were once plentiful on both coasts of Florida, but now a few carefully guarded near Miami alone remain. They still wallow in all the inlets and estuaries along the Gulf coast of Central America; and the South American nail-less species is one of the commonest game animals of the Amazon and Orinoco basins, incessantly hunted by both Indians and white men for the flesh and the oil. Dampier's opinion of the edibility of the animal in Campeachy was this: —

"Their Flesh is white, both the Fat and the Lean, and extraordinary sweet, wholesome meat. The tail of a young cow is most esteemed; but if old, both Head and Tail are very tough. A Calf that sucks is the most delicate meat; Privateers commonly roast them: as they do great Pieces cut out of the Bellies of the old ones."

Here, did it fall within my plan, would follow the history and account of the whales, grampuses, porpoises, and related marine mammals, of the order *Cetacea*. The leading authorities for unscientific readers on this group of animals are Beddard,[255] Bullen,[256] Scammon,[189] and the publications of the United States Bureau of Fisheries.

WHALEBONE IN MOUTH OF A BALEEN WHALE.

403

THE GNAWERS — Order, RODENTIA

WE come now to one of the most numerous, widespread, and familiar groups of mammals, — the rodents, or animals that gnaw. They are smallish, furry or spiny, vegetable-eating animals, sharply distinguished by their dentition. The characteristic and most important teeth are the incisors, — the gnawers. These are two only in each jaw (except in the rabbits and pikas), and are very long and strong, their roots extending back through the jaws to the hinder part of the skull, where they have "persistent pulps," that is,

Teeth.

the formative organ remains active, so that the tooth continues to grow throughout the animal's life.

This provision maintains in the teeth the length and strength needed for the continual gnawing upon which the animal depends for its livelihood. It is equally requisite, however, that they should always be sharp, and this is provided for by having the general substance of the tooth a comparatively soft dentine, while the front is coated with a layer of much harder, glasslike material called enamel. The end of the tooth is chisel-shaped, and as the dentine wears away faster than the enameled front, a sharp cutting edge is always maintained; this, too, wears away somewhat, but is steadily pushed forward by the active growth at the root to make

LOWER JAW OF A BEAVER.

Showing the vast length of the ever growing incisor (*i*), and position of the molars (*m*), characteristic of the dentition of rodents.

up for the loss, so that the rodent always has his tools in good order. In the best gnawers these incisors are thicker than wide, and are often brown or yellow, and perhaps grooved, upon the outer surface. Another provision of interest is, that inside the mouth, behind the incisor, there is a hairy ingrowth from each cheek, which meet and form a barrier against the passage into the throat of chips and dust dislodged in cutting wood or digging in the ground.

The back teeth have a similar growth in certain kinds, but more often are rooted and grow only for a limited period like ordinary teeth ; "are quite straight and perpendicular, and their crowns, worn flat by mutual attrition, present an intricate and endlessly varied pattern of the enamel folds," useful in distinguishing the different groups and species. No rodent has more than three molars, but the premolars when present vary in number. The brain is primitive in type, but in the larger rodents shows furrows in proportion to the animal's size, according to the general rule that large creatures have brains with more surface convolutions than little ones; an odd exception, however, is the beaver, which, although comparatively big, and manifesting superior intelligence, has a remarkably smooth brain.

The rodents embrace an enormous number of genera and species. "They are distributed all over the world, including the Australian region, and, being small and often nocturnal, and by no means particular in their diet,

MEADOW MOUSE.

Showing how the cheeks close in behind the incisors.

have managed to thrive and multiply to a greater extent than any other group of living mammals. They are chiefly terrestrial creatures, and often burrow or live in ready-made burrows. Some, however, such as the voles, are aquatic; others, *e.g.* the squirrels, are arboreal, and there are 'flying' rodents exemplified by the genus Anomalurus." It is evidently needful to sort this immense and diversified assemblage into natural groups in order to examine it. The incisor teeth, which form the most characteristic feature of the order, afford a basis at once for a prime division into two suborders thus: —

I. *Duplicidentata*, — having four upper incisors; and

II. *Simplicidentata*, — having two upper incisors.

The first of these suborders (also termed Lagomorpha) contains two families of "double-toothed" rodents: (1) the pikas, small, short-eared and tailless; (2) the hares, larger, long-eared and tailed.

The second, "single-toothed," suborder contains all the remainder, — several hundred species. It is evident that here convenience, at least, requires a still further classification. Examining the mass, it becomes plain that this suborder has developed along three distinct lines, represented respectively by the porcupine, the rat, and the squirrel.

The rodents are a very ancient race, traceable by fossil forms as far back as the early part of Tertiary times. The types mentioned above are plainly to be distinguished **Ancestry.** in the oldest Miocene, but the Eocene has as yet produced nothing but the lowest, or squirrel, type. The striking fact about this history is that no essential change has taken place in the rodent type since the Miocene; and it is probable that the divisions of the Rodentia are descended from corresponding groups of a single primary source. This primary source, in the opinion of Professor Cope, a high authority here, may have been the group Tillodontia. Other indications point to derivation from ancestral Marsupialia, with or without the intervention of the Tillodontia.

The Tillodontia are a small group of primitive mammals, fossil in the earliest Tertiary strata, chiefly of North America, which developed perhaps at first in advance of the Rodentia, and later beside them. They are very generalized in structure, having, for instance, in the upper jaw not only the three pairs of incisors of the normal mammalian set, which have been lost wholly or in part by the rodents, but also having definitely marked premolars. Already, however, the canines had disappeared to mere rudiments, the outer pair of incisors had been greatly reduced, and the second pair been much enlarged. Moreover, while those of the earliest tillodonts do not seem to have grown from persistent pulps, the incisors of the later genera (as Tillotherium) did do so. Similar features tending toward the modern rodents are seen elsewhere in the structure. Nevertheless, the tillodonts seem not to have been in the direct line of ancestry, and came to an end with the close of the Miocene period. The largest of them was the most recent form, Tillotherium, which was as big as a small bear.

We may now take up the Rodentia in order, beginning with the Duplicidentata, because they are of a more primitive type, as shown by the dental resemblance to the tillodonts, in having two pairs of incisor teeth in the upper jaw, although the inner pair is small and hidden behind the big outer pair; and sometimes there appear in earliest infancy traces of a third pair.

EUROPEAN RABBIT.

The hares and rabbits form a compact family (Leporidæ) of some sixty species, scattered in all divisions of the globe except Australasia and Madagascar; but only one species occurs in South America, and the family is most numerous in northerly regions, where these animals form an important food resource for man and beast. All are much alike in the long, high-haunched hind legs, which give great leaping and dodging power; tall, erectile ears; divided upper lip; short scut; and grizzled gray brown coat, with various specific markings of white and black. The only exceptional one is the "hispid" hare of northeastern India, which has small eyes, bristly short ears, short hind legs, and much the manner of a rabbit.

The term "rabbit" has wholly replaced "hare" in America, because the common small hare of the eastern United States, **Rabbits.** quickly seen by the first English settlers, looked to them more like the rabbit they had known at home than like their bigger hare; and they ignored the difference in habits as they did so many other facts in their careless naming of the animals of the New World after those of Europe. It must always be remembered that the first Pilgrims, Puritans, and southern "adventurers" were mainly from cities, and knew little of rural things, to which ignorance, by

Brownell, Phot.

AMERICAN COTTONTAIL RABBIT.

the way, they owed most of their early misfortunes in the colonies.

The true rabbit or "cony" differs from its relatives by its small size (average weight two and a half to three pounds), short ears and hind legs; but more in its habits, for its young are born naked, blind, and helpless, and it is comparatively slow-footed. Hence it has been compelled to become a burrower for the safety of both itself and its babies, and, as is usual with animals become burrowers, has acquired the habit of gathering in communities, whose crowded diggings or "warrens" are labyrinths of subterranean runways. Even this, however, would hardly suffice to preserve this timid and nearly defenseless race were not several litters of five to eight young (leverets) produced by each pair annually to make good the loss from enemies and disease. The original European wild rabbit is grayish brown, becoming foxy on the neck, but this rabbit has been domesticated since ancient times, and alterations of coloring as well as of form have been produced. Ten or more distinct breeds are recognized by fanciers, some of which, as the lop-eared, the great Belgian, and the Angora, are far away from the original type. All are described, and methods of rearing and caring for rabbits are taught in several books by Knight,[70] Morant,[71] and other fanciers.

Their amazing fecundity has caused rabbits to multiply into an almost uncontrollable pest since they were unwisely introduced into Australia and New Zealand, where the scarcity of beasts of prey allowed them to increase without bounds.[104] In a few years, therefore, the whole country was overrun by millions, which threatened to devour not only all the crops but every bit of wild herbage; even in Europe, when for any reason their subjection is neglected, they do great damage to gardens, orchards, and plantations of young trees. Writing about 1895, Dr. Lydekker recorded the result of the introduction of a few rabbits about 1850 into Australia, and about 1875 into New Zealand, as follows: —

"The inhabitants of the colony soon found that the rabbits were a plague, for they devoured the grass which was needed for the sheep, the bark of trees, and every kind of fruit and vegetables, until . . . ruin seemed inevitable. In New South Wales upwards of fifteen million rabbit-skins have been exported in a single year; while in the thirteen years ending in 1889 no less than thirty-nine million were accounted for in Victoria alone. To prevent the increase of these rodents, the introduction of weasels, stoats, mungooses, etc., has been tried; but it has been found that these carnivores neglected the rabbits and took to feeding on poultry, and thus became as great a nuisance as the animals they were intended to destroy. The attempt to kill them off by the introduction of an epidemic disease has also failed. In order to protect such portions of the country as are still free from rabbits, fences of wire netting have been erected, one of these fences erected by the government of Victoria extending for a distance upwards of one hundred and fifty geographical miles. In New Zealand . . . its increase has been so enormous, and the destruction it inflicts so great, that in some districts it has actually been a question whether the colonists should not vacate the country rather than attempt to fight against the plague."

At present further use is being made of the rabbits by "packing" their edible flesh in various forms as an article of preserved food, which is finding a wide market; and probably the pest will be abated in course of time by natural processes. √ Thus far no notable changes have taken place in these colonial rabbits; but elsewhere, *e.g.* in Malta, special local varieties have

SOUTHWESTERN JACK RABBIT AND KANGAROO MOUSE.

arisen from the imported stock, upon which Darwin has discoursed at length in illustration of his opinion that variations are often due to altered environment.

Returning to the hares, not much need be said as to particular species. All dwell either in open grassy country or else **Hares.** among rocks and bushes. They do not flock, nor make any sort of shelter, but each inhabits a certain small district, where it makes a smooth resting place called its "form." To this it will return day after day for a long time unless frightened; and in such a form the young are born and are left concealed, when still in the suckling age, under a cover of leaves and vines, or even of fur plucked by the mother from her own loose coat and felted into a sort of blanket. They seek no better shelter than this in winter, except that some, as our common little cottontail, will creep into the mouth of an old skunk's or woodchuck's hole or within a hollow stump, to seek protection from the "cauld blast." The "jacks" of the Plains are so well furred that even the soles of their feet are warm mats of hair; and they are the only small animals able to survive outside of burrows the in-

tense winter cold and gales of those bleak up-lands. This hardihood is due primarily, of course, to the fact that hares are able to find nutritious forage all through the winter, and so keep up their bodily heat.

All species have great speed, — their principal means of safety, — and the swiftest hounds are hardly able to run them down; while they also have astonishing skill in suddenly halting and turn-ing, or "doubling," by which they gain a fresh

MOLLY COTTONTAIL.

start before their more clumsy pursuers can perceive what has happened, and change their course. Chasing them with grey-hounds is a regular sport called "coursing." Along with this goes extreme timidity and watchfulness, in which their big ears serve a most useful purpose, rising to the slightest sound, but dropping out of the way as the animal makes off in a series of tremendous leaps; and the hare can make faster time uphill than down, ow-ing to the greater length of the hind legs—a decided advantage.

Knowing these tricks, most of its enemies resort to counter-strategy, — a stealthy approach and quick rush; and an excellent picture of these wiles, and poor Bunny's efforts to meet them, may be read in Seton's tale of "Raggylug," and in such delightful writings as those of Audubon and Bachman, Godman, Kennicott, Lockwood, Abbott, Robinson, Sharp, Cram, and some others. Even the least of the tribe, however, is able to make a defense which often completely disconcerts the foe, and the means are found in its strong hind feet. Mr. Sharp[72] gives an American illustration: —

"Molly feeds the family shortly after nightfall, and always tucks them in when leaving, with the caution to lie quiet and still. She is not often surprised with her young, but lingers near on guard. You can easily tell if you are in the neighborhood of her nest by the way she thumps and watches you, and refuses to be driven off. Here she waits, and if anything smaller than a dog appears she rushes to meet it, stamping the ground in fury. A dog she will intercept by leaving a warm trail across his path, or, in case the brute has no nose for her scent, by throwing herself in front of him and drawing him off on a long chase.

"One day as I was quietly picking strawberries on a hill, I heard a curious grunting down the side below me, then the quick *thud! thud!* of an angry rabbit. Among the bushes I caught a glimpse of rabbit ears. A fight was on. Crouching beside a bluish spot, which I knew to be a rabbit's nest, was a big yellow cat. He had discovered the young ones, and making mouths at the thought of how they would taste, when the mother's thump startled him. He squatted flat, with ears back, tail swelled, and hair standing up along his back, as the rabbit leaped over him. It was a glimpse of Molly's ears as she made the jump that I had caught. It was the beginning of the bout — only a feint by the rabbit, just to try the mettle of her antagonist. The cat was scared, and before he got himself together, Molly with a mighty bound was in the air again, and, as she flashed over him, she fetched him a stunning whack on the head that knocked him endwise. He was on his feet in an instant, but just in time to receive a stinging blow on the ear that sent him sprawling several feet down the hill. The rabbit seemed constantly in the air. Back and forth, over and over the cat she fled, and with every bound landed a terrific kick with her powerful hind feet, that was followed by a puff of yellow fur. The cat could not stand up to this. Every particle of breath and fight was knocked out of him at about the third kick. The green light in his eyes was the light of terror. He got quickly to a bush and ran away, else I believe that the old rabbit would have beaten him to death."

In addition to this familiar eastern cottontail we have in the United States several other species, as the little marsh hare and the big water hare of the southern states; the large northern varying hare; the arctic hares; the various long-eared, long-legged "jack rabbits" of the Plains and Rocky Mountains, a particular account of which has been given by Palmer [73]; and several lesser species, more or less common on the Pacific coast. The "varying hare" is so called because, as is the case with several foreign northern hares, its brown summer coat when shed as usual on the approach of winter is replaced by one which is white. The purpose and process of this change with the seasons has been explained elsewhere.

Porcupines, Chinchillas, and Cavies

This brings us to the suborder *Simplicidentata* or rodents with only one pair of upper incisors, which consists, as we have seen, of three groups: (1) porcupinelike; (2) ratlike; and (3) squirrel-like; but many members of each bear little outward resemblance to their types.

The porcupines are stout-bodied animals, protected by an armor of stiff, sharp, quill-like spines. In the European species these are twelve or fifteen inches long in some places, and on the back are solid, but on the tail are hollow. When the creature is angry or trying to look dangerous, it lifts these spines until they stand out in all directions, shakes its tail to give a clicking noise, and perhaps makes an odd bayonet-charge *backward*, at which the enemy usually flees *nem. con.* A mane of long, whitish bristly hairs flows back from its forehead. Several very similar species inhabit Asia and South Africa, and some others in the East Indies have long tails with a tuft of quills at the end, whose rattling, when the animal gets excited, recalls that of a rattlesnake. These Old World porcupines dwell in burrows of their own digging, or in con-

Brownell, Phot.

THE NORTH AMERICAN OR "CANADA" PORCUPINE.

venient and softly bedded hollows among rocks, whence they sally forth at night in search of edible roots, etc., and to damage gardens and fruit orchards; they never climb trees, and hibernate in winter when they live in a cold country.

Our American porcupines, on the contrary, are first-class climbers, and remain as much awake in cold weather as in warm, — which is no very high praise for their activity. They are further distinguished by the fact that the spines are shorter and are intermingled with hairs; the sole of the foot is rough and the toes are furnished with long claws, so that the paws are well fitted for holding to the branches of the trees in which our porcupines spend most of their time; and in many the tail is prehensile. Lastly, the food is mainly bark and leaves.

Our eastern porcupine (there is a similar far-western "yellow-haired" species) is numerous and well known wherever coniferous forests remain and rough hills give it a safe place to make its den; and it passes its time lazily browsing in the hemlocks, or at night in wandering about near its lair, picking up a variety of vegetable fare, and rejoicing in an occasional find of bones or cast antlers or the saline scraps of a lumber camp or a hunter's bivouac, which it enters with the fearlessness of innocence, and rummages without doing any great harm. It does not hibernate, resisting the cold as long as food holds out; and this is so simple and easily obtained that the animals have nothing to do but to go from one tree to another, which they are loath to do as long as a leaf remains. Under this lack of stimulus to exert themselves they have become as lethargic in mind as in body. In my "Wild Neighbors" [36] will be found a somewhat extended biography under the title "A Woodland Codger."

The porcupine led our Indians to one of the most distinctive native American arts, that of ornamentation by its quills, — an art unknown in primitive Europe, but practiced all over North America, and often giving an exceedingly pretty effect. The quills were **Quills.** sometimes drawn into, or sewed in patterns upon, garments, moccasins, robes, tobacco pouches, bow cases, and similar things made of buckskin or fur; were combined with feathers and beads in the ornamentation of war bonnets, pipes, and various ceremonial objects; were bent and woven into baskets, mattings, canoes, and many small articles formed of birch bark; the short ones were strung like beads for fringes; and in many other ways the quills were made to serve an artistic purpose. Usually, they were tastefully dyed with vegetable juices, since their own colors faded or were easily soaked out. These decorative designs cost much time and were the "fancy work" of the squaws, who often exercised notable skill and taste, and produced thereby a truly native art.

In Central and South America live a number of species of smaller and more thoroughly arboreal porcupines which have prehensile tails and otherwise differ from those of North America; in one, the spines are little better than bristles.

Associated with the porcupines anatomically, though very unlike them in form and mode of life, are the chinchillas, cavies, **Chinchilla.** spiny rats, and some other little beasts which next demand attention. The chinchilla, whose delightfully soft, silver-gray fur is so highly prized, is a small, long-eared, squirrel-like, nocturnal creature, living gregariously in the high Andes, where it follows the customs of the pikas, except that it often digs burrows for itself, and that its food is mainly roots. It is becoming rare. Another genus (Lagidium) are also mountain dwellers, but their fur is inferior.

Closely allied to them are the viscachas or "bizcachas,"

BRAZILIAN TREE PORCUPINE.

as Darwin spells it, which have been so particularly described **Viscacha.** by Hudson,[35] and which take the place on the plains of Argentina of our prairie dogs, and are equally pestiferous. Formerly they were extremely numerous, but now have been greatly reduced by the farmers whose fields they damage. Viscachas are grayish animals, about twenty inches in length, with black and white faces, and with much the form of rabbits except that the ears are short and the tail rather long

VISCACHA.

and bushy. They live in companies of twenty to thirty, and dig deep and complicated burrows, often branching and communicating, and having large craterlike openings, around which the earth is soon bared of vegetation; and they have a habit of dragging on to these hillocks of cast-out earth not only the remains of their food, which consists of grass, roots, seeds, thistle stalks, etc., but any bright object near by, so that when a traveler loses a small article he at once searches the nearest viscachera. These hillocks are the homes of several birds — one a small ground owl, the coquimbo, which, like our burrowing owl, lays its eggs in some unused tunnel entrance or often excavates a little cave for itself; another a small passerine bird, one of the wood hewers, which digs a nesting hole in the mound; and the third a swallow, which breeds in abandoned burrows, as also do sundry foxes, snakes, etc. These last are enemies, but the viscachas are plucky in defending themselves, and "will attempt to rescue their friends if attacked by a weasel or a peccary, and to disinter those covered up in their burrows by man." The under surface of the viscacha's upcurled tail is padded with a thick, naked, horny skin; "and when the animal performs the curious sportive antics in which it occasionally indulges, it gives rapid, loud-sounding blows on the ground with this part of the tail." The pelt is of no value, and the flesh is not well liked, though equal or superior to that of the hare.

South America is the principal home of the porcupine group, and that it has always been so is shown by the abundance of their remains in the rocks there, carrying their history back far into the Tertiary period. The bones of one species, found in the Lower Pampas formations, indicate an animal closely related to the modern viscacha, but as big as an ox! It is not surprising then to find many existing relatives in that continent, — agoutis, pacas, capybaras, cavies, and so forth.

One of the best known of these in former times, when it was extremely numerous all over Argentina, was the tall Patagonian cavy or mara, which Mr. Darwin called "aguti," **Agoutis.** and which had the singularity of not being nocturnal, but of wandering and feeding by day, enjoying the hottest sunshine. The true agoutis, as we now use the term, are forest-loving animals ranging from the borders of the pampas northward. They are odd, golden-brown little creatures, with squirrel-like heads, high round haunches, a mere excuse for a tail, and slim legs with practically only three toes on the feet, and these armed with hooflike claws, so that, excepting its head, the agouti looks like a sleek little pig.

"They are mainly nocturnal, remaining concealed during the day in hollow trees, or in cavities or burrows among their roots; . . . Their movements are extremely active and graceful. When going slowly they advance at a kind of trot, but when running their pace takes the form of a series of rapid springs which succeed one another so quickly as to give the appearance of a gallop. 'Cutias,' as these animals are called on the Amazons, can swim well, but are unable to dive. Their food consists of the foliage and roots of ferns and other plants, as well as fallen fruits; their sharp incisor teeth enabling them to perforate the shells of the hardest nuts. In cultivated districts they do much harm to plantations of sugar cane and plantains. Of their reproduction in a wild state, comparatively little is known. They breed, however, at least twice in the year. . . . If captured at a sufficiently early age, agoutis can be readily tamed; and it is not uncommon in South American houses to find one or more of these animals roaming at large. . . . They are much hunted by the natives for the sake of their flesh." Thus far, Lydekker.[10] Turning to Rodway,[88] we find him much pleased at the wily ways of this small

A PACA.

strategist of the woods. "If chased," he tells us, "he will run along the shallows of a creek to hide his scent from the dogs, or swim over and back again several times for the same purpose. He never runs straight when pursued, but doubles, often hiding until a dog has passed, and then making off in a different direction. Like the fox, he has been hunted for a very long period; and, like Reynard, has grown wiser with every generation." A smaller species, the aguchi, inhabits Central America and some of the West India Islands.

One of the most prominent of the smaller Brazilian mammals, particularly in view of the fact that its flesh is excellent eating in a country where wild meat is scarce, is the paca, **Pacas.** a cousin of the agoutis and connecting their family with that of the cavies, presently to be introduced. Wallace and others declare its meat is the "very best the country produces, being fat, delicate, and very tender," whereas agouti flesh is dry and tasteless. The habits of the pacas — there is a second smaller species in the uplands of Ecuador — are very like those of the agouti, that is, they are nocturnal and burrowers; but their appearance is very different, for they have five-toed paws on short, strong legs and the general shape and attitude of big, tailless woodchucks, richly brown in color and ornamented with rows of white spots. This beautiful pelt is of no commercial value, however, on account of its thinness.

Copyright, N. Y. Zoölogical Society.

Sanborn, Phot.

CAPYBARAS IN THE NEW YORK ZOÖLOGICAL PARK.

Of these specimens Mr. Hornaday writes: "The capybara is not at all difficult to keep in captivity. The swine-like appearance of the animal is also reflected in its temper and disposition. These two are not only tame, but even affectionate, and fond of being petted. While seeking attention, or being handled, they utter a queer clicking sound indicative of goodwill. Their outside cage is supplied with a bathing tank."

The largest of all this group not only, but the biggest of existing rodents, is the capybara, carpincho, or water hog, which **Capybara.** reaches a length of four feet and a weight of one hundred pounds, and looks like a gigantic roughcoated guinea pig, as, in truth, it is. It is to be met with all over Brazil, the Guianas, and Uruguay, and not only forms the principal food of the jaguar and other large beasts of prey, but its veal-like flesh is well liked by both Indians and whites, who also kill it because of its depredations on their fields of sugar cane, plantains, etc. The capybaras are thoroughly aquatic in their habits, swimming wholly immersed except their faces, diving well, and having the trick of hiding for a long time among aquatic weeds with only their nostrils poked above the surface; their feet are hairless, partly webbed, and look more like a duck's than a mammal's. Darwin [77] and Bates [25] describe them at length, and Aplin [89] has recorded their habits in Uruguay, where they are seen usually in small herds, and utter a curious grunting bark, or, when they are pleased, a queer little quavering warble, very pretty. They may be tamed.

The capybara belongs to the cavy family, of which there are a dozen or so other kinds, — all small, gregarious, nocturnal animals, inhabiting open regions from the Andes of Peru to the plains of Patagonia, some always digging burrows in connected warrens, others sometimes doing so and again contenting themselves with natural hollows; while the small Brazilian rock cavy, or hoki, lives in crevices of rocks, where the Indians seek it eagerly for the pot. The most familiar one, probably, is the aperea of the La Plata Valley, whence, it used to be said, came our guinea pigs — which are not pigs and have nothing to do with Guinea or even with Guiana! It is now known that these amusing pets are a modified form of Cutler's cavy of Peru, which has black fur with the flanks and under parts brownish. This one was domesti- **Guinea Pigs.** cated by the Peruvians before their conquest by the Spaniards, and Pizarro's men sent live specimens to Spain. Since then the cavies have been bred by fanciers into many varieties of size, color, and character of coat; and books describe the show points of these pets, but do not explain who gave them the absurd name they bear.[115] It would be better to call them *cavies*.

There remain to be mentioned within this suborder only
an extensive family (Octodontidæ) of "rats," many of large
size, and nearly all burrowers or swimmers or both, agreeing
in several peculiarities of structure, one of which is that spines

THE COYPU.

or bristles are min-
gled with the fur or
else form a comblike
appendage on the
hind feet. The group
belongs mainly to
tropical America, but
a few are African,
prominently the big
"cane rat," so de-
structive to sugar
plantations, yet of
much importance as
a food resource of
the negro field-hands.

Several of the American forms make some special claim
upon our interest, as, for instance, the quaint hutias of Cuba
and Jamaica, which are known nowhere else; the noisy Argentine tuco-tuco, — a curious little creature with the habits of a
mole and nearly as blind, eyes being of no service to it underground; and that big water rat called in Chile coypu, on
Coypu. the Argentine pampas quuiya, and in the fur
trade nutria (Spanish for "otter"), because it
furnishes a fur which became a substitute for beaver; and
like that animal it was nearly exterminated before the fashion
for wearing felted fur hats was changed (about 1825) to
that for the silk "tile" of the present mode, giving both
animals a respite. The coypu looks and behaves much like
a muskrat, but has a round tail, and swims by means of
webbed hind feet.

Mice, Rats, and Such Small Deer

Now we come to an immense assemblage of small mammals, embracing more than one hundred genera and perhaps ten times as many species, which must be sketched very rapidly, although full of interest for the naturalist and often prominent in our daily life. This is the murine or myomorphic section

A JERBOA, SHOWING TUFTED TAIL.

of the Rodentia, distinguished from the other suborders by certain peculiarities of the skull, and by the circumstance, associated with their speed and leaping powers, that the long bones (tibia and fibula) of the leg are united into a cannon bone; and containing the jerboas, rats, mice, lemmings, and their kin, whose fare is mainly vegetable, and which for safety and warmth dwell in holes, and go abroad by night rather than by day.

Most of the species are very small, one of the largest being the Cape jumping-hare of South Africa, which looks like a rabbit wearing a big squirrel's tail. It is a burrowing, **Jerboas.** nocturnal, far-leaping animal of southern Africa, and is a cousin of the tiny, pug-nosed and comical jerboas of the desert country of northern Africa, Arabia, and central Asia. The accompanying sketch shows how they look; the largest is no more than seven inches long, and the smallest scarcely half that, not counting the long balancing pole of a tail. All are softly fawn color, matching the sands over which they skip like birds in tremendous leaps, and at such a rate that a swift horse cannot overtake them. The pretty Egyptian jerboas, which are often tamed by the Arabs into the most charming of pets, have only three toes on the hind feet, but the larger number of species have five toes; for example, the big alag-daga, everywhere seen in Turkestan, and an important source of food to the Kirghiz of the Steppes. All the jerboas live in companies which unite to make a network of underground tunnels as a permanent home.

A very near relative of these is our North American jumping-mouse, but it dwells in the woods and fields, not in deserts, and is not gregarious. Late in summer this mouse weaves a globular ball of grass blades, and occupies it with his mate until cold weather approaches, when the pair find a deep cranny among rocks or dig a hole a little way into the ground, and there, in a snug bed of shredded bark, leaves, and so forth, go sound asleep with the first severe frost, and never wake up before May day. None of our mammals is so deep a winter sleeper. The several species are much alike in color, — dark along the back, reddish yellow on the flanks, and whitish underneath.

In a neighboring family are grouped another lot of North American mice, — the agile, graceful pocket mice, kangaroo **Kangaroo Mice.** rats and their fellows, which abound in the arid Southwest. The kangaroo rats would surely attract an artist, if Seton is a good reporter.

"Just the loveliest, daintiest, fawn-brown little creature that I had ever seen in fur — large beautiful eyes like a fawn's — No! not like a fawn's, for no fawn that ever lived had such wonderfully innocent orbs of liquid brown, ears like thinnest shells of the sea, showing the pink veins' flood of life. His hind feet were large and strong; but his fore feet — his hands, I mean, were the tiniest of the tiny — pinky white, and rounded and dimpled, just like a baby's, only whiter and smaller than the tip of baby's finger. His throat and breast were snowy white — however does he keep himself so sweetly clean in such a land of mud! Down the outside of his brown velvet knickerbockers was the cutest little silvery white stripe, just like that on a trooper's breeches.   His tail . . . was remarkably long, and was deco-

A KANGAROO RAT.

rated to match the breeches with two long white stripes and ended in a feather duster, which was very pretty, but rather overdone, I thought, until I found out that it was designed for several important purposes.

"Soft as a shadow, swift as an arrow, dainty as thistle down, bright-eyed and beautiful, with a secret way to an underground world where he finds safety from his foes — my first impression was not so very far astray. I had surely found the Little Folk."

These charming fairies of the desert are extraordinarily numerous and varied, and find abundant food in the seeds of grasses and weeds, and in sundry insects, which they gather and carry in their pouched cheeks during the night.   By day they are hidden in a labyrinth of connected runways beneath some hillside, where a large colony dwell snugly all the year round, carefully closing the tunnel entrances with loose sand each morning to keep out both enemies and heat.   Hence these most beautiful and lively of our mice are rarely seen or even trapped, for they are extremely wary.

Every one in the open western half of the United States and Canada is, however, familiar with their big relatives, the pocket gophers, so called because of their "pouches," and also to distinguish them from the northern "striped gophers," which are ground squirrels. They are about the size of large house rats, "of squat bunchy shape, with short thick limbs, a short tail, very small or rudimentary ears, small eyes, no appreciable neck, and thick blunt head." Like the pocket mice they possess capacious pouches in each side of the head, which are not connected with the interior of the mouth, but open only by wide vertical slits beside the jaw; they are lined with fur, and in reality are deep infolds of the skin. Their loose inner walls meet behind the front teeth and prevent the dirt dislodged in tunneling from falling into the mouth and throat. These gophers are almost as completely subterranean as the mole, and their fore limbs, though not twisted and mis-shapen like the mole's, are broad and strong, and provided with long digging claws.

Gophers.

In his monograph [81] upon the group, Dr. Merriam tells us that in working their way through the ground they use the strong, overhanging, grooved incisors as picks to loosen the soil, while the fore feet scratch and push the earth backward until a large quantity has been loosened; the animal then turns around and pushes this back to an opening in the tunnel and out upon the surface, where a hillock is soon formed. In these runways the gophers trot backward as readily as forward; and the naked ratlike tail is so sensitive to touch that it gives instant warning of anything wrong. The food consists prin-cipally of roots, tubers, and other hard vegetable substances, but grass and juicy plants are sometimes eaten. Thus the animals may be highly mischievous, destroying potatoes and root crops, gnawing off the roots of fruit trees, and spoiling much ground in fields of grain or fodder by making water channels. They are busy hoarders, carrying away to underground store-

WESTERN SPERMOPHILE; OR, STRIPED GOPHER

WESTERN POCKET GOPHER

FRANKLIN'S SPERMOPHILE

WESTERN GROUND SQUIRRELS

houses vastly more stuff than they consume. The one inhabiting the Gulf states, which the Georgians and Floridans call "salamander," is particularly injurious to orange orchards and sweet-potato plantations; and the Californian species are exceedingly destructive to fruit trees and vines. Another charge is that they spread the growth of certain troublesome weeds. On the credit side, their continual overturning of the loam, and accidental burial of much vegetable refuse, is a practical plowing and manuring of great utility in developing fertile soils. Many interesting details of the habits of all this group are related by Vernon Bailey in his account of Texas animals.[68]

In these operations they make constant use of their pouches, cutting the food into small pieces, and then by swift and dexterous motions with the fore feet packing it into the pouches, usually filling one before the other. They do not drink at all. The pouches are emptied by putting a paw behind each and squeezing the contents out. Thus stores are carried by the bagful to the big central chamber in which their tunnels concentrate, where the gopher is really "at home" with his mate, and where the young are reared on a bed of grass, leaves, etc.; but pairs may be found together only in early spring. To their solitary mode of life, gophers probably owe the vicious pugnacity so characteristic of them. None seems to hibernate. Two or three young only are born annually; but this small rate of increase is balanced, as Bailey points out in his paper [82] on their habits, by the safety from enemies, storms, and other dangers gained by their mode of life. Thus the reddish prairie gopher (*Geomys bursarius*) remains exceedingly numerous and troublesome all over the well-

CHEEK POUCHES.

settled prairie region; the salamander (*Geomys tuza*) in the southern states; the smaller gray gopher (*Thomomys talpoides*) throughout the Northwest; and a large number of other species southwest of these districts, in spite of great efforts made for their extermination.

Brownell, Phot.

A HOUSE MOUSE.

Africa has some related forms, such as the big mole rats of the Cape of Good Hope. One of the most remarkable is the Egyptian spalax, which stores in closets along its complicated runways beneath the desert sand quantities of bulbs of a grape hyacinth, and that only; so far as we can see the distribution, if not the existence, of the animal is dependent on this plant. Here, too, come the large edible bamboo rats of many kinds, familiar in India and eastward. The last, and several others, are good eating.

This brings us to the populous family Muridæ, or typical rats and mice, whose distinguishing marks are a long, nearly **House Mouse.** hairless or scaly tail, and naked soles. The genus Mus, which contains about one hundred and thirty species of "true" rats and mice, is confined exclusively to the Old World, and is absent there only from Madagascar. The type of the group is the house mouse, which probably originated in Asia. Its special characteristics are its relatively large ears, long tail, and the nearly uniform brownish coloration; but this last varies greatly in different countries and climates. Town mice, for instance, are always darker, especially on the under side, but fanciers have bred many pied and even pure white varieties. It has also been tamed and taught tricks. Quite as distinctive as its form and color are the partiality of this mouse for human habitations, and its omnivorous appetite;

wild mice often come into houses for a time, but desert them as soon as house mice arrive. Its bodily and mental activity are both noteworthy; it is as ingenious as it is curious, will leap long distances and run up vertical walls, so that it is extremely difficult to put things out of its reach. Its acuteness has been the theme of many anecdotes, and its attentiveness to musical sounds and ability to make them are well known. It is not surprising, then, that the mouse should figure largely in the folk-lore and fables of all peoples.

Equally domesticated and even less welcome are the big gray brown, blunt-nosed rats of cellars, ships, warehouses, granaries, and grain fields all over the world. So **Rats.** completely have they allied themselves with man and his works that their primitive home is unknown, but is thought to be Mongolia. The advent of this rat in Europe, and its dispersion thence by shipping to all parts of the globe, are more recent than is generally assumed, since rats first became noticeable in southern Russia by migrating from the East in large numbers and swimming the Volga. The immigrants then spread rapidly over Europe, reaching London about 1730, — "the only wild animal," remarks Boyd Dawkins,[83] "which is known to have invaded Europe since the Pleistocene Age, with the exception, perhaps, of the true elk."

Wherever it went it overcame and partly exterminated the smaller, more timid black house rat, now very scarce — itself a world-wide wanderer in the paths of commerce. The popular belief in Great Britain that the brown rat was introduced there in Norwegian timber ships, gives it the name "Norway rat"; at any rate, European ships carried it to all parts of the world. It reached our eastern ports in 1775 and was popularly credited to the hated Hessian soldiers, — a queer echo of the London idea that it came there with the Hanoverian train of the present reigning house. By 1830 it had reached the Mississippi, and by 1857, at least, was numerous in California.

Long previous (1554, according to Erxleben) the European black rat had established itself in the eastern states; and also (in the South) a white-bellied variety of it, native to Egypt and the Mediterranean shores, known as the Alexandrine rat, or "roof rat," which has never appeared north of the Carolinas. Baird thought it probable that the early Spanish discoverers and conquerors carried this variety to America in their vessels, and thus introduced it on the continent long before the brown or even the black rat. An odd result of this ancient importation was that an idea got abroad, and into early books, that these black rats were indigenous American animals which had emigrated to Europe. In America, as elsewhere, the big brown rat has beaten its earlier but weaker brethren in the competition for livelihood, and the latter has become scarce or has taken to the woods.

This strong brown-coated invader succeeds by its adaptability to all climates and foods, its enormous fecundity, its quick-witted intelligence, and its willingness and ability to fight for whatever it wants to get or to keep. Its usefulness as a scavenger is a small offset to the vast evil it does as an agent of infectious diseases. To the rats of the East is largely due, for example, the epidemic spread of the bubonic plague, whose germs are carried in the filth frequently attached to their feet and fur. When this pest began to appear in Korea and Japan in 1903–1904, the Japanese authorities, who were about to put great armies into the field, and were preparing to prevent their decimation by camp diseases, caused the collection of all the rats the people could be hired to kill. Each corpse was examined for bubonic microbes, and when these were found it was destroyed. The result, aided by other means, was the extirpation of the plague in that part of the world; and the clean skins furnished ear tippets for every soldier campaigning in Manchuria.

The true mice of this group are numerous throughout the world, and show many local peculiarities. One of the smallest and prettiest is the diminutive harvest mouse, weighing only a sixth of an ounce, and familiar in English grainfields, where its ball-like nest of woven grass blades is suspended near the tops of the stalks. It is often carried home with the harvest and remains in the barn or stacks

Mice.

all winter, but otherwise it digs a tiny tunnel and hibernates underground. A singular mouse of the desert region has so very spiny a fur that "when it has its spines erected it is almost indistinguishable from a diminutive hedgehog." Another desert genus imitates the jerboa in form and habits; and the Barbary mouse is prettily striped. Peculiar genera are restricted to various African and Asiatic regions, or to single East Indian islands (bamboo rats); and Australia possesses several species — the only native mammals not marsupials except bats. One of them is the beaver-rat — a large dark brown species of Hydromys frequenting creeks like the European water rat, and having a beautifully soft, beaverlike skin.

The water rats proper, the "voles" of the English, form a group with many representatives in the United States, and are of rather stout, clumsy build, with short ears and short hairy tails. The water rat and bank vole are familiar ones in Great Britain, dwelling in holes in every stream bank, and swimming in ponds, though their feet are not webbed. Another very small vole is the ordinary field mouse of Europe, which every few years, by reason of plentiful food and other favorable conditions, suddenly becomes excessively numerous in some region and appears as a "plague." Millions of these mice will devastate the local fields for a year or two, and then gradually, by enemies and disease or starvation, will fall away to their original numbers. In South Russia, Hungary, and similar countries, such plagues have sometimes caused extensive famines. The same thing has happened in Nova Scotia, and is liable to arise in our prairie states.

To this group belong our short-tailed meadow or field mice, wood mice, pine mice, lemming mice, and muskrats.

The meadow mice (genus Microtus) exist in many species and varieties all over the continent north of the Tropics.

"They live," says Miller, "in an endless variety of situations, from sea beaches to marshes and alpine mountain tops, and from open plains to the densest forests. They are perhaps most numerous in well-watered grass lands. In localities where they are abundant most of the species **Meadow Mouse.** make their presence known by trails or runways traced through the vegetation near their burrows. Occasionally, however, they occupy hollows in decaying logs or among loose rocks, and use natural crevices instead of beaten paths. While the great majority

MEADOW MOUSE.

of the species spend much of their time on the surface, protected by the overhanging vegetation, a few live almost exclusively under ground, and in consequence of this habit have acquired numerous modifications which fit them for the needs of a subterranean life. Others are amphibious, and never occur at any great distance from water. At least one member of the subfamily is said to live among the branches of trees (Douglas spruce, in Oregon). The food is chiefly vegetable, though most species occasionally eat animal food. The vegetable food consists principally of grass stems, though roots, bark, leaves, seeds, and fruit are at times eaten in varying quantities. As voles are readily caught in traps baited with meat, it is probable that flesh forms part of their normal food. Mollusks are eaten freely when they can be obtained.

"The voles and lemmings breed very rapidly during the warmer part of the year. The number of young in a litter varies from one or two to ten. . . . The young are born in nests made of soft vegetable fibers. The nests are usually placed in a burrow or beneath shelter of some kind, and vary with the size of the animals."

Every American book of natural history has much to say of these little creatures, one of the best accounts being that by Kennicott,[56] from whose writings, buried in the Smithsonian Reports, I have made somewhat extensive quotations on this subject elsewhere.[36, 94] See also the books of Audubon, Thoreau,

Abbott, Sharp, Cram, and others. A small cousin of the common eastern meadow mouse plentiful in the woods and fields of the northwestern states is the red-backed mouse; the prairie region has a gray, harshly haired species; while the pine mouse is numerous in the South, and is the smallest, reddest, and most subterranean of its kind.

Closely related to these are the lemmings of northern regions, which in general are larger, more thick-set animals, with powerful digging feet, long, dense fur, and very short tails.

In one (Dicrotonyx) of the American genera, the fore feet are strangely altered every winter, apparently to fit them better for the incessant digging which must be done in moving about under the snow or soil, whereas in summer this mouse spends most of its time above ground. The thumb of the fore foot is a mere tubercle, but the other toes are well developed and clawed, especially the two middle ones, and in summer are not at all remarkable. As winter comes on, however, a great horny pad forms underneath each of the two middle claws and remains there until spring, when it gradually loosens from the nail and sloughs off.

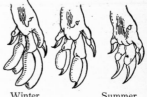

Winter   Summer

PADDED TOES OF DICROTONYX.

These lemmings all live in high latitudes or among cold mountains, and hence are more given to the protection of underground houses and a long winter hibernation; but their food **Lemmings.** and habits are not greatly different from those of their more southern relatives. Several related species exist in northern Canada, and like their arctic European brethren turn white in winter; but interesting is the true lemming of Scandinavia, whose celebrated migrations have never been satisfactorily explained, but are evidently similar to the "plagues" of mice alluded to above.

The lemming is about three inches in length on the average, but is very variable in size and color, with a triangular, prettily striped face, scarcely visible ears and tail, and strong curved claws; and the beadlike eyes seem always to notice objects above them rather than those in any other direction. During the summer they form their nests under stones, and in winter push long galleries through the turf and under the snow in search of their vegetable food, since they lay up no stores.

NORWEGIAN LEMMINGS.

"In England," says Crotch, who contributed a most observing account of the animal to *The Popular Science Review*, new series, Volume I, page 143, "we fail to perceive how much active life goes on beneath the snow, which in more northern latitudes forms a warm roof to numerous birds, quadrupeds and land insects, which are thus enabled to secure an otherwise impossible sustenance. At the same time . . . a fearful struggle for existence is carried on during the long autumnal nights before the snow has become a protection rather than a new source of danger to all save predaceous animals."

At intervals, averaging about a dozen years apart, lemmings suddenly appear in cultivated districts in central Norway and Sweden, where ordinarily none live, and in a year or two multiply into hordes which go traveling straight west toward the Atlantic, or east toward the Gulf of Bothnia, as the case may be, regardless of how the valleys trend, climbing a mountain instead of going around it, and, undeterred by any river or lake keep persistently onward until finally some survivors reach the sea, into which they plunge and perish. The Norwegian peasants have many superstitions relating to these migrations, and will assure you that the lemmings rain down. Almost as illogical is the theory formerly held by the learned that these movements are prompted by an ancient instinct which forces the animals to seek, at times, a mythical land of plenty, — an Atlantis, — now submerged in the ocean, whence their ancestors came ages ago. It is more rational to suppose that under specially favorable conditions the lemmings multiply so fast that their natural habitat in the high central mountains fails to supply sufficient food, and thus a movement outward from that center begins. As the lemmings reach cultivated ground, the abundance of food and a warmer climate lead to a marked increase, and as the females when only six months old bear young, and then produce several litters annually, their number soon becomes countless, and the swarm must spread. This leaves unaccounted for their inveterate attempt to reach the sea. It is plain that the ancient notion that they go under a mysterious impulse to commit suicide, is absurd. Their impulse is simply to keep going, — why always straight east or west, we cannot say; probably simply because the valleys and dip of the land is in that direction. Certainly there is no reason to believe that they know or care anything about the ocean at all; and the truth probably is, that when they come to the strand they enter the water with no idea of its breadth or depth.

"They descend from the Kolen [Mountains], marching in parallel lines three feet apart; they traverse Nordland and Finmark, cross lakes and rivers, and gnaw through hay and corn stacks rather than go round. They infect the ground, and the cattle perish which taste of the grass they have touched; nothing stops them, neither fire, torrents, lakes, nor morasses.

The greatest rock gives them but a slight check; they go round it, and then resume their march directly without the least division. If they meet a peasant they persist in their course, and jump as high as his knees in defense of their progress. They are so fierce as to lay hold of a stick and suffer themselves to be swung about before they quit their hold. If struck they turn about and bite, and will make a noise like a dog. Foxes, lynxes, and ermines follow them in great numbers, and at length they perish, either through want of food, or by destroying one another, or in some great water or in the sea. They are the dread of the country, and in former times spiritual weapons were exerted against them; the priest exorcised them, and had a long form of prayer to arrest the evil." So wrote Thomas Pennant,[174] more than a century ago; and it forms a vivid illustration of the way in which rodents would devastate the earth were it not for the constant repression exercised by their natural enemies the carnivores.

Scandinavia suffers most because that peninsula has comparatively few flesh-eating animals to police her valleys. Mr. Crotch supplies an interesting detail, showing how unfit these little animals are to endure their ill-considered journeys: "On calm mornings my lake, which is a mile in width, was often thickly studded with swimming lemmings, every head pointed westward, . . . and never did frailer barks tempt a more treacherous sea, as the wind swept daily down the valley, and wrecked all who were then afloat. It was impossible not to feel pity for these self-haunted fugitives. A mere cloud passing over the sun affrighted them; the approach of horse, cow, dog, or man alike roused their impotent anger, and their little bodies were convulsively pressed against the never failing stone of vantage whilst they uttered cries of rage."

Muskrat. The American muskrat is only a big vole, adapted to a thoroughly aquatic career, but is one of the most celebrated and noteworthy of our quadrupeds; it is to be met with throughout the whole continent, to which it is peculiar, but not south of Arizona. That of Newfoundland and the muskrat of the Dismal Swamp, in Virginia, are called distinct species by the specialists.

Although so widely distributed and abundant, the muskrat is not often seen, as it is mainly nocturnal in its habits, and during the day remains in its burrow or house especially when it fears it will be observed. Its home either is built of sticks, mud, and grass, and forms a heap the size and appearance of a small haycock, or else is dug out of the bank of a stream or pond as a burrow, the entrance to which is under water. Where there is an extensive swamp, or stretch of shallow water, so that the houses will not be ordinarily exposed to wandering enemies, muskrats seem to prefer them; but where they live in or about a narrow stream, with little swamp, the bank burrow is the usual shelter. This is sometimes only a few feet in length, and often has a concealed land entrance as well as a subaqueous one. The houses are always entered through the basement from water deep enough not to freeze to the bottom in winter; and are usually swept away by the spring freshets, so that a new one must be erected each autumn.

Brownell, Phot.

THE AMERICAN MUSKRAT.

The muskrat is omnivorous, eating roots (especially of the pond lily), fruits, vegetables, insects, worms, mollusks, etc., and is especially fond of sweet corn and apples, in search of which it often wanders far from its home, and finds its way occasionally into barns and cellars. In some localities fresh-water mussels are a favorite article of food, and large heaps of the empty shells are sometimes found near musk-rat burrows, due to their preference for dining day after day in the same place. In some places, and irregularly, probably, they store up in their habitations considerable quantities of apples, lily roots and similar provender.

The body of the muskrat is about a foot long, and the tail eight inches. The animal is rather stout and thick set, the head is rounded, and the ears are small and close. The front feet are rather small, while the hind feet are stout, with five partially webbed toes, well fitted for swimming, yet the sculling movement of the much-compressed tail is the principal means of progress in the water. The pelage consists, as is usual with aquatic mammals, of an under coat of dense soft fur and an outer coat on the back and sides, chiefly of long, dark, shining, smooth hairs which are pulled out when the pelt is dressed. So much air is held by these outer hairs that in ordinary excursions the under fur is hardly wetted. The color above is dark umber brown, darkest on the middle of the back and on the tail, while beneath the prevailing shade is gray. The musky odor from which the animal gets its name is due to the secretion of a large gland between the thighs, which is present in both sexes; and to similar secretion, excessive in amount, is due the name "muskrat" applied in India to a very different animal, — a large shrew (*Crocidura*).

Brownell, Phot.

A MUSKRAT'S DINING-TABLE.

Showing an accumulation of mussel shells (Unio), the remains of many meals.

The flesh of the muskrat is good eating and was formerly much used by the Indians; and the skins form an important item in the fur trade. Hence muskrats are extensively trapped, chiefly in the winter, by setting small steel traps at the entrance to their houses or burrows or in runways where they come ashore, and hundreds of thousands are killed annually. Their numbers nevertheless do not decrease, partly because their natural enemies are now fewer, but chiefly because of the fact that the making of slack-water spaces, by damming rivers and the digging of canals (whose banks they seriously damage), have greatly extended waters suitable for them in various parts of the country.

Another housebuilder is the wood rat, of which one sort is not uncommon in the woods of the Appalachian region, another on the Gulf coast, and others in the Rocky Mountains. About the size of house rats, their hairy tails, larger

Pack Rat.

ears, thick, soft fur, and redder tinge sufficiently distinguish them. They live in wild places and gather masses of sticks, shredded bark, and other stuff into a nest often of considerable size and shapeliness; and Western men call them pack rats.

"These animals," Hornaday tells us, "are nocturnal, and their nest-building and other work is done at night. The most remarkable thing about them is their habit of entering houses and playing practical jokes upon the inmates. A pair of wood rats that I knew by reputation at Oak Lodge, in Florida, first carried a lot of watermelon seeds from the ground floor upstairs and hid them under a pillow. Then they took from the kitchen a tablespoonful of cucumber seeds and placed them in the pocket of a vest which hung upstairs on a nail. In one night they removed from a box eighty-five pieces of beehive fixtures, and hid them in another box, and on the following night they deposited in the first box about two quarts of corn and oats. Western frontiersmen and others who live in the land of the wood rat relate stories innumerable of the absurd but industrious doings of these strange creatures."

The bushy tailed pack rat, in particular, makes the acquaintance of every settler and is quick to adapt the conveniences of cabin or barn, or a roadside mail box, to his ideas of comfort. He is not altogether welcome, however, for he is rather too frequent and bold in his visits to house and pantry, stealing and dragging to his own stores all sorts of small articles, as well as a great accumulation of grain, fruit, leaves, and the like, little of which he really needs. But otherwise he is a harmless little creature, as pretty, cleanly, and lively as a squirrel. This species occurs from Utah to the Yukon Valley; other species range southward into Mexico.

This wood rat is a large edition of that exquisite little wanderer, the white-footed mouse, the many species of which compose the genus Peromyscus, and form a charming band, peculiarly North American. They are the graceful, large-eared "deer" mice of our woodlands often seen about country houses,

White-foot Mouse. and are richly fawn-color above, with pure white under parts and feet. The common whitefoot is active, agile, hardy, and has as miscellaneous a bill of fare as a red squirrel, eating all sorts of seeds, thin-shelled nuts, berries, small fruits, insects, and scraps of flesh and bone. These mice are largely responsible for the disappearance of cast horns

EASTERN WHITE-FOOTED WOOD MOUSE.

of deer, and of animal skeletons left in the woods. "Like squirrels," remarks Cram,[52] of New England examples, "they often find a way into granaries and farmhouses in search of food, particularly in the winter, when times are hard; for though they lay up generous stores of nuts and seeds, and hibernate to a certain extent, large numbers of them are up and doing at all times in spite of the weather." Elliot's "Synopsis" recorded in 1901 no less than forty-two alleged species in North America; and several other populous genera are closely allied. Related mice well known in the South are the cotton rat and rice-field mouse, while the American harvest mice are widespread in the West. In the Old World occur the large and interesting hamsters (Cricetus) whose skins make pretty robes, etc.; and in South America the extraordinary, aquatic, fish-eating rats of the genus Icthyomys, recalling the Australian beaver rats.

Africa possesses many exclusive groups and genera, of which

only a few can be noted. One of the most unusual is the large webber or crested rat of the eastern half of that continent, whose long harsh hair forms a roach of bristles on the back and tail, so that the animal resembles a miniature porcupine. We

know little of its habits except that in Arabia it sits upon its haunches and whistles, and climbs wild date palms to feed on the fruit. The deserts of Africa and Arabia are also the home of gerbilles of many species — small mice with jerboalike appearance and habits.

So distinct from the foregoing rats and mice as to constitute a separate family

Shepheard-Walwyn, Phot.
A HIBERNATING DORMOUSE.

are the dormice, which in some of their many forms are found in Africa, Asia, and Europe, but not in America. Typical of the group is the European dormouse, which is much like our whitefoot in habits and food, but is more nocturnal and looks like a miniature squirrel. An English correspondent, Mr. H. W. Shepheard-Walwyn, favors me with the following notes on this celebrated sleeper: —

"This quaint little animal spends some six months of the year wrapped in a profound sleep. Motionless — save for the rhythmical heaving of the furry body as it draws its deep, long breaths — the sleeper is by no means silent, inasmuch as its wee nostrils emit a terrific snoring, which can even be heard across a fair-sized room. The specimen here depicted included a small but shrill note in its somnolent wheeze, and the noise which it produced by this means was really tremendous, considering the diminutive size of the animal. Cold to the touch, and apparently lifeless, the little yellow body might, to all intents and purposes, be that of a cold-blooded animal; and it has even been rolled about the room without attempting to uncurl its tightly folded form or evincing the faintest signs of returning animation. Naught but the voice of summer — barring such artificial methods as exposure to a hot fire — will open again the great, pathetic eyes, for all the world like a couple of black boot-buttons, or rouse into being the active life which lies dormant within the sluggish limbs."

Squirrels, Scaletails, Prairie Dogs, Woodchucks, and Beavers

In this third company of the rodents we shall find many familiar and engaging friends, — none more so than the squir-

Brownell, Phot.

SAUCY RED SQUIRREL.

rels, — agile, graceful, alert, curious, full of business, noisy, irascible, "fat and sassy," finding their home in the trees, under the double umbrage of the foliage and their own shady tails. These long, bushy tails, curving so gracefully over the back, forming so warm a blanket when wrapped about the sleeping owner, and always so expressive, are the badge and pride of the tribe. In color, squirrels range from gray, with black varieties frequent, through various browns and foxy reds to the deep chestnut or orange markings of some Oriental and Mexican beauties; and in general are so variable that too eager naturalists have been misled into giving specific names to hundreds of mere varieties. Even now no less than ten geographic races of our red squirrel alone are recognized.

This common species illustrates the contrast between summer and winter coloration prevalent in this family. In summer the red squirrels are truly foxy red all over the upper parts, and snowy white on the under surfaces, with only a faint suggestion of a dark line along the side separating the two color areas; but this is replaced in winter by a new coat of yellowish gray, divided from the dull white of the belly by a prominent black band, and only along the spine is there any redness. The young, usually born in April, are reddish, and the black side band is strongly marked. Squirrels seem also peculiarly sensitive to climatic influences, especially of excessive dryness or moisture, as affecting both their colors and form.

EUROPEAN COMMON SQUIRREL.

Squirrels inhabit hollows in trunks of trees or among their roots, make globular summer nests of leafy twigs on lofty branches, and bear once a year about four young, which remain with the mother until the ensuing autumn or spring. Nuts form their staple food, but berries, fruits, roots, funguses, insect-grubs, etc., offer changes in fare with the recurring seasons. Sometimes great ingenuity is displayed in getting at this food; for instance, the black-tailed northwestern variety of the red squirrel called Richardson's, feeds almost exclusively on the seeds of pine and fir, especially the whitebark.

"The scales of the cones are very thick, and are firmly glued together instead of being separate as usual among conifers. To reach the seeds the squirrel gnaws a hole in one side of the cone by means of which he extracts all of the seeds, just as our eastern squirrels obtain the meats of the larger nuts. . . . Squirrels ordinarily reach the seeds of conifers by stripping off the scales from the cones." [113]

Carnivorous tastes prevail among them, and trappers are constantly annoyed by these little meddlers springing the traps baited with flesh for martens and the like. Some species are arrant robbers of birds' nests, and now and then kill and eat small birds and mammals; and the older males are resolutely kept away from their babies by the mothers for fear of their teeth. This catholic appetite, and their willingness to wander from place to place in search of things seasonable, enable squirrels to find food of some sort every month of the year, yet most species have the forethought to lay up in more or less secret places a winter supply of provender; consequently no species (of Sciurus) hibernates, strictly speaking. Their pretty way of sitting up on their great haunches and holding a nut in the fore paws while they cut through its shell, is characteristic of the tribe. Their fur, especially of the big Siberian species, is an important article in commerce; and their flesh is eaten largely in all of the colder countries.

Any detailed account of our eastern squirrels is needless, but some western species are less well known. Familiar in **Western Squirrels.** California and Oregon is the sprightly Douglas squirrel, in summer olive-brown with orange breast and feet; there is a black lateral line, and the tail is reddish black above, fringed and lined with orange. In the Rocky Mountains lives Fremont's squirrel, which is mainly yellowish gray. A large tufted-eared relative of the Southwest is Abert's, found only in the lofty pine forests, the behavior of which has been portrayed by Dr. Merriam [112] : —

"It is common everywhere in the pines, and is particularly fond of the large seeds of *Pinus flexilis*. . . . It builds large covered nests of green pine branches, but also avails itself of holes in trunks. . . . On reaching the tree of its choice, it climbs to the very top and then, unlike any other squirrel with which I am familiar, crawls out to the small end of a branch about which it curls and remains motionless. When in this position it is exceedingly difficult to see, though considerably larger than our eastern gray squirrel; and even the white under side of the bushy tail is so coiled about the body as to aid in deceiving the observer. The long and handsome ear-tufts are shed in the spring, and the new ones do not attain their full growth until the early part of winter; hence specimens taken in summer have naked, or nearly naked, ears."

Sanborn, Phot.

MALABAR SQUIRREL.

Mexico and Central America have several species of their own, mostly brightly colored — none more so than the gray-backed, red-bellied one common in the mountains of eastern Mexico. Hornaday thinks, however, that the most attractive squirrel in the world is Prevost's of the Malay Peninsula, whose "colors form a beautiful pattern of gray, brown, black, white, and buff." Another of very striking coloration, — above bright chestnut brown with sides and abdomen yellow, — and the largest of its race, is the Malabar squirrel, inhabiting the hills of southern India. The common squirrel of England (and eastward to Japan) is nearly like our red squirrel in appearance with the important difference that its ears are heightened by a long fringe and pencil tip of stiff hairs.

The flying-squirrels form an allied arboreal group, in which the furry hide is extended in a loose flap or cloak to the feet, and, in various Oriental species, also from the wrists to the neck, and from the ankles to the base of the tail.

This expansion forms a sort of parachute, or "patagium,"

sustaining the creature in the air when he spreads his limbs and makes his long leaps. We call it flight, but "sailing" is a more exact word, because there is no power of accelerating the speed, and little of changing direction; hence these animals may properly be regarded as offshoots of a wingless stock, which have developed the skin expansions as an aid in leaping, until now the smaller species will glide one hundred feet or so from some high limb to a lower one in another tree, and the big East Indian round-tailed ones much farther. A recent discovery is that among the cliffs of the high

Fisher, Phot.

AMERICAN FLYING-SQUIRREL.

western Himalayas lives a woolly flying-squirrel eighteen inches long, exclusive of the tail; and it was first described from a skin long used as a robe in a baby's perambulator at Simla!

There is to be found in Africa, only, a flying-squirrel so different in structure and relationships that it is held to represent a separate order by some zoölogists,—the anomalurus or "scaletail." Externally it looks much like an ordinary one; but its dentition is different, the cartilaginous support of the patagium extends from the elbow instead of from the wrist; and especially the under base of the tail is coated with a series of stiff, overlapping scales thought to be helpful in climbing. More lately a similar African animal has been discovered, peculiar in having almost no patagium, and considered by Lydekker [65] as representing the ancestral form from which sprang these queer imitators of our northern type.

Anomalurus.

Our own flying-squirrels are scattered all over North America south of Hudson Bay, and are numerous, but so secretive and nocturnal as to be rarely seen. They lodge in **Flying-squirrel.** holes and crannies of decaying tree trunks, — often in old woodpecker nests, — where they make warm beds of soft materials, including much of their own shed fur. Frequently they come into the garrets of houses built near woods, and are likely to gather into communities. Their food is the smaller sorts of nuts and berries, together with many insects, and they have a strong taste for meat, catching and killing birds and robbing their nests. Whether or not they hibernate seems to be determined in each case (or with many other animals) by the circumstances as to a winter supply of food. At any rate,

Fisher, Phot.

FLYING-SQUIRREL AT HOME.

while the smaller, more southerly, variety seems usually to sleep in winter, even where the climate is not excessively cold, those of Canada and the Adirondacks will remain active throughout the much colder winter whenever they live in forests yielding beechnuts and similar provender in plenty. They are almost the softest, "cutest" animals in creation; have too little intelligence to show much fear of man, often, indeed, seeking his hospitality; cuddle in one's pocket or bosom with loving content; and exhibit the most charming activity in a spacious cage, or when turned loose in a room in the evening. Nevertheless, they are likely to be mischievous and destructive unless kept well under control. Entertaining accounts of their tricks and manners wild and tame have been written by Audubon,[90] Kennicott,[56]

447

Merriam,[48] Cram,[100] and in *The American Naturalist* for 1873 and 1883.

    The ground squirrels are members of a group of genera well represented in all countries, which dwell in burrows in the

Chip-munk. ground instead of in holes or nests in trees, and have acquired a trimness of form, slenderness or brevity of tail, and other traits, such as small close ears and eyes, strong claws and teeth, cheek pouches, etc., adapted to their career as miners. Our lively chipmunks and spermophiles, and the

COMMON EASTERN CHIPMUNK.

similar susliks of Russia, are good examples. Africa abounds in ground squirrels (genus Xerus), having a fur so harsh that in some species real spines are scattered among the hairs. All dig elaborate tunnels in the soil, in which to breed in summer and secrete themselves in winter, and make extensive stores of imperishable food upon which to subsist, hidden but not hibernating, during the months when the woods are bare and the ground is frozen and snowy. Thus protected from enemies and from famine, they are able to survive numerously even in the midst of civilization, and provide a constant supply of flesh for carnivorous mammals, birds, and reptiles.

The storing of winter provender is a feature of animal economy well worth consideration. It has been forced upon small animals wherever the climate, either by reason of cold, snowy winters or very hot, dry summers, causes an annual failure of the food supply for a time. A moment's thought will show how, by the falling of the leaves, the drying of bark, the death of green herbage, and the hardening and burial of land and water under ice and snow, a northern winter cuts off more or less completely all means of making a living from most of the smaller rodents and from various other animals. If regions with such a climate are to retain their animals, some extraordinary means must be found for avoiding or enduring this season. The insects die, but leave inert larvæ to revive in the ensuing spring and so continue the race. Many of the lower animals, as snails, reptiles, etc., go into the ground or the mud of swamps and ponds and rest in a more or less torpid condition. Fishes and the aquatic life generally seek the deeper parts of their home waters, and exist beneath the ice, or go down to lake or sea. Most of the insect-eating birds migrate to southern regions, where food is constantly procurable.

None of these methods is wholly available to the nervous, warm-blooded mammals, which, unless they have acquired a strength, hardihood, and breadth of taste which belong to only a few of the rodents, must either be able to go into the cold-trance of hibernation or else save enough from their plenty of autumn to keep them alive during the following months of famine. The same difficulty arises from opposite causes in deserts, where the excessive drought and heat of midsummer destroy the food of some mammals so completely that they must go into a heat trance (estivation) or else, like the mole rat, must stock their burrows with enough bulbs or other proper edibles to last them until the next rains begin.

I have never seen any explanation of this foresighted habit, but it must have arisen in such a way as this: It is the natural custom of most ground-keeping animals not mere grazers to take as much of their food as they well can to some favorite eating place. This practice is observable in a wide range of creatures, and is prompted by various motives, of which the strongest, no doubt, is the desire for security from robbers and enemies; also in some cases the sharing of the meal with their family. Now one of the foremost characteristics of animal conduct is the desire to do things by rule, — to go accustomed rounds and repeat acts and operations in precisely the same way. Hence the habit of seeking the same place for a regularly recurring purpose, like eating, will be quickly confirmed, especially in such animals as these rodents, which have acquired the ability and practice of making and living in permanent burrows or houses. They are feebly endowed with powers either for defense or for escape outside their homes, and when gathering their food must not loiter much to eat as they go, but must pick up what they can carry and hasten to the safety of their doorways. This is the reason why surviving species of such animals have acquired cheek pouches, in which they can transport a fair meal of their food to be eaten at home at leisure.

Origin of Food Storing.

During the larger part of the year food is scant, and these rodents get into the way of picking up every bit they can find, and some seem so restless and energetic that they bring to their homes quantities of things not edible, as we have seen in the account of the viscacha. Similar instances of a habit of accumulating stuff, edible and otherwise, may be found among birds of the crow tribe and elsewhere, but it has not been developed among them beyond the careless, accidental stage which makes the action miserly rather than thrifty. In the case of our store-saving mice, hamsters, beavers, and their ilk, however, necessity and advantage together have led to a far more advanced

THE GRAY SQUIRREL.

451

development of the habit, until finally it has crystallized into an instinct of self-preservation.

The process of acquirement may have been something like this: Remembering that the search for food is the foremost anxiety and occupation of these little creatures, it would be increasingly stimulated as the ripening season of the seeds and nuts on which they depend advanced, and the impulse to incessant industry, so necessary in the poorer parts of the year, would now be overworked, and each animal, in his haste to be up and doing, would constantly bring home more food than would be consumed, so that it would pile up in the accustomed "dining room." The gradual failure of outdoor supplies, as winter came on, would lead to the eating, with increasing frequency, of those fragments casually saved in and about the burrow or house, which, from their nature, would not have decayed. The animal which had been most busy and clever in food gathering would own the largest amount of the leavings of these autumnal feasts. Having the most food he would be among those of the colony or neighborhood strongest and most likely to survive, and to give to his offspring the tendency to strength and industry which had been his salvation. This would be continued and shaped by the process of natural selection into a valuable, instinctive habit of gathering food in large quantities as winter provender.

Another noticeable point in the habits of these miners is this: Although often the very image of nervous activity, these and other burrowing animals shut themselves for long periods into almost air-tight apartments under ground, and yet seem to suffer no harm; but it is possible the scarcity of oxygen, or, rather, the accumulation of carbonic elements, may aid in inducing the trance of hibernation, to be considered when we come to the marmots.

As to the ways of the chipmunks (ground squirrels of the genus Tamias), and of the "gray gophers" or prairie ground squirrels (genus Spermophilus) of the western plains, one cannot speak here in much detail. Our literature[103] abounds in accounts of them, and every one may easily learn their ways for himself by a little useful observation, since there is no lack of specimens. As our eastern chipmunk is the genius of the rail fences and stone walls that bound the country lanes, so is his four-striped western brother **Western Ground Squirrels.** of the woods and thickets of the Rocky Mountains. The moment one camps anywhere these delightful little visitors will introduce themselves with an air as chipper as their voice,

and become as entertaining as they are saucy. Many's the night I have had them dancing all over me as I lay rolled in my blankets under the tall yellow pines of the midland, or the spruces of the higher mountain shoulders; or have been awakened as they dashed across my face by the soft pricking of tiny toe nails. Similarly in California and

Carlin, Phot.
WESTERN GROUND SQUIRREL.

Oregon (where, according to Merriam and his hair-splitting school of systemists, there is a different "species" in almost every line of hills), the vagabond camper is investigated with friendly impudence not only by many kinds of chipmunks and pine squirrels, but by the lovely golden-backed spermophile.

"In camp," writes an explorer of Mt. Shasta, "they made frequent visits to the mess box, which they clearly regarded as public property, approaching it boldly and without suspicion, and showing no concern at our presence — in marked contrast to the golden-mantled squirrels, which approached silently, stealthily, and by a circuitous route, in constant fear of detention. If disturbed while stuffing their cheek pouches with bits of bread, pancake, or other eatables, each chipmunk usually seized a large piece in its mouth and scampered off, returning as soon as we withdrew. In fact, they made themselves perfectly at home in camp."

All the large Plains gophers (spermophiles) are gregarious, and dig extensive burrows so that they are a serious pest to both cultivators and grazers, and must be dealt with by poisoning or otherwise. Their most complete biographies have been written by Coues [106] and by Bailey.[68, 114.]

Closely related to the ground squirrels are the prairie dogs, — a name given by the early French explorers and trappers of **Prairie Dog.** the West, more from their cheerful, puppylike actions, I suspect, than from their cry, which could hardly be called "barking"; yet Lewis and Clark, who first described the animal formally, called it "barking squirrel." It is a denizen of the dry plains east of the Rockies, while two or three other species inhabit the mountains, the Utah basin, and southward into Mexico. This animal is sometimes confused towards the north with the larger gray gophers, especially the Columbian and Franklin's, so that we wrongly hear of "prairie dogs" on the Canadian plains; it is to be distinguished by its slightly larger size, distinctly brownish color, and very short tail (two inches), which is flat and black toward the end.

The prairie dog is about a foot long, and robust, with strong limbs and claws. It dwells in colonies, whose permanent "towns" or burrows, each marked by a hillock of earth about the entrance, spread densely over many acres under the natural prehistoric conditions, but now sometimes cover hundreds of square miles. The burrows are deep and extensive, and at first go down at a very steep slope to a depth of twelve to fifteen feet, when they turn horizontally, and here and there branch into chambers, some of which are family rooms, while in others fodder is stored, or refuse and dung are deposited. The mound about the hole is packed hard, not only by the tramping of the animals, but by crowding it down with their noses; this hillock prevents water from running into the burrows when the plain is flooded by heavy rains, and also serves as a tower of observation. Following is an account of their habits and evil work which I prepared from original sources for the *New International Encyclopedia*, and which covers the subject in a condensed way: —

"The prairie dogs feed upon grass and herbage, which is soon exhausted near the burrows, compelling the animals to go farther and farther away for food. This they dislike to do, as it exposes them to attack from enemies; and after a time they prefer to dig a new burrow nearer a supply of food. Thus a 'town' is always spreading and contains many empty burrows. Like other animals habituated to desert regions, they do not drink at all, and the early belief that subterranean pits were dug by them, down to a water supply, has been proved erroneous. Artesian wells within dog towns have failed to strike water as often as elsewhere. The animals are diurnal and most active morning and evening. They come out daily during the winter, except when it is very stormy; but this practice varies with the latitude and climate.

Brownell, Phot.

A PRAIRIE DOG AT THE MOUTH OF HIS BURROW.

"They are prolific, especially in the southern half of their territory, and would multiply with excessive rapidity were it not for numerous enemies, especially rattlesnakes and other serpents. These are courageously resisted by the prairie dogs, who sound the alarm the moment a snake enters a hole, gather, and proceed to fill the entrance with earth, packing it down, thereby sometimes entombing the snake forever. Probably few snakes go down the passages, which are so steep they could with difficulty climb out, but depend upon lying hidden in the grass and striking down the young squirrels when out at play or in search of food. This is the method of the coyote, kit fox, wild cat, hawks, and owls, who find the dog towns a profitable hunting ground. Badgers, however, can, if they will, easily dig up a burrow and devour the helpless family. The worst enemy is the black-footed ferret, a weasel of the plains, which easily penetrates the burrows, and against whose ferocity and skill the squirrels can make little defense. Every prairie dog town is also tenanted by many little burrowing owls.

"All these conditions together served in the natural state of things to hold the prairie dogs in check, but the changes brought about by civilization have been so favorable to these little animals, by the reduction **A Pest.** of their enemies on the one hand, and the augmentation on the other hand of their food supplies by the farmers' plantations of meadow grass, alfalfa, and grain, that they have increased into a very serious pest. Dr. Merriam stated in the *Yearbook* of the United States Department of Agriculture for 1901 that colonies twenty to thirty miles in length were then not rare; and one in Texas was known to cover an area of twenty-five hundred square miles, with a probable average of twenty-five holes to an acre and of one animal to each hole. At this rate the prairie-dog population of this district would be forty millions; and on the carefully studied estimate of students that two hundred and fifty squirrels will devour annually the same amount of grass as a cow, the pasturage consumed by this great colony would support over 1,500,000 cattle. When such a colony spreads over a district devoted to farming, the loss is increased, for the space occupied by their mounds is a waste of valuable land; the animals are likely to cut irrigation canals, draining off the water, and they devour the planted crops, especially of alfalfa. Both the federal government and local authorities have tried various methods for relief, but are almost helpless in view of the large spaces between cultivated districts, where the pest can only be overcome by public and united effort, and also by coöperation among the ranchmen. The squirrels may be killed by poison in various ways; but best by the use of bisulphide of carbon. A teaspoonful of this cheap liquid is placed upon some absorbent substance (a nodule of dry horse dung or half a corncob will serve the purpose well), and dropped down the hole, which should then be stopped with earth. The fumes are heavy, sink into the depths of the burrow, and kill the inhabitants."

These ground squirrels and prairie dogs naturally bridge the gap between the tree squirrels and the marmots, as they are styled in the Old World, or "woodchucks," as we **Marmots.** know them in the northern states, or "ground hogs," as they call them in the South. Marmots are of stouter build than gophers or susliks, with short, strong limbs, broad heads, no cheek pouches, short ears and tail, the first toe of the fore foot rudimentary, and rather harsh fur of a uniform grayish, reddish, or yellowish tint, deepening to blackish along the spine. In Europe there are two species, the big (twenty inches) Alpine marmot, and the lesser bobac of Russia and Siberia; several more kinds inhabit central Asia north of India.

"The districts inhabited by all the marmots of the Old World," says Lydekker, "are desolate and barren; being in most cases scorched with fierce heat in summer, while in winter they are subject to intense cold. . . . The occurrence of fossil remains of the alpine marmot in many parts of Europe . . . leads to the conclusion that western Europe had at one time a more or less steppe-like climate. As milder and more genial climatic conditions supervened, the alpine marmot gradually retreated to the nearest mountain ranges; and we thus have a complete explanation of its present isolated distributional areas. The habits of all the marmots of the Old World appear to be very similar; all the species of these animals living in large companies, and excavating burrows in which they pass the whole of the winter buried in profound slumber. . . . All the species are diurnal in their habits; and their food is purely of a vegetable nature, consisting mainly of roots, seeds, and leaves of various plants. In the Himalaya the burrows are very generally constructed beneath the shelter of a plant of the wild rhubarb; and the tenants on a fine day take up their station on the mound at the entrance, or journey for a short distance in search of food. At the least alarm they rush at once to the entrance of their burrow, while they sit up on their hindquarters to survey the scene and detect the danger. If the enemy approach too close, the loud whistling scream is uttered, and

A MARMOT.

the animal dives headlong into its burrow. . . . The flesh of marmots is said to be of good flavor, and is largely consumed by the inhabitants of the Siberian Steppes."

To this company belong our American woodchucks, and one of them, the Rocky Mountain "siffleur" or whistler, is a larger **Wood-** counterpart of the Alpine marmot, whose wild **chuck.** eerie whistle seems the voice of the spirit of the windy solitudes above timber line, where it makes its home. It is hunted eagerly by Indians for both its flesh and its fur.

Brownell, Phot.

THE WOODCHUCK.

Our sober eastern "ground hog," however, has forsaken the prairie-dwelling traditions of the tribe and taken to the woodlands, whither he is likely to retire for his winter refuge, even after spending a summer in open fields. He is to be found everywhere east of the Plains, except along the Gulf coast, and northward to Labrador; other species of larger size occur west of the Plains and in the wooded Canadian Northwest. The habits of all of them are much the same as those of their cousins across the sea, and abound in queer, comical ways. The woodchuck affords a most striking example of hibernation; that is, the going into a deep sleep in winter, as a means of passing safely that part of the year.

When the temperature sinks below a certain figure the vital energy of certain animals becomes so diminished that they fall into a more or less profound torpor. Semper's pet prairie dogs (living in Germany) began to get drowsy at about 48° F. As the sleep deepens, the temperature of the body falls nearly to that of the surrounding air. Howath, quoted by Semper,[107] found that one of his zizels (ground squirrels), when hibernating in a room cooled down to 2° C. (35.6° F.), had a bodily temperature exactly the same; and another in a room 9° to 10° C. had a temperature of 8.4° C. or 46.1° F. As the ordinary blood warmth of these animals in active life is about 100° F., it will be seen, as Semper remarks, that "during their winter sleep warm-blooded animals become cold-blooded"; and he adds that only such as are able to effect this change can become hibernaters. The true cold-blooded animals, and especially their eggs and young, can survive much lower temperatures than the warm-blooded ones, even to being partly frozen; but no warm-blooded one can endure that. Hence the hibernating mammals, to which we are now confining our attention, place themselves in situations protected from severe cold by digging deeply into the ground, or creeping within hollow logs or stumps, and surrounding themselves with blankets of dry leaves, grass, and so forth. Moreover, all are warmly clothed in fur, then at its longest and best condition. These things tend to keep the bodily warmth up to the low measure needed by the reduced necessities of their inactive condition. But during this time, in the real hibernaters, which lay up no stores of food, nothing is eaten, so that no fuel is received to be converted into bodily heat by the oxidation of the blood through breathing; on the contrary, the lungs almost cease to work. There is an occasional respiration, — a sighing inhalation of breath, — but the most of the time the only oxygen which enters the lungs is the trifle reaching them by the effect of the slow beating of the heart, and by the process of the diffusion of gases. A mirror held before an animal in this condition is not clouded by its breath. The creature may be placed under water, or in a jar of carbonic acid gas, for an hour or more, and will not drown nor be suffocated; nevertheless, respiration and other functions do not wholly cease.

What, then, supplies even the meager warmth required? It is the slow absorption and combustion of the fat stored up under the skin by the abundant feeding in the summer and autumn. That this is so, is shown by the fact that when they come out in the spring they are thin and weak; curiously too, their awakening is followed by a period of failure, when they become so emaciated that often a late storm will kill them before they begin to pick up by voracious feeding. Their awakening must be gradual, too — the sudden forcible arousing of hibernaters, as by sudden warmth or handling or electric shocks, is likely to cause their death. Here a curious fact may be mentioned: in spite of their comatose condition, — which has been equaled by human beings in a trance state, — they are sensitive to the slightest touch; merely blowing on the hair will induce an instantaneous response, although not in the least arousing the sleeper.

The period of hibernation varies not only with different kinds of animals, but with the same kinds under different or even the same circumstances. One woodchuck experimented upon by Dr. Mills,[108] though kept (in Canada) under precisely the same conditions as others which slept profoundly, "did not hibernate for an hour the whole winter, though he drowsed and slept enough."

In spite of so much data we must confess that we are not yet certain what really causes this winter sleep; but that it is of a

THE AMERICAN BEAVER.

highly protective character cannot be doubted, since the true hibernaters are those whose food altogether fails in winter, and which is of such a nature that it could not be stored up, at least in sufficient quantity. Dr. A. S. Packard has discussed the whole subject ably in his article "Hibernation," in the New International Encyclopedia.

The beaver! How shall I tell of him and his works in the few pages at my command; and how keep you interested without repeating or even enlarging the marvelous tales upon which his reputation rests?

Beaver.

In the first place, this big water squirrel — for so he is, just as the muskrat is a giant among the meadow mice — is not wholly American, but a native of the north of the Old World as well. None has been known wild in England since historic records began; but their bones show that they must have been common enough there when the Roman pioneers landed, and they lingered in Scotland and Wales, according to Harting,[109] until the twelfth century. On the continent they fared much better. A century ago they swam and worked in most of the larger German, French, and Austrian streams, and are not yet quite exterminated there, though the Swiss and Italian lakes, where they were so numerous in the days of the Neolithic lake dwellers, know them no more. It is less than a century since the animal abounded in Poland and western Russia, in the Caucasus, and even among the upper valleys of the Euphrates; but they are now scarce even in the remoter rivers of Siberia, whence formerly came bales of their skins. Everywhere, in fact, they may be said to exist only by the protection of some powerful landowner.

Whether these European beavers, called *Castor fiber*, are really a different species from our *Castor canadensis*, is a matter of dispute, and of small importance; to all intents and purposes they are the same.

This is only one of many examples of substantial identity in the animal life of North America and Eurasia. The brown bear, gray wolf, white and red foxes, sable, lynx, certain seals and cetacea, bison, wapiti, moose (elk), bighorn, beaver, lemming; many falcons, owls, sea birds and shore birds of many kinds, waxwings and several finches; and certain fishes, especially of the salmon family, — are prominent examples of cases in which convenience, rather scientific candor, causes separate species to be named. The reason of this identity, of course, is the nearness of the two continents to each other in the far north, and the fact that they have actually been connected since modern forms of animal life arose, so that the ancestors of these now separated races were presumably a continuous stock in the North, where we know a milder climate existed in the Tertiary period than at present. No department of natural history is more interesting or enlightening than that of the distribution of plants and animals on the face of the earth; and the relation of this distribution, past and present, to the habits and habitats of the several groups and species.

In America our beaver seems to have dwelt everywhere that suitable woods grew and waters ran, from northern Florida and the mountains of Mexico, northward as far as birch and willow trees grow. As for one hundred and fifty years its fur has been one of the most highly valued spoils of the trapper, and only recently, and in the more civilized parts of the continent, has its getting been at all restricted by law, it is not strange to learn that the animal survives only in a few isolated colonies east of the northern Rockies and south of the Canadian wilderness. That any are left is due, probably, more to the disuse, half a century ago, of its fur in hat making, following the invention of silk hats, than to anything else. Even now fifteen to twenty thousand skins a year are collected by the Hudson Bay and other fur companies, which, however, are now taking precautions against diminution of the supply by setting apart certain islands in northern Canada as preserves.

The beaver is the largest of the rodents except the capybara, is about two feet long, without the tail, and weighs thirty to thirty-five pounds. As it is a dweller in cold waters, it has an exceedingly fine, close fur, with a dense under fleece and a thick skin which, when stripped off, forms an almost round mat. Its hind feet are webbed and are powerful swimmers, while the fore feet are small and as handy as those of a squirrel. The great yellow chisels of the front teeth are always sharp, and the tail is a most interesting organ; it is about a foot long, very strong, and expands into a flattened, oval mass of fatty tissue, clothed in a lustrous black horny skin that looks as if scaled.

This remarkable tail has been called a trowel, and has been described as used to spread and pat the mud plastered upon the dams and lodges; also that it serves as a sledge which the other beavers load, and thus haul earth and stone. In reality, it is of great service in swimming and diving, and the loud slap it may give as an alarmed beaver dives acts as an effective signal of danger; but it takes no part in the constructive work. The food of the beaver is wholly vegetable, and mainly the bark of deciduous trees, especially birch, poplar, and maple — never of evergreens; but the bulbous roots of lilies and other aquatic plants are also well liked.

A beaver colony begins with the settlement upon some woodland water, in midsummer, of a pair of young immigrants. Their first work is to dig a burrow in the bank, **Dams and** entered from beneath the water. This done, two **Lodges.** conditions are needful to maintaining the homestead: one is that there must remain enough water in front of the burrow to cover the entrance, and bar out such enemies as wild cats and foxes, and the other, that the water must be too deep to freeze

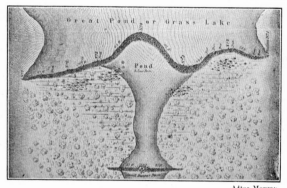

After Morgan.

MAP OF THE GREAT BEAVER DAM AT GRASS LAKE, MINN., IN 1830.

to the bottom. As the lowering waste of late summer admonishes them of danger in these directions, the beavers choose a point in their stream where the bottom is firm, and begin to make a dam high and strong enough to hold back the water at a proper height throughout the winter.

They start by cutting saplings leafy at the top, and dragging or floating them to the place. The current straightens these out, with the brushy tips downstream, and they are forced to the bottom and made to lie there by having stones and mud heaped upon them; it is astonishing what large stones the animals are able to roll and push into this service. This work is performed mainly at night, each animal doing what he thinks proper. The fine old stories of a superintendent who sets tasks, are as fanciful and untrue as the fable that they construct five-story houses, and make wattle-work like an Indian fish weir. They do nothing of the sort, but continue to heap up old sticks, earth, and stones anyhow, until they have formed some kind of a barrier, — always moving the materials with hands or teeth.

Now this dam is always begun in the center of the stream. If the current is slight, it will run straight across, but where the current is fast the dam is likely to show a decided curve on its upstream side. This has been represented as an intelligent employment of the strength of the arch form against the current; but more probably it is simply the result of the action of the stream pressing down the wings of the first, central, obstruction. The water does not pour over the top of these dams, but filters through them, and its washing necessitates constant repairs, which are made on the inner (or upper) face, leaving the outer front a mere tangle of sticks and poles. Sometimes, however, a short high dam will get so filled in with earth that it becomes a solid, tree-grown dike; and some relics of this kind may be several centuries old. The length of a dam, of course, depends upon its site. In a flat valley, the most advantageous situation for a beaver colony, a pond will broaden rapidly, and the original channel-barrier must be extended to prevent the water running out beyond its wings; and thus a few old dams in the level swampy woods about the sources of the Mississippi exceeded one hundred and twenty-five yards in length.

The young beavers of which I have spoken probably spent their first winter in a burrow, but when, next May, half a dozen young ones arrived, they would begin to build a lodge above ground. A beaver lodge is a hollow mound on the bank or on some islet, three or four feet high and eight or ten in outer diameter. It is erected in the same way as is the dam, of sticks, earth, and stones heaped around a hollow center, the floor of which is a little higher than the surface of the pond. As the dam grows and the pond expands and rises, the floor of the chamber is raised by hollowing out the interior overhead, and piling more stuff on the roof to equal the loss. It has two entrances, always beneath the water, for an opening into the air would admit both cold and enemies. The walls of such a lodge may be three feet thick and as solid as masonry. The beavers heap on patted mud, and drag over it astonishingly big limbs, so

A Wet Republic

BEAVERS AT WORK.

that when the mass freezes the enormous strength of a bear or wolverine is hardly able to break it down; but in summer both these marauders, and especially the latter, frequently tear it to pieces. The domed chamber within an old house will be six or seven feet in diameter, and in winter is snugly bedded with grass. Such a house stands a great many years — is a permanent habitation, in fact; but never contains at once more than one family, which consists of the parents and two successive broods of young; the third year the oldest youngsters leave, or are driven out to set up for themselves. In summer, however, when the babies are arriving, the old "buck" beavers all leave home and wander widely, keeping (or kept) away from their wives and little ones.

There is, then, no real community life, even in a large beaver colony, except in the ownership and care of the waterworks, and there each works as he pleases, though all share the benefit of his labors. Each separate family builds and repairs and occupies its own lodge, and provides its own store of food.

This food, as I have said, is mainly birch, poplar, and maple bark, and it can be obtained only by gnawing down trees. This **Food.** the beavers do as often as necessary, but mainly late in autumn, in preparation for the impending winter. At that season they attack large trees, — sometimes eighteen inches in diameter, — and gnaw them off by standing on their hind legs and biting all round them until they fall. Having felled a tree, the family busies itself in saving a store of bark for winter use. For this purpose the smaller brushy parts of the limbs are first cut off and dragged or floated nearly to the door of the house, where they are sunk to the bottom of the pond, and somehow fastened there. The larger limbs are then cut into manageable lengths and put into the same place; and there they stay until one by one, during the winter, they are dragged into the lodge and stripped for food. Then the denuded logs are thrown out and form the materials for repair work in the spring. This, as you will see, is hard work, and after the trees have been cut from near the bank of the stream the animals would be com-

pelled to leave it, were it not for further ingenuity in engineering. The continual raising and extension of the dam deepens and spreads the pond, and little by little makes fresh trees accessible; but the clever little woodsmen do more than this, for they dig regular canals, sometimes hundreds of feet in length, where the ground is low, in order to reach groves of desirable trees, and so get stores of bark out of reach were they obliged to carry it over-

After Morgan.

FOREST CANAL CUT BY BEAVERS.

land. There is perhaps no more useful part in the whole service of a beaver dam than the keeping full of these water roads, for they are the highways of both food and safety to the whole community.

The beaver was at the foundation of our national wealth, and is still one of the important objects of the fur hunter and trader. It has excited enormous interest, and has been made the subject of at least two special books.[110] Lately, many descriptive articles, illustrated by instructive photographs, have been printed in American magazines, but they seem to have added nothing beyond their pictures to the accurate and exhaustive studies of Morgan. These animals do well in the semicaptivity of park streams, and most zoölogical gardens, especially those at New York and Washington, contain flourishing colonies, while they have been successfully reintroduced into Great Britain on the estate of the Marquis of Bute and elsewhere.

The last to be mentioned of the rodents is a small and secluded group of animals of the northwestern coast of the United States, known in books by their Indian names sewellel and showtl, but locally in their Oregon home as mountain beavers, or boomers, — the last in reference to the hollow cry. They have some relationship to beavers, but are set apart by the latest students of their position into a superfamily Aplodontiæ. They are small, robust creatures, about a foot long, and are brownish, with close fur, short ears, minute eyes, very long stiff whiskers, and stubby tails. They dwell in colonies in wet mountain meadows, burrowing long tunnels through the marshy soil, making small heaps of sticks and rubbish, or "houses," above the principal entrance to the underground residence, and feeding on bark, herbs, roots, etc. Some of this seems to be stored, although they do not hibernate in winter, but come out daily, even in snowy times. Their flesh and fur were both highly valued by the Indians. These animals are nocturnal, shy, and not well known; but what has been learned of their habits may be found in the works of Coues and Allen,[267] J. K. Lord,[268] and in *The American Naturalist*, 1877, page 434, and 1878, page 10.

ANT-EATERS, SLOTHS, AND ARMADILLOS — Order, EDENTATA

It follows naturally from the rise of the animal world, as a whole, by development from simply organized forms to those more complex and specialized, that as we descend from higher groups to lower, we shall find the latter of more and more ancient stock. We have now arrived at the *Edentata*, among the lowest of the eutherian orders, and we find not only that their beginnings are lost in the obscurity of a very remote past, but that those now living are mere enfeebled remnants of an order formerly of leading importance. It is not surprising, then, to find also that all the edentates inhabit South America, since that is the most ancient and unchanged of all the continents, save Australia. A few sorts of ant-eaters, sloths, and armadillos, — small, frightened, dull-witted creatures of no practical account — are all that remain; but in the early periods of the Age of Mammals living species were reckoned by hundreds, and stood foremost in the animal world of their time.

The great Brazilian ant-eater, tamandua assu or yurumi, is a shaggy animal about eighteen inches tall, grayish black, marked by a black-and-white pointed stripe or "banner," as the Brazilians say, reaching back **Ant-eater.** from the throat to the hips. The total length may reach seven feet, but this is mainly head and tail.

This tail is the biggest thing of the kind in the mammal world, I guess, and has set many heads at thinking of what use it is. Wallace [27] says: "During rain it turns its long bushy tail up over its back and stands still; the Indians, when they meet with one, rustle the leaves and it thinks rain is falling, and, turning up its tail, they take the opportunity of killing it by a blow on the head with a stick." In contrast to this is the suggestion of Bigg-Wither,[252] who believes that the tail serves well to keep off annoying insects, especially bees, which, although stingless, are liable to settle in myriads upon any animal raiding their nests, — but we do not know that this animal ever robs these bees. The tail is, in fact, a useful mantle wrapped about the creature when it sleeps, warding off insects, hiding its colors from view, shedding rain, and keeping the temperature about the body equable. It is ordinarily trailed.

The ant-eater's long neck tapers into an equally long head, with very small eyes, ears, and nostrils; the skull, indeed, re-

GREAT ANT-EATER, OR TAMANDUA.

sembles that of a bird, and contains small room for brain. The hind feet are normally plantigrade and bearlike, but the fore feet are lifted upon the toes, and so bent in at the wrist that the weight rests upon the outside edge, with the great hook-like claws bent under. The animal never leaves the ground, and evidently no great activity is possible to it with such a club-footed deformity; its utmost efforts at speed are a shuffling run, easily overtaken by a boy. The purpose of the great fore paws (as of the precisely similar ones of the pangolin) is to enable the animal to tear to pieces the earthen mounds or rotting stumps and logs sheltering the ants which form its sole food. The instant their homes are wrecked, the insects rush out in swarms, whereupon the ant-eater throws out its very long, narrow, ribbonlike and sticky tongue, — a living fly paper, — to which the insects are glued and then brought into the mouth. This operation is repeated with lightning-like rapidity until no more ants remain. The viscid saliva is contained in two bags (glands), which reach far back through the throat and over the chest, the orifices of which in the mouth are under muscular control. As a result of this copious supply, the animal slobbers too much to be a pleasant object.

"It seems almost incredible," remarks Azara,[131] "that so robust and powerful an animal can procure sufficient subsistence from ants alone; but this circumstance has nothing strange in it to those who are acquainted with the tropical parts of America, and who have seen the enormous multitudes of these insects, which swarm in all parts of the country to that degree that their hills often almost touch one another for miles together."

Notwithstanding its powerful digging tools, the ant-eater does not burrow, but "has a regular lair, or, at least, an habitual place of resort, generally situated among tall grass, where it spends the day in slumber, lying on one side, with its head buried in the long fur of the chest, the legs folded together, and the huge tail curled round the exposed side of the body." As to the animal's defensibility, much confusion of statement is met with in books. That it either can defend itself, or is well protected by some quality, is plain from the fact that it is widespread and fairly numerous; also that it produces but a single offspring annually, which remains with its mother for eighteen months or so, when young riding about on her back. The Indians and woodsmen have always insisted that although by careful management you could drive one right into camp, when it was aroused or assaulted it became a very dangerous customer, and was capable of killing even the jaguar by the terrific strength of its fore arms in striking and hugging an antagonist. But Azara, who writes at length on the animal's habits, ridicules this, and assures us that a jaguar would knock an ant-eater dead before it got ready to resist. Here is an actual occurrence in Costa Rica, reported in *The Field* of Nov. 12, 1892, which shows what happens when an ant-eater is incautiously assailed: —

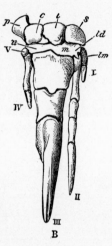

EDENTATE CLAWS.

Bones of forefoot of the lesser ant-eater: I–V, digits, showing the vast enlargement of the third toe; *u–lm*, wrist-bones.

"One of these animals was creeping slowly amongst the stumps and fallen logs, and poking its long snout into the crevices in search of its insect food. We were unarmed, but thought we could make an easy capture of such a harmless-looking beast. When the ant-eater saw that it could not escape, it threw itself upon its back, and D. rather imprudently seized it by the neck; immediately the brute struck out one of its paws and buried its formidable claws deep in the palm of his hand. It was impossible for him to free himself from the grasp of this monster, though he knelt upon its stomach and tried his best to choke it, suffering excruciating pain all the time. Fortunately, B. was near at hand, and after a little delay found a heavy stick and with some difficulty, succeeded in stunning the brute, when its claws relaxed. We thought the animal was dead, and carried it between us on a stick to the house, but hardly had we put it down on the ground when it recovered itself, and made a fresh attack, and seized B. by the leg, making a deep gash. Thinking it was too dangerous a beast to keep alive, we now killed it and preserved the skin. The skin was remarkably thick, and the fore legs or arms exceedingly powerful. . . . The Spaniards when they saw it said the ant-eater was a dangerous animal to encounter, and that they had seen dogs killed on the spot, with the claws of the ant-eater actually interlocked in their bodies. This animal measured six and a half feet, including its bushy tail, which is two feet long."

The lesser ant-eater or caguari is not more than half as large as the other, and lives altogether in trees, curling up to sleep in a crotch. It has a shorter head, large ears, short bristly hair of variable light tints, and a long, strong, terete tail, naked, scaly, and prehensile toward the end. The whole animal smells abominably. It is more powerfully clawed than even its cousin, rips up bark and dead wood in search of termites, or tears open the nests of wasps to get the honey and grubs; and, judging by the viciousness with which it will fight cats and dogs, is well able to defend itself against natural enemies.

Finally, northern Brazil and the Isthmus region possess a species, the silky "two-toed" ant-eater, no larger than a rat, bright yellow in color, and seldom seen, for it is nocturnal and keeps in the tree tops, aided by a prehensile tail. It seems to live mainly on wasp grubs. Von Sack [257] gives an interesting account of one he kept in confinement, which reminded him by its behavior of a miniature sloth.

The sloths, forming the family Bradypodidæ, and known through all the forested lowlands of tropical America, are really pretty close counterparts of the ant-eaters in organization, but have more the form of apes, being **Sloths.** very hairy, and having exceedingly long and muscular limbs, ending in double or triple hooks rather than in anything like ordinary hands or feet. These hooks are the long curved claws by which these animals, which spend their whole lives in trees, hang back downward beneath a branch, or slowly scramble about. This, and clinging to one another's shaggy coat, are almost all the hands and feet are ever asked to do. The food is nothing but leaves, plucked with the lips and swallowed with little crushing, for the creature's only teeth are a few in each cheek, without any coating of enamel and fixed in the jaws like pegs. There are two types of sloth, — one, the ai or tardo, having two toes on the fore feet, and the other, the unau, three

toes. The former is the more specialized, widespread, and celebrated. The two differ in their teeth and certain other anatomical points, and also in the particular tinge of green on the
coarse, brittle hair.

This greenness of the hair is not only singular as a mammalian color,
but in its nature, for it is due to a growth of microscopic plants (algæ),
which become rooted in the crevices of the surface of the hair, and flourish
there as long as the
animal lives. The
hairs of the two kinds
of sloths differ in
structure, and sup-
port different species
of alga; and the
plant does not be-
gin to grow in the fur
of the young (from
spores caught from its
mother's fur) until it
approaches adulthood
and goes away by it-
self.[65] This fact, and
the broader one that
it helps to make the
animal less easily
visible in the foliage,
causes this growth of
algæ to be regarded
as a protective adap-
tation. Attention was
called to it long ago.
Thus Van Sack notes

Copyright, N. Y. Zoöl. Society.   Sanborn, Phot.
TARDO, OR TWO-TOED SLOTH.

that "the color and even the shape of the hair are much in appearance like withered moss, and serve to hide the animal in the trees, but
particularly when it gets that orange-colored spot between the shoulders,
and lies close to the tree; it looks then exactly like a piece of branch
where the rest has been broken off, by which the hunters are often deceived." The color disappears from stuffed skins, because the minute
vegetation dies after the animal itself ceases to live.

That the creature which Buffon declared needed only one more defect to put an end to its race altogether, should have all the assistance in hiding it can get, is evident, for it is quite incapable of making any serious defense — or even trying to. "Here we have," says Tschudi, "a symbol of life under the utmost degree of listlessness, and of the greatest insensibility in a state of languid repose. This emblem of misery fixes itself on an almost leafless bough, and there remains defenseless; a ready prey to any assailant." Big weasels climb the trees and fasten upon its throat; harpies tear it loose and carry it off to their eyries; cats, large and small, take one when they find it without making any exertion; "a hungry bear collects a family of sloths as he would gather a bunch of grapes;" and a hungry Indian or negro does the same, when he is not too lazy to climb and search the tree from which some evening he hears the tardo's wailing cry. The sloth does his best, however, to escape notice, remaining all day in motionless simulation of some feathery tuft of moss or mistletoe, and making his slow excursions about the branches only after dusk. If you shoot him, he will probably hang dead by his hooks until decomposition relaxes the muscles.

No one has written of the sloth more knowingly than Dr. Felix Oswald,[120] who has told us so much of the intimate life of the animals of Mexico; and those who cannot get access to his book may find large quotations from it in the excellent "Standard Natural History." Other worthy sources of information are Alston,[114] who quotes in his account a long and quaint description by old Dampier; and the ever readable writings of H. W. Bates[25] and Thomas Belt.[26]

As to the armadillos, the bony armor by which all are more or less protected, and which is unique among living mammals, is only one of many extraordinary features in their anatomy. Not only are they considerably removed in structure from the sloths and ant-eaters, but they **Armadillos.**

differ greatly among themselves. All have numerous peglike teeth, and the giant armadillo (Priodon) may have more than forty in each jaw.

The most distinctive feature of the group is the "quasi coat of mail," as Theodore Gill calls it, in the form of a carapace, which covers all the back and sometimes the head and tail also. It is formed like a mosaic by the

Copyright, N. Y. Zoöl. Society.   Sanborn, Phot.

AN ARMADILLO, THE PELUDO.

union of many small bony pieces formed within the skin and later overlaid by a horny pellicle. Each piece or "scute" of the mosaic has a shape and surface-sculpturing characteristic of the species. This armor may be all in one piece, but usually consists of several, giving needed flexibility to the body. On the abdomen and limbs, or wherever, indeed, there is no armor, the skin is clothed with hairs, which also sprout out between the zones of plates. "The armor is doubtless useful against the attacks of their many carnivorous and reptile enemies. It assists them in burrowing, keeps off pressure, and may protect those which live in forests against a falling bough. They are passive creatures, mostly nocturnal in their habits, and their skeleton is strengthened in some parts in relation to its armor and its office."

The most advanced of the armadillo race is the Brazilian one, about eighteen inches long, named Scleropeura, and given highest place because it has almost no carapace, mere traces of armor mingling with the hair which clothes the body, so that it is approximated to the ant-eaters.

Of the typical armadillos the leader is the "giant" armadillo of the Amazon Valley, which may measure three feet from its nose to the root of its rather long tail. It has tremendously powerful claws, and is reputed to dig up corpses, but in fact lives mainly on ants and termites. Its armor looks like a uniform coat of mail, but really is disposed in five belts.

Peludo.

Nearly as large, and more extended in its range toward the south, is the tatouay, with a short, nearly naked tail and twelve or thirteen bands of plates. To the south of this, all over Paraguay and Argentina, are found several other much smaller species, as the peludo, of which Hudson [35] has written at such length. It lives on the pampas, where in some places its burrows are so numerous as to make riding dangerous.

Wherever a horse dies, or other carrion lies, these little animals gather and devour the putrid flesh voraciously. They also eat much plant food, but their chief diet consists of insects, mainly worms, which they detect underground by scent and then obtain by boring holes with their triangular armored snouts, turning round and round with their noses pushed into the soil, like animated gimlets, until they reach and seize the grub or earthworm they are after. Hudson describes the cleverness with which a tame one he had would trace a wild mouse to its lurking place by quartering the ground and following the scent; also how they search for the nests of ground-building birds and devour the eggs or fledglings; and especially how they kill snakes by leaping upon them, settling down across their writhing bodies, paying no attention to the reptiles' striking and biting at their shells, and then swaying their bodies back and forth until the jagged lower edges of the shield have literally sawed the serpent into halves, when it is eaten. This and its related species are scarcer and more wary than formerly, not only because they disappear rapidly and unaccountably as soon as a district is settled, but because they are hunted for the sake of their flesh by the help of dogs trained to rush and seize them before they can reach their burrows or disappear in impromptu excavations. Some of the smaller species are said to make their way so rapidly in the loose pampas soil that a man must fairly tumble off his horse if he means to catch one before it has put itself below the surface.

Differing from these in various ways are several other armadillos, of which one kind, the little "apars," have very solid bucklers over their fore shoulders and rumps, but the central zone separated into three narrow bands; and these are the armadillos which roll themselves into tight balls, which a dog or wild cat may tumble about till they are tired but can get no tooth into; then the apar lets the kinks out of the special muscles which enable him to curve and hold his shell around him, uncoils and trots away on the very tips of his toes in the most

APARS, ROLLED INTO BALLS.

comical of pony gaits. The apars are noted, indeed, for their lively and restless manners. As for the peba, that is a "nine-banded" species chiefly interesting because so common in Mexico and western Texas, and the only member of its clan counted among Uncle Sam's animal citizens. It is equally numerous and familiar in all the drier parts of South America, and is best liked of all when nicely baked in its own shell. Pleasantly told anecdotes of their ways as they potter about, "respectful of others' rights, but calmly confident in their tooth-and-claw-proof armor," may be read in the Beebes' "Two Bird Lovers in Mexico" — a delightful book.

Quite separate from all these there is or was, for perhaps none are left, on the western border of the Argentine pampas, a miniature pink and white armadillo, not larger than a mouse, the pichiciego, whose armor is constructed after a very different plan from the others. Lydekker [10] describes its peculiarities in detail.

What has been the history of these queer little creatures? In no group of mammals is the contrast between the present and the past so striking as in these edentates. As **Ancestry of** to their remote beginnings, little or nothing is known, **Edentates.** but representatives of the three South American groups have been obtained from nearly the whole breadth of the Tertiary formations. The fossils show that the ant-eater-sloth type was sepa-

APAR, OR THREE-BANDED ARMADILLO.

rated very early from the armadillo type, and never have had associated with them any Old World fodients. In the earlier Tertiary strata of Patagonia, there occur the remains of animals which have slothlike characteristics in skull and teeth, but are evidently not arboreal, and therefore have been called "ground sloths." They measured only about three feet in total length, had no armor or weapons of defense, and, as they were surrounded by big, rapacious beasts, it is surmised that they must have been burrowers, since otherwise they could not have existed so long and plentifully as they did; their strong, well-clawed fore limbs certainly imply digging powers. It is apparent that these comparatively pygmy ground sloths were the ancestors of the megatheres and their relatives, which later were among the most gigantic beasts of the ancient world.

Some of these huge edentates became known long ago, for in 1789 a nearly complete skeleton of one of them, named *Megatherium* by Cuvier, was exhumed near Buenos Aires and sent to Paris, where it was mounted **Megatherium.** and may still be seen at the Museum of Natural History. Many other specimens, and the skeletons of allied species, have since been found in the Pampean formations of Pleistocene age, when these mighty animals flourished. The megatheres were very bulky, the largest measuring about eighteen feet in total length (yet the tail was not long, although extremely massive), and had big, roundish, slothlike heads, and short, massive limbs, especially as to the hinder pair, where the haunches were of enormous breadth and strength. The structure of the fore foot is essentially that of the modern ant-eater, the inner toe being rudimentary, the next three, and more especially the middle one, enormously enlarged and furnished with huge claws; and during life the creature rested on the outside of the fifth claw and the backs of the three large toes in ant-eater fashion. Its hind foot, however, was not at all ant-eaterlike, for that animal stands upon a flat sole while the megathere walked only on its outer edge; the great middle toe, which constituted nearly the whole foot and was armed with a terrible claw, does not seem to have touched the ground in walking, and so the claw was not dulled. "Some idea of the gigantic proportions of the megatheres," Lydekker tells us, "may be gathered from the circumstance that its hind foot measured nearly a yard in length."

The mouth of the megathere contained teeth in the form of square prisms, with a length of more than ten inches and a diameter of one and a half inches. These teeth were rootless and continued growing, and their arrangement shows that between them lay a huge tongue that probably could be stretched far out. The structure of these teeth and of other parts shows that the megatheres were far removed from being sloths; but the gap is somewhat filled by the mylodons, contemporary and somewhat smaller animals of the same general appearance, the special feature of which was the presence in their skins, near the outer surface, of a great number of bony nodules like beans. There was still another group of related animals at that time, — the great scelidotheres, — differing decidedly from those already mentioned in having elongated narrow skulls, so that when alive they must have resembled ant-eaters.

It is evident from their massiveness that these ground sloths were terrestrial; their limbs and feet show that they must have been very slow and clumsy in movement, and no creature so heavy and short-legged could climb a tree. Nevertheless monstrous creatures like these could not have obtained sustenance in a treeless region, such as that of the pampas now is, and we may assume from this and other circumstances that in their day the Argentine plains were forested. "Browsing on the leaves and perhaps on the smaller branches of forest trees, the ground sloths probably obtained their food by rearing themselves up against the trunks, supported on the tripod formed by their massive hind limbs and powerful tail." That they continued to inhabit the land after humanity had invaded their haunts, is testified to by undoubted evidence, including bones wounded with stone arrowheads, and pictures left upon the walls of caves once human homes. These prehistoric draughtsmen hunted the megatheres and ate their flesh; there is evidence even that they had domesticated some of the ground sloths — probably as a reserve supply of food. In certain dry caves of Patagonia have even been found large fragments of their hides, still clothed with long coarse hair; and it is plain that they came to an end only a few thousands of years ago — how or why is one of the mysteries of zoölogy.[187]

Ground Sloths.

Even more extraordinary were the forerunners of the armadillos, the glyptodons, perhaps the most astonishing of all extinct mammals. Instead of the movable plate armor of the armadillos, their cousins of the late Tertiary had bodies protected by a bony shell or "carapace," which gave them a striking outward resemblance to turtles; but anatomically they were very unlike those reptiles, for the carapace had no attachment to the skeleton, but was composed of a mosaic of little plates of bone formed within the skin, varying in shape and sculpture according to species, joined by their edges, and covered with a horny coat. Each bit of the mosaic

Glypto-dons.

enlarged as the animal grew. As some of these glyptodons, which fall into several genera, had shells several feet long, the weight carried was relatively enormous. Consequently the legs and feet, especially those of the hinder pair, are short and massive, with the soles planted flat and firm, and "nearly the whole of the vertebræ are welded together so that a large portion of the backbone forms a continuous solid tube." The head is protected by a bony helmet. The tail in most species was nearly as long as the body, and its vertebræ also, as the animal attained to full size, united into a slender hollow cone armed or ornamented with rings of spikes and knobs, "forming a protective case against which little short of a steam hammer would have been of any avail." Woodward[60] gives a fine figure of this armor.

None reached so great a size or so bizarre an aspect as did the club-tailed glyptodon (Dædicurus) of Patagonia. In this monster, sometimes twelve feet in total length, the carapace is humped in outline and each piece in its mosaic is rhomboidal in form, and pierced with from two to five large circular holes. Woodward[60] considers these simply the passages (foramina) by which blood vessels and nerves reached the surface layers of the skin; but Dr. Lydekker regards them, from the analogy of the living hairy armadillo, as the exits of large bristles or quills, making the whole animal look like a gigantic porcupine. He says: —

Dædicurus.

"Still more extraordinary is the conformation of the huge tail, which had a length of about five feet. At its base this appendage was encircled by about half a dozen double bony rings, nearly as large at the base as the iron hoops in the middle of an ordinary beer barrel, their component plates being pierced by the aforesaid holes for bristles. The whole of the terminal half of the tail is formed by one continuous piece of hollow bone, which . . . is almost as much as a man can lift. Starting at its base in the form of a nearly cylindrical tube this sheath rapidly expands at the sides, and becomes flattened on the upper and lower surfaces, until at the tip it finally assumes the form of a depressed, flattened club, which would have formed a most effective weapon for a giant. Along the sides of its extremity this club is marked by a number of oval, depressed disks, showing a sculptured pattern of ridges and grooves radiating from the center, and some of them attaining a length of six or seven inches. From the structure of their sculpture it seems evident that during life these disks formed the bases of huge horns projecting at right angles to the tail, which would thus have formed a veritable *cheval de frise*. If, as is quite probable, these horns were as long as those of the common African rhinoceros, the tail of the dædicurus must have presented a most extraordinary appearance as it dragged on the ground behind its owner (for it is impossible to believe any muscles could have raised such a stupendous structure). The use of these horny appendages is, however, hard indeed to guess, since the creature was amply protected by the underlying bone; and it is therefore probable that they must come under the category of ornamental appendages. Be this as it may, with its bristle-clad body and horned tail, the club-tailed glyptodon may well lay claim to the right of being one of the most extraordinary creatures that ever walked this earth during the whole of the Tertiary period." [65]

These ring-tailed glyptodons seem to be the direct descendants of the pygmy ancestors with which the race began in the early Tertiary. Their habits were probably much like those of modern plant-eating armadillos (for the glyptodons were exclusively vegetable feeders), and the big ones seem to have been fond of retiring into caves.

"When standing with the edges of its impenetrable carapace resting on the ground, its mail-crowned head partially withdrawn within the front aperture of its shell, and only the lower portions of the limbs exposed, a glyptodon must have been safe from all foes save savage man, and even he must have had a tough job to slaughter the monster, if, indeed, he ever succeeded in doing so. That man did exist with the later glyptodons . . . is proved by more than one kind of evidence. Probably the empty carapaces of the larger members of the group were employed by the primitive inhabitants of Argentina as huts; and it is said that they are sometimes even so used at the present day by the Indians." [65]

In his interesting and valuable book, "Notes of a Naturalist in South America" (London, 1887), Mr. John Ball, F.R.S., mentions the scientific labors among the Indians near Bahia Blanca, on the northern border of Patagonia, of a learned gentleman, M. Georges Claraz, who told him that he had collected evidence among the Indians "which seemed to prove, that the Glyptodon survived in Patagonia down to a comparatively recent period, and that the tradition of its presence is preserved in the stories and songs of the natives."

Along with these great "tortoise armadillos" — the glyptodons — lived the ancestors of the true armadillos. Their remains are not numerous in museums, but such as have been studied are very similar to their modern descendants, showing how conservative this group has been, and, incidentally, how little change has taken place for ages in the climate or geography of South America.

Some rather obscure fossils of the lowest Eocene rocks of North America, deemed by some authorities ancestral to the Edentata, are classified in an order *Ganodonta*.

OLD WORLD ANT-EATERS — Order, FODIENTIA

ALTHOUGH in their outward form and habits there is considerable resemblance between the American edentates and the scaly ant-eaters and termite-hunting aard-varks of Africa, and although until lately the latter have been included in the order Edentata, the differences of structure between them and the three American families are so deep-seated that modern care in classification compels their being set apart in another order; the propriety of this is emphasized by the fact that no extinct forms allied to either group have ever been found in the hemisphere of the other. Furthermore, the distinctions of structure between the aard-varks and the pangolins are, in the view of some good naturalists, quite as important as those separating both from the ant-eaters, etc., of the New World, and hence they would assign each to an order by itself; but for the present it may be considered that the aard-varks and pangolins stand together in the order Fodientia. This group is inferior in general organization to the Edentata, and so far as we know has had no such a history in geological time. It represents an independent line of development "converging" toward a likeness with the American edentates through having followed a similar method of making a living.

The aard-varks are among the strangest of animals — in form somewhat like a thinly haired, yellowish bear, with a pig's snout, donkey's ears, and kangaroo's tail! A full-grown one may measure six feet in total length. One **Aard-vark.** kind inhabits South Africa, another northeastern Africa, and two others are known as fossils in the Pliocene and Oligocene rocks of southern Europe. They feed wholly on ants and termites, digging at night into the bases of their hills, and also making deep burrows for living quarters, where a single naked

AARD-VARK, OR CAPE ANT-EATER.

and very feeble "earth pig" is born each spring. Though these animals are almost never seen, their burrows show that they have been numerous until recently throughout eastern Africa; now they are becoming scarce, because the natives hunt them incessantly for the sake of their hides. The aard-vark has an almost full set of teeth, but of a very unusual structure.

There seems to be no real affinity between the aard-varks and the American edentates, and hardly any between them and the **Pango-** toothless pangolins or "scaly ant-eaters" of the family **lins.** Manidæ. The scales which give the latter quaint little animals their spruce-conelike armor are horny and overlap, and between them grow hairs, but they are totally unlike the bony armature of the armadillo. At birth the scales are soft but quickly harden, and at full age are so thick and strong as to resist the tooth and nail of any enemy. A pangolin, when attacked, instantly draws in head, legs, and tail, and becomes a scaly ball which a leopard, for instance, might well roll about as a plaything but could get no further satisfaction out of. It puzzles a strong man to persuade one to "open up." They subsist wholly on ants and termites caught at night by scraping open their nests and licking up the insects.

Oriental writers relate a legend, widespread among Malays and Japanese, that the pangolin "erects his scales and feigns to be dead; the ants creep between the erected scales, after which the ant-eater again closes its scales and enters the water; he now again erects the scales, the ants are set floating, and are then swallowed by the ant-eaters."

Three species are West African, one reaching an adult length of six feet, and one, the "phatagen" of the ancients, living mainly in trees. Three species of smaller size are East Indian or Malayan, the latter hunting mainly in the tree tops of the forest, and dwelling in hollow trunks.

WEST AFRICAN PANGOLIN, OR MANIS.

THE MARSUPIALS — Order, MARSUPIALIA

THE marsupials are a group of mammals so peculiar in their structure and distribution that for a long time they were regarded as constituting a subclass completely apart. Their most striking peculiarity is their method of reproduction. The female's internal reproductive organs are double throughout, whereas in all the mammals heretofore described these organs are paired only in the ovaries, from which ducts lead to a single sac (uterus) in which the offspring begins its growth. The fertilized egg there becomes attached to a particular part of the interior wall and develops in organic connection with the mother, her blood circulating through the veins of the embryo, and nourishing it by means of an intervening temporary modification of the surface of the uterus called the "placenta"; and there the embryo remains growing until it has reached an advanced age of readiness. Such mammals are said to be "placental." In marsupials and more primitive monotremes, however, the internal reproductive organs of the female are more or less perfectly paired in all their parts; and the embryos have no organic attachment to the wall of the uterus, so that these mammals are "implacental." Hence, instead of remaining within the mother's body until they are grown into a condition where they can almost take care of themselves as soon as born, the embryos in this group escape from the uterus and body of the mother at a very early stage, when utterly helpless and minute, being, even in the case of the largest kangaroos, hardly as big as mice. It would be fatal, of course, to turn them loose upon the world; and therefore the mother is provided with a fold of skin, forming a more or less

Reproduction.

perfect pouch (marsupium) on the hinder part of the abdomen, within which are the numerous teats.

The instant an embryo is dropped the mother picks it up with her fore paws and places it within the pouch, where it crawls about until it touches and instinctively takes hold of one of the threadlike teats.

The minute creature, soft, blind, and naked, has as yet no properly formed mouth, but instead a temporary arrangement of muscles by which it clings automatically to the nipple. It cannot suck, and is nourished by the mother forcing jets of milk down its throat; and lest this should choke its breathing, its windpipe is extended up to a junction with the nostrils, which state of things continues for several weeks, or until the animal is able to

A ROCK WALLABY, WITH YOUNG IN POUCH.

some extent to shift for itself. It then wakes up, stirs about, and leaves the pouch now and then, but returns to it for nursing, sleeping, and protection when alarmed, until finally it departs altogether.

This arrangement, with which many minor peculiarities are associated, was long regarded as more primitive than the placental method of reproduction, although an advance upon the egg laying of the monotremes. Upon it was based the former separation of the marsupials as a subclass *Metatheria*, of equal rank with the *Eutheria* or higher mammals, on the one hand, and with the *Prototheria* or monotremes on the other. Since it has been found that in the bandicoots (Perameles) there exists a true allantoic placenta, this distinction breaks down, and naturalists are forced to the conclusion that instead of being an independent primitive stock, the marsupials "have sprung from a stock with an allantoic placenta," — that is to say, its origin was the same as that of all other groups of mammals except (as it now appears) the monotremes. When the divergence in the methods of reproduction began, paleontology gives little indication. It is a noteworthy fact that now the pouch is least perfect (occasionally absent) in those forms which are of most ancient and general type.

Very characteristic of the group are the presence of two detached bones in the epipubic region; and also the fact that the hinder extremity of the lower jaw is always bent inward, or "inflected," — a reptilelike feature of much weight in determining the affinities of the earlier fossil remains, which so often consist of only a half of a lower jaw. The brain of all marsupials is "very small in proportion to the size of the head and body, while its external surface exhibits comparatively few foldings and convolutions, thus indicating that the brain power and general intelligence of these creatures are of a low grade." The experience of hunters and also of those who have made pets of many species, and found them gentle, amusing, and quick to learn, does not bear out this deduction. Doubtless, the marsupials, like other animals, have quite as much intelligence as their several circumstances require. Many clever acts have been reported of them. Nevertheless, the type of brain, the character of the dentition and other features detailed by Parker and Haswell,[2] Beddard,[37] Lydekker,[258] and other specialists, show that the marsupials must be placed near the foot of the list in respect to organization.

Many of the earliest mammals of which we have any certain information were of this race, and such were all of that division (polyprotodont) represented by the bandicoots. As far down in the rocks as the Triassic, at the base of the Mesozoic series (dawn of the Age of Reptiles), are found in various parts of the world, including North America,[59] a few jawbones and teeth indicating that some of the diminutive forerunners of the Mammalia — able by reason of their minuteness to run and hide and nibble in a world filled with ravenous reptiles — were marsupial in organization. Some of these early types lasted into or through the Jurassic period, but are not met with subsequently as fossils, except in Australasia and Patagonia. After a long interval marsupials again appear, in the Middle Tertiary rocks of the Old World, and soon after in similar formations in the New World. During the later Tertiary marsupials flourished, as did all other orders in that heyday of mammalian life. Such details of this part of their history as seem to be called for will be given when I come to speak of the families; at present I wish only to direct attention to the fact that in the past marsupials of all kinds were scattered all over the globe, whereas now, except the American opossums, no living member of the order is known outside of Australasia, where they constitute almost the entire mammalian fauna. This fact was very hard to explain until the discovery of many fossils supplied the key to a part, at least, of the puzzle. Dr. Lydekker [258] has sketched this interesting matter concisely in the following sentences: —

Mesozoic Mammals.

"Having their headquarters in Australia and New Guinea, where they form the dominant part of the mammalian fauna . . . the marsupials gradually diminish in number and importance in the islands of the Northwest, being largely mingled in Celebes and the neighboring islands with types of mammals characteristic of the Indian or Oriental region. If, however, we pass westward across the deep channel separating the island of Celebes from Borneo, or its continuation which runs between Lombok on the east and Bali, at the extremity of Java, on the west, we shall find all the islands lying to the westward of that line devoid of marsupials and possessing a mammalian fauna akin to that of India. The line of the channel in question is, therefore, evidently a very important one as regards

Distribution.

distributional zoölogy; and since this importance was first demonstrated and explained by the great explorer and naturalist, Dr. A. R. Wallace, it is now by common consent appropriately denominated 'Wallace's Line.' To the eastward marsupials extend as far as New Ireland and the Solomon Islands, but they are unknown in Polynesia proper, as, indeed, they are in New Zealand, where, by the way, there are no indigenous mammals at all."

This localized condition of a great group is explained by the statement of scientists that Australia and its neighboring islands were connected with Asia previous to the Jurassic period, but since that time have been separated from it by the deep channels along Wallace's Line; at that time Australia seems to have been much more extensive than at present, embracing within its mainland Tasmania, New Caledonia, and other present islands. It is a fair inference that previous to and during the Jurassic period Australia, as a part of the Asiatic continent, became peopled with the only mammals then in existence — the small primitive marsupials. Then the island-continent was cut off, and they were left to work out their destiny undisturbed by any immigration of alien competitors or destructive enemies. To this fortunate isolation, perhaps more than to anything else, they owe their immeasurably long survival, for before the close of the next era the influences and competition abroad in Europe and Asia had killed off all the marsupials that had remained there. A similar fate seems to be slowly overtaking the long-preserved Australian remnant, apart from anything man is doing. There is evidence of the existence during the Pleistocene of many now extinct forms of kangaroos and wombats, by the side of which the largest existing species would be as dwarfs. "The cause of this universal extinction (for universal it is) of the most gigantic mammals throughout the world soon after man made his appearance on the earth is one of those problems which has not yet received a satisfactory answer, as not even a glacial period could have made a clean sweep of the whole globe." Such is the substance of the present view.

There is this to be said, however, at this point: It is a possibility that this whole matter of the spread of primitive marsupials (and of some other of the older types) has been viewed "wrong end to." Various facts and indications point to the probability that the **Antarctic Origin?** Southern Hemisphere received its animal life first from original centers of birth and distribution in the South Polar region, then mild and fruitful in climate. If this were so, then the adjacent Australian country would have become populous first, and the spread of marsupials would have been onward into Asia and Europe, until the more distant were cut off by the water gap opened early in the Cretaceous era along Wallace's Line; and the early disappearance of this race from the mainland would be more readily understood than on the supposition that it originated there. Such a hypothesis (direct evidence of which must always remain hidden for the most part under the antarctic ice) would also explain the curious fact that the only marsupials now living elsewhere than in Australasia are in South America, one species, our opossum, ranging north to the central United States. Fossil remains of primitive marsupials abound in the early Tertiary rocks of Patagonia, and by the time of the Oligocene opossums had spread over all North America and Europe. The notable faunal and floral resemblance in general beween Australia and South America, increasing as it is traced backward in geologic history, can be explained only by some sort of former land connection now submerged, presumably antarctic. The great objection to this hypothesis is a negative one; namely, that thus far no fossil forms of Mesozoic age have been found in Australia.

It is in suggesting such large thoughts as this that the marsupials become interesting, rather than in what they nowadays are or do.

The marsupials present another engaging aspect in showing themselves to be an epitome of the whole mammalian world, and so illustrating on a large scale, and in **Adaptations.** the most conspicuous way, how the necessity and habit of making a living in a particular manner brings about a suitable modification of structure, by such methods of adaptation as Morgan [260] has elucidated. In Australia these animals found themselves confined in a comparatively small, sharply limited space, including both plains and forests, with a fair uniformity of climate and products. There was an abundance of insect, reptilian, and bird life; but no other mammals save a few bats and mice blown or drifted thither from the North; for the dingo, finally to prove so severe an enemy, was doubtless a late immigrant. In this complete freedom, and under favorable conditions, the marsupials soon became sufficiently diversified within their type to take advantage of all their opportunities, as in the more spacious outside world the more numerous other groups of mammals have been separated and fitted for a still wider variety of modes of life.

AUSTRALIAN BEAVER-RAT.

"We have, for instance," remarks the latest monographer of the order, "both terrestrial and arboreal types, while one form recently discovered passes an underground existence like the mole. Some, again, are carnivorous and others herbivorous; while among the former certain kinds live on flesh and others on insects, an equal diversity obtaining among the vegetable feeders, some of which live on roots, others on grasses or leaves, others on fruits, and yet others on honey or the juices of flowers. . . . It is, however, very remarkable that not a single Australian representative of the order is aquatic in its habits, so that such an animal as a 'marsupial otter' does not exist in that region. The place in nature thus left vacant by the marsupials has been seized upon by the duckbill, and by two members of the rodent order (otherwise so poorly represented in Australia), of which the best known is commonly termed the 'beaver-rat.'"

A valuable discussion of the Origin and Evolution of Marsupials, by B. A. Bensley, will be found in *The American Naturalist* for 1901.[266]

The order Marsupialia is divisible into two sections: —

I. *Diprotodontia* — with numerous incisors. Kangaroos, phalangers, and wombats; herbivorous; specialized and recent.

II. *Polyprotodontia* — with rarely more than two incisors. Bandicoots, pouched mice, and opossums; carnivorous; generalized and ancient.

The kangaroos stand at the head of the list, and are the largest, most highly developed, and familiar of their race. They form a family (Macropodidæ) which is spread **Kanga-** over both Australia and New Guinea, and includes **roos.** over fifty species. While the majority inhabit open grassy plains, others brushy districts and rocks, and a few dwell in trees, the kangaroos proper include half a dozen of the largest kinds, the commonest of which is the great gray "boomer" or "forester," of the colonists, whose discovery in 1770 astonished Captain Cook and his men, and which was described at length by Sir Joseph Banks, the naturalist of the expedition. This kangaroo, which occurs all over Australia, Tasmania, and New Guinea, stands four to five feet tall, with a tail thirty to thirty-six inches long; but this size is considerably exceeded by that of the red or woolly kangaroo, of eastern and southern Australia. Furthermore, fossil remains show that in the Pleistocene era kangaroos far bigger than even these existed there in numerous extinct species, — one, for instance, whose skull alone measured nearly a yard in length. One of the best accounts of kangaroos ever written is that by Henry Wheelwright (under the pen name "An Old Bushman") [261] which in part is quoted below: —

"The singular form of the kangaroo is doubtless familiar to all who are likely to look into these pages; it is one of the few animals whose habits are strictly terrestrial, which, although by nature furnished **Gait.** with four legs, use only the two hind ones as organs of progression. . . . In form the hind leg is similar to that of a hare, and when in an upright position the kangaroo rests on its hind feet and haunches after the manner of a squirrel; the tail stretched out at full length along the ground, not, as I have seen it represented in a picture, curled up like that of a rat, for the kangaroo cannot bend its tail. When running, it springs from the ground in an erect position, propelled by its powerful hind legs and balanced by its tail, holding its short fore arms well into the chest, after the manner of a professional runner. Thus it bounds lightly and easily along, clearing any obstacles such as trees and even low fences in its stride. I never fairly measured one of these strides or springs, but I am

RED OR WOOLLY KANGAROO.

certain, when hard-pressed, an 'old man' or 'flying doe' will clear nearly ten yards at a spring. The long tail materially assists them in running, and its measured thump may be heard on the ground long before the kangaroo itself appears in sight in the thick forest.*

"The countenance is mild and placid, but, like the sheep, we rarely see two exactly alike. The eye is bright; the nostrils not very wide; the ears large and pricked; and many of the males have a marked Roman nose, like that of an old ram. In bush parlance, the old male kangaroo is called an 'old man'; the young female a 'flying doe'; and the young one, till eight or ten months old, a 'joey.' The weight of a full-grown doe or

* Whether or not this is correct is a matter of dispute. That the tail is a support when the animal is at rest or walking slowly is certain; but good observers insist that it is held clear of the ground when the animal is leaping at speed, and say no trace of its touching appears when the kangaroo races across soft ground.

young buck, just killed, will vary up to about 120 lbs. Some of the 'old men' reach to an immense size, and I have often killed them over 2 cwt.

"In habits the kangaroo much resembles both the sheep and the fallow deer. Timid and shy, their senses of sight, hearing, and smell are most acute. Like the hare, they appear unable to see an object **Habits and** directly in front of them when running; at least I have often **Food.** stood still and shot one down as it came running straight up to me in the open forest. It is not a ruminating animal, and the four long front teeth, two in each jaw, are sharp, flat, and double-edged, peculiarly adapted for cutting or browsing; and the thick blunt crushing molars betoken a purely herbivorous animal. They are very gregarious, and are always to be met with in smaller or larger droves. I have often seen as many as 150 in a drove, and our general mobs used to average 50 or 60. After the rutting season, the 'old men' will often draw away from the mobs and retire by themselves to the thickest scrub. Each drove frequents a certain district and has its particular camping and feeding grounds. The mobs do not appear to mix, and when the shooter once obtains a knowledge of the country, he has no difficulty in planting himself for a shot. Their camping grounds are generally on some open timbered rise, and they have well-trodden runs from one ground to another. They feed early in the morning and at twilight, and I think also much by night. . . . The meat is dark in color, soon dries, and in appearance and taste is similar to poor doe venison.

"The kangaroo lies up by day during the hot summer weather, in damp, thickly scrubbed gullies, in the winter on dry, sandy rises. Here, unless sturbed, they will remain quiet for hours; and it is a pretty sight to watch a mob camped up, some of them playing with each other, some quietly nibbling the young shrubs and grass, or basking in the sun half asleep on their sides. About Christmas the young ones appear to leave their mothers' sides, and congregate in mobs by themselves. I have seen as many as fifty running together, and very pretty they looked. The kangaroo is a very clean animal. Both sexes seem to keep together, and, except in the rutting season, when desperate battles take place between the old males, they appear to live at all times in a state of domestic felicity. Like sheep, they can be driven in almost any direction that suits the driver, and, . . . like sheep, they always follow a leader. Their principal food appears to be the tender sprouts of small shrubs and heather, quite as much as grass; but there is a small kind of spike grass, brown on the under side, called the kangaroo grass, to which they are very partial. They will also come at night into the small bush inclosures, and nibble off the young blades of wheat, oats, etc.

"Although harmless and inoffensive when unmolested, nature has furnished the kangaroo with a dreadful weapon of defense in the powerful hind claw, with which it can rip up a dog, like the tusk of a boar; and I have seen a large kangaroo take up a powerful dog in its fore claws, bear-fashion, and try to bite it. I never but once had one turn on me, and this was an old male which I had knocked down, and when I went up to it on the ground, it sprung up and came at me; it luckily fell from exhaustion as I stepped back. Like deer, when wounded, they will often take to water, and, if they get a dog in their claws at such a time, always try to drown it. But I do not believe in the fiction that they will carry a dog to a water hole for that purpose."

The smaller kangaroos are called "wallabies" or "brush" kangaroos, since they frequent scrub jungle and rocky places rather than open plains. These smaller species **Wallabies.** furnish most of the leather and furs sent to market, and also the best venison; their skins are exported in vast quantities (350,000 were disposed of in the London sales of 1905), yet certain species remain numerous. There are also other wallabies, as the rock wallabies (Petrogale) of central Australia, which leap and climb about their rough resorts with remarkable agility, fleeing to deep holes when pursued. "When on precipitous cliffs they ascend the rocks in groups, jumping from side to side, and alighting on such small ledges that it seems almost impossible for them to obtain foothold. During the day they remain concealed in caves and holes from which they issue forth at evening, while on moonlight nights they may be seen abroad at all hours . . . they also have the power of easily ascending the sloping trunks of trees."

A genus (Onychogale) of similar mountain dwellers is distinguished by having a horny nail on the tip of the tail. A third genus is that of the hare-wallabies (Lagorchestes), of which Gould [262] gives some interesting notes.

"I usually found it solitary and sitting alone on a well-formed seat under stalks of a tuft of grass on the open plains. For a short distance its fleetness is beyond that of all others of its group that I have had an opportunity or coursing. Its powers of leaping are also extraordinary. While out on the plains of South Australia I started a hare kangaroo before two fleet dogs. After running to a distance of a quarter of a mile, it suddenly doubled and came back to me, the dogs following close to its heels. I stood perfectly still, and the animal had arrived within twenty feet before it observed me, when, to my astonishment, instead of branching off to the right or to the left, it bounded clear over my head, and, on descending to the ground, I was able to make a successful shot. . . . It is strictly nocturnal."

The dorca kangaroos (Dorcopsis) of New Guinea form a transition from the ground-running kinds to the tree climbers of that island and north-ern Australia, whose fore arms are relatively long in adaptation to their arbo-real habits; the Queens-

JERBOA RAT KANGA-ROO.

"Their appearance," says Gould, "when leaping toward their nests with their tails loaded with grasses, is exceedingly amusing." It is an interesting fact that our North American opossums use their tails in the same way.

land species is notably pretty in its blended colors, — golden brown and white, with black-gloved hands and feet. Add-ing the thicket-loving "banded" kangaroo of West Australia, we complete the catalogue of this subfamily.

To another group belong the diminutive rat kangaroos, which are ratlike in form, colors, and manners, running rather than leaping, and dwelling among "scrub" and grass, scratching the ground all day in search of the **Rat Kan-garoos.** roots upon which they feed, and making havoc in the fron-tiersman's potato patches. Several of them have prehensile tails, which they use apparently only to carry to their intricate underground homes the long grass of which they make their beds. They associate in "towns" of connected burrows like a rabbit warren. Closely related but more active in its habits, being a tree climber, and more miscellaneous in its fare, which includes insects and worms, is the musk kangaroo, whose body exhales a strong odor.

We come now to a distinct family, the phalangers, which the Australians "persist in misnaming 'opossums.'" This **Phalan-** family is widespread, and is regarded as representing **gers.** the most ancient type of diprotodont marsupials.

"In their modes of life," Lydekker remarks, "the phalangers and their allies are essentially arboreal creatures, the great majority of them being highly assisted in their climbing by their highly prehensile tail. Some, however, have 'gone one better' than this, and have developed large parachutelike expansions of skin from the sides of the body, by means of which they are able to take long flying leaps from bough to bough, and thus from tree to tree. And it may be mentioned here as a somewhat remarkable circumstance, that the different groups of these flying-phalangers, like their analogues, the flying-squirrels, have developed their parachutes, independently of one another, from distinct groups of their non-volant cousins. . . . While the great majority of the members of the family are purely vegetable feeders, subsisting chiefly on leaves and fruit, a few feed either entirely or partially on insects, while others have taken to a diet of flesh."

Entitled to first notice is that quaint little creature, the "native bear" or koala, whose portrait sufficiently describes him, when I add that he is about 32 inches long, and is gray with whitish under parts, rump, feet, and ears. Like the sloth, of which his sluggishness reminds one, he spends his days asleep in a tall tree top, or lazily feeding upon eucalyptus shoots, but at night descends and prowls about, scratching up edible roots. These comical little chaps have a single addition each spring to the family, and it is toted about for a long time by the mother, clinging to the fur of her back while she scrambles through the gum tops. Its flesh is good to eat and its hide tans into excellent leather.

Somewhat similar in habits, but more lemurlike in appearance and disposition, are the queer cūscūses, several species

KOALA, OR AUSTRALIAN "NATIVE BEAR."

of which inhabit northern Australia, New Guinea, and the islands west to Celebes, where they were met and described by both Wallace [31] and Forbes.[3] They are about the size and shape of ferrets, have dense woolly fur, and a tendency toward piebald coloring, which gives them the name "tiger cat." Like the koalas, they dwell in tree tops, feed on leaves and the like, and sleep in a decayed hollow; and the natives of the Moluccas, at least, hunt them to eat.

Of similar habits are the typical phalangers, of which the best known is the common one, always called in Australia "opossum," — an odd instance of the travels of an American Indian word. It is of the soft, richly colored skins, 80 to 120 sewed together, of this and some related species, that the

famous opossum rugs are made; and so numerous and prolific are these animals, in spite of the fact that three millions
or more of their hides are consumed annually (2,500,000 in
London alone, during 1905), these phalangers are still in
thriving abundance. The common "opossum" is about the
bigness of a cat, and lives mainly in peppermint gums, whose
aromatic leaves are its favorite food, and so taint its flesh that
nobody but a blackfellow cares to eat it; but some of the
smaller "ring-tailed" phalangers are said to be excellent on

THE COMMON "OPOSSUM," OR VULPINE PHALANGER, OF AUSTRALIA.

the table. Wheelwright[261] gives a very full account of the animal, and tells us that when one is shot it will often hang by
the grip of its prehensile tail long after life has departed.
Protective laws have recently restricted the killing of them.

It was to be expected that among creatures of these squirrel-like ways some would grow to have a squirrel-like form.

Flying-Phalangers. This has happened, and they have added to the
large balancing and seizing tail the faculty of flight,
as has been intimated. Thus we have flying-
phalangers. One is the dark green taguan or "tooan" of
Queensland and Victoria, about 17 inches long, with a
tail measuring 20 inches, noted for its piercing scream
when alarmed or in flight. Another well known is the yel-
low-bellied, of which Bennett wrote so particularly in his

AUSTRALIAN MARSUPIAL SUGAR-SQUIRREL

excellent book;[263] he raised a captive to be a most engaging pet and says: —

"It holds a raisin or almond in its forepaws, licking and nibbling it. It is often seen lying on its back at the bottom of the cage when feeding, and when drinking milk holds the small vessel containing it between its forepaws, lapping like a kitten. It is evident from the fondness of this animal for sweets that, when the eucalypti are in flower, it subsists upon honey, which the blossoms yield in very large quantity (the honey is in such abundance as to afford subsistence to honey-eating parrots and other birds, as well as to these animals, and also to myriads of insects of various species). When these have disappeared it lives upon nuts and young foliage, and, probably, as is usual with honey-eating animals, also upon insects."

Seen and loved everywhere in New South Wales is another species, the sugar squirrel (*Petaurus sciureus*), one of the most beautiful of mammals, as may be seen by the colored plate herewith. It is only about nine inches long, plus nine or ten inches of evenly bushy tail; and its fur has so exquisitely soft and silky a quality that it is superior even to chinchilla. Many are the stories told of its astonishingly long and graceful flights in the moonlight among the honeysuckles, which are its favorite haunt; and the people are satisfied that it has power to change its course to a certain extent in mid air. They relate how, on one occasion, one which had the run of a ship at sea leaped from a masthead just as the vessel gave a great lurch. The squirrel's course would undoubtedly have landed it overboard, but it was seen to swerve in mid flight and alight safely on deck. All this sounds very much as if said of American flying-squirrels; and the two kinds of animals look and behave as nearly alike as possible, though developed on opposite sides of the globe and in separate groups. The "flying-mice" (Acrobates) are miniature volant phalangers, no larger than house mice.

Equally striking is the resemblance of their smaller cousins, the dormouse phalangers, to the European dormice both in appearance and habits, except that they inhabit tree tops.

Another phalanger of great interest is the long-snouted tait of West Australia, which lives mainly on honey extracted from the tubular flowers so common in that country, and blooming on one or another tree throughout the year. To this end it has acquired its long nose and a tongue which can be thrust far

WOMBATS, CALLED BY AUSTRALIANS "NATIVE BEAR."

out of its mouth and is roughened toward its tip and capable of being curled into a scoop. Such fare implies the taking of a good many insects sticking to the liquid sweet; but all the phalangers are to some extent fond of grubs, and quick at grasping insects that fall in their way. Very different animals are the wombats (Phascolomyidæ) of southern Australia and Tasmania.

Wombats. "Heavily made and short-limbed creatures, with incisor teeth curiously resembling those of the rodent mammals, the wombats may be regarded as filling in Australia the place occupied in the northern hemisphere by the marmots, and in South America by the viscachas.

. . . Like most marsupials the wombats are essentially nocturnal animals, remaining concealed throughout the day in their subterranean quarters, whence they issue forth at night to feed. . . . Their food consists partly of grass and other herbage, but mainly of roots, which their powerful front teeth are admirably adapted to gnaw. From specimens kept in confinement it appears that the female usually produces from three to four young at a birth, which are tended with great care and solicitude, until such time as they are able to shift for themselves. By no means active in their movements, and shuffling along with an awkward gait which calls to mind the progression of a young bear, the wombats are gentle and somewhat stupid in disposition."

It may be added that the wombats, like the koala, have cheek pouches, and both animals store temporarily masses of food, and are otherwise of considerable likeness. Nearly 130,000 "wombat" skins were sold at the fur auctions in London alone in 1905.

Last of the diprotodonts are the two small species of opossum rat (raton runcho) of Colombia and Ecuador, the sole survivors of an almost extinct family (Epanorthidæ), represented by many fossil remains in the Miocene rocks about Santa Cruz, Patagonia. The foremost peculiarity is that the toes of the hind feet are wholly free, not somewhat webbed as in the kangaroos and all other diprotodonts. Their pouch is almost rudimentary, their food is not vegetable, but mainly birds and their eggs, insects and the like; and all together these small American cousins of the phalangers stand at the foot of the list. With them we easily pass to the bandicoots, and so take up the Polyprotodontia.

The distinction regards the teeth, which here, by numerous incisors, strong canines, and sharp cheek teeth, in- **Polyprotodonts.** dicate a flesh diet and predatory habits. The dentition of a bandicoot is much like that of a shrew, and an opossum has teeth like a weasel's. This implies similar tastes and methods; and within this section will be found insect hunters as active, and beasts of prey as fierce, as any developed outside the marsupial world.

Before taking up the group, however, a word should be

said about the marsupial "mole" discovered in 1891. It lives in an arid part of southern Australia, is a burrowing creature, **" Mole."** has a silky coat, pale golden red, and in many ways is a most striking counterpart of the South African "golden mole," which is no more a true mole than is this, but is an insectivore. Interest in the close similarity between them, internal as well as outward, deepens when it

AUSTRALIAN MARSUPIAL MOLE.

is added that the Tertiary rocks of Argentina contain a fossil insectivore (Necrolestes) closely allied to the Cape species. The marsupial mole is not only blind, but its eyes have been more completely lost by degeneration than in any other known case; and its anatomy abounds in curious adaptations to an underground existence evidently antique.

The true bandicoots are animals like bush rats, from nine to sixteen inches long, plus a tapering tail, which inhabit wooded **Bandi-coots.** places, some on the high, dry, interior mountains, and other species in the southern swamps. Some are handsome; but in outlines and colors they vary greatly. All make a compact nest of grass, etc., looking like a mere heap of rubbish in a hollow of the ground, in which a family hides until the coming of dusk arouses it from its dozing and sends it forth to feed. In this, and in their nocturnal digging of bulbs to add to their diet of leaves, fruit, mice, insects, worms, etc., they closely resemble in mode of life our American wood rats (Neotoma). Krefft [264] describes a happy captive which became an adept in mice catching; and says it would tumble the mice about with its fore paws, break their hind legs, and then, as a rule, eat only the head. Less typical and carnivorous are the rabbit bandicoots, which, although very long-eared, owe their name more to their harelike manners, food, and taste, than to similarity of appearance; and the out-of-the-way, now rare, "pig-footed" bandicoot of southern Australia, which also has much the habits of a rabbit, but makes grass nests and subsists largely on insects, never, apparently, hunting mice, as do the bandicoots proper. All the bandicoots are regarded as pests by the Australian farmers, because they dig and tunnel in their fields after worms and roots, and so do the same sort of mischief as our ground squirrels. One remarkable feature in the bandicoot family (Peramelidæ) is the fact that the hind feet are almost precisely like those of kangaroos, although it is probable that this feature was independently acquired, and that the bandicoots are an offshoot from the next family, the dasyures, rather than near relatives of the kangaroos, to which they bear a greater outward resemblance.

The dasyures (Dasyuridæ) are the marsupial beasts of prey. The limbs are of nearly equal length, the feet of the ordinary digitigrade type, the dentition thoroughly carnivorous (doglike), the digestive apparatus fitted for **Dasyures.** flesh food, and the form and habits much like the wolves, civets, and weasels of northern climes; but all are pouched, and, as in the bandicoots, the pouch opens backward. The foremost of this predatory group, and the largest, is a ferocious creature known as "Tasmanian devil." It is uniformly black and shaggy, has a head somewhat like a bear, with jaws and teeth strong enough to crush big bones; and in size, strength, and diabolism is an imitation of the wolverine. It lives in self-dug burrows like a badger, whence it prowls at night, doing immense damage in poultry yard and sheepfold, and few dogs have the nerve to face it; but now it has been almost exterminated, and is likely to be gone before several unknown points as to its breeding, etc., have been learned. Harris, who first described the creature in 1808, said they were gladly eaten by the early settlers of Van Diemen's Land, tasting like veal, and were easily taken in meat-baited traps, but proved "untamably savage," two captives that he kept fighting continually. "Their quarrels began as soon as it was dark (as they slept all day) and continued throughout the night almost without intermission, accompanied by a kind of hollow barking not unlike that of a dog." A bigger and worse "devil"

A DASYURE, THE TASMANIAN DEVIL.

infested the Australian mainland in the recent past, as we know from bones in caves.

The dasyures proper, or "native cats," consist of half a dozen kinds of active little carnivores, which fill the rôle there of our northern martens and weasels. Some are Australian, others Tasmanian, others denizens of the Papuan Islands; and most of their time is spent in trees, although some are more fond of hunting amid rocks and brush. None is larger than a small house cat, and with their sharp muzzles, brightly colored and usually spotted coats, and long, ornamented tails, they remind one of civets. This is especially

COMMON DASYURE, OR AUSTRALIAN "NATIVE CAT."

true of the common little Australian one. Naturally bird hunters and nest robbers, all are pests to farmers interested in chickens or pigeons. Their haunts and habits are much the same as those of a weasel; but they are more apt to take to a tree for refuge when chased by a dog. They have a weasel's reckless boldness and bloodthirst.

"They prefer to take up their abode with civilized man when they find out that he keeps plenty of meat about his habitation or rears poultry. They are very savage for their size, and five of them kept in a cage without sustenance for a day only had almost reduced themselves to the state of the famous tabbies of Kilkenny. They are stubborn in the extreme, and appear to care about nothing. We have noticed them to come quite unconcerned into a tent at night, and take up a cosy place near the chimney, from which a fire stick only could dislodge them." [264]

Near relatives of these alert marauders are a large number of tiny dasyures of the genus Phascologale, which are widely scattered and in places very numerous. The Australians call them "pouched mice," for none are as large as a rat, but they are really more like the Malayan tree shrews, scrambling about the bark and branches after the insects which form

their chief diet, and nesting in their hollows. The larger ones
kill eagerly such birds and mice as they can catch; and all
make pretty pets. Besides these several other species behave
like shrews, living wholly on the ground; and one of the larger
desert kinds (Antechinus), whose principal enemies are hawks
and owls, carries the similitude farther by leaping when it moves
just like the true jumping-shrews of the deserts of North Africa.

BANDED AUSTRALIAN ANT-EATER.

There seems no end to the way in which circumstances have
produced in these Australian marsupials forms and aptitudes
like those of the placental mammals elsewhere exposed to
similar conditions of soil, climate, etc.

Another example is found in the last of this family, the
banded ant-eater, which has the general look of a large
Banded Ant-eater. reddish squirrel irregularly banded with white
across the back, digs open ant-hills, and then licks
up their denizens by means of a long glutinous
tongue — an adaptation in structure like that of the true ant-
eaters, just as their needs and pursuits agree. Its habits otherwise are little known, for it is rare and local. Another interesting fact about this animal is that its teeth, which are very
small and delicate, though numerous (54), are unlike those
of any other marsupial, and exhibit (as also does the palate)
suggestive points of resemblance to the dentition of the mono-

tremes (see page 523); they more closely resemble, however, the type of teeth seen in the fossil jaws (the likeness extends to the jaw bone itself) of such most primitive relics as Amphitherium of the Jurassic, which is among the most antique of recognizable mammalian remains. It may be that this little Australian ant-eater is a direct survivor from the Secondary fauna.

An allied but separated group is represented by the Tasmanian "zebra wolf" or thylacine. This much-dreaded beast is a long-bodied, short-legged, long-tailed, dog-headed animal, with the look of an ancient creodont and the manners of a modern wolf. As will be seen by the photograph, the head is large, the jaw powerful, the gape of the mouth extending back behind the eye, which is large, prominent, and very dark. The incisors do not

Copyright, N. Y. Zoöl. Society.   Sanborn, Phot.
THYLACINE, OR TASMANIAN WOLF.

correspond with those of our carnivores, being eight in the upper and six in the lower jaw. The canines are strong and fully an inch in length. A full-grown one is nearly six feet long to the end of the tail; and the coat is short, close, and of a dusky-tawny hue, marked upon the hinder part with about 16 blackish transverse bands. Its home is Tasmania, where it lurks among the rocky ravines of the interior mountains, sometimes as high as the snow line. When the island first began to be colonized it was numerous, finding plenty of native prey; but as soon as sheep were introduced it naturally took to killing them, and thus aroused a war of extermination. So well armed are its great jaws and so courageous is its fury that even a pack of dogs will refuse to attack an old "wolf" with his back to the wall. They rarely show themselves by daylight, and then seem slow, dull-witted, and half blind, but make their forays at night, each hunting alone, and with no more voice than a low growl. A few have been caught alive and soon adapt themselves to captivity, so that all the larger zoölogical gardens now exhibit them and even cause them to breed. Mr. R. Gunn, who sent a female to the London "Zoo," wrote of her as follows:—

"The present one, in giving suck to its young, used to lie down like a dog, the skin of the pouch being thrown back so as to admit of the young ones getting easily at the teats. When alarmed, the young ones crawled in with their backs downwards, the mother assisting by lowering her hind quarters to facilitate them getting in, and by also placing her rump against the side of the cage to give the cubs a purchase with their hind legs against the cage, and thus push themselves in."

A word or two here about the pouch. In the kangaroos and their kin this organ is most highly developed and longest used by the young. As **Relation of Pouch to Rank in Development.** the line is approached separating the diprotodonts from the polyprotodonts, the opening of the pouch changes from front to rear, and when the smaller dasyures are reached it is seen to be very restricted and to open by a slit straight downward; and the kittens make little use of it after once getting out. In the pouched mice, despite their name, it is so small as practically to be wanting; and in Antechinus and the ant-eater there is no pouch at all, the teats being protected merely by the long hair among which the young cling until they mature. This deficient condition characterizes the opossums, with two specialized exceptions. These very exceptions, in the opinion of Dr. Lydekker, "demonstrate that this organ is primitively an essential characteristic of marsupials, and not one that has been specially developed to suit the exigencies of the various modes of life of the Australian members of the order. Consequently those forms, like the majority of the opossums and the banded ant-eaters, which have either no pouch or merely a rudiment thereof, may be safely assumed to have lost that organ through specialization. The reason of the loss of such an organ, which appears so admirably adapted for the protection of young born in the imperfect and helpless condition characteristic of all the marsupials, is hard to divine." Beddard's "Mammalia" [87] (pages 14–18) should be consulted for fuller treatment of this subject.

The origin of the pouch, as an advantageous feature, is probably due to the arboreal habits which are believed [226] to have been characteristic of all the ancestral marsupials, the coming down to earth (assumption of terrestrial habits) being a comparatively modern matter affecting only certain groups of this class.

In regard to the early history of this group, Dr. W. D. Matthew writes me as follows: —

"Recent studies by W. J. Sinclair have shown that the thylacine, although now found only in Australia and Tasmania, is the last survivor of a group of carnivorous marsupials which inhabited South America during the Tertiary period, and took the place in that continent of the true Carnivora of the northern world. Since none of these animals, living or extinct, has been found in any of the northern continents, it appears most reasonable to suppose that the thylacines reached Australia from South America (or vice versa) through a former land connection by way of the Antarctic regions, an hypothesis supported by many other resemblances between the animals and plants, recent and extinct, of the three southern continents. About the middle of the Tertiary period Africa became connected with Europe, and at a later epoch South America with North America, the south polar land connections having in the meanwhile sunk below the ocean. The more active, powerful, and intelligent carnivorous animals of the northern world were thus enabled to extend their range into the southern continents, and soon displaced and destroyed all their marsupial predecessors in those regions, while Australia, still separated by ocean from the northern land masses, retained its ancient population of marsupial carnivores."

The true opossums are a family (Didelphidæ) related to the dasyures, but never represented in Australia. It is the lowest family in rank of organization and the one most ancient in lineage, for it seems to have become well **Opossums.** established in the Cretaceous, and widely distributed throughout the northern world during that and the Eocene periods. No other marsupial group, so far as known, approaches this in antiquity, save the banded ant-eaters; yet so little change has occurred that teeth from the Laramie formations of Wyoming are hardly distinguishable from those in the jaws of our 'possum-up-a-gum-tree to-day. No wonder the quaint creature is hoary and wrinkled; he is a very Methuselah among mammals, and looks it! All opossums seem to have disappeared from

THE NORTH AMERICAN OPOSSUM.

Europe, however, before the close of the Miocene, but continued to survive numerously in South America, and that continent to-day is the headquarters of the race. They probably owe their long career, in competition with animals of so much higher grade, to their small size, forest life, nocturnal habits, ability to eat all sorts of food, and, most of all, to their great fecundity.

With all this historical background, the gray, snarling, pilfering, dunderheaded, and motherly opossum of our southern woods becomes respectable. You may make his acquaintance from New York to Iowa and California and southward to Patagonia, and will note several varieties of tint in his ragged, "mussed-up" coat. He (and she) are almost as familiar in Dixie as rabbits, and have been laughed at in parlor, cabin, and camp ever since Captain John Smith reported among the wonders of Virginia: "The Opassom hath a head like a Swine, a Tayle like a Bat, as bigge as a Cat, and hath under her belly a Bag wherin she carrieth her young." Then there was another man, quoted in "Purchas His Pilgrimage" (London, 1617) who declared: "They have a monstrous deformed beast, whose fore part resembleth a Fox, the hinder part an Ape, excepting the feet which are like a man's; beneath her belly she hath a receptacle like a purse, wherin she bestows her young, until they can shift for themselves, never coming out of this natural nest but to sucke."

This must have been both startling and puzzling to the readers of that day, yet it was not so wide of the mark if we recall that then "monstrous" meant simply marvelous, and the likeness of the feet to a man's referred to the plantigrade tracks they left. The statement that the young came out of the pouch to nurse was only the first of a long list of errors in respect to the strange reproductive processes of this little beast, which, it must be remembered, was the first marsupial with which naturalists became familiar, and that the early zoölogists had little help from Australia in solving the problem. Dr. John Bachman, who wrote the extended and excellent account of this animal (as of most others) in Audubon and Bachman's "Quadrupeds," [90] appears to have been really the first to penetrate the mystery, or at any rate to make its explanation known; and he did not learn it all. He tells us that 15 days elapse between conception and the birth of the young, and that they remain in the pouch about five weeks before they first begin to climb over their mother. They are then, to use Sharp's words, about the size of full-grown mice, and the dearest of wood babies.

"They have sharp, pink noses, snapping black eyes, gray fur, and the longest, barest tails. I think that the most interesting picture I ever saw in the woods was an old mother opossum with eleven little young ones clinging to her. She was standing off a dog as I came up, and every one of the eleven was peeking out, immensely enjoying this first adventure. The quizzing snouts of six were poked out in a bunch from the cradle pouch, while the other five mites were upon their mother's back, where they had been playing Jack-and-the-beanstalk up and down her tail."

An old number of *The American Naturalist* (September, 1886) contains a capital story of the wild creatures which used to come at night about the cabin of the writer, I. Lancaster, who had made a temporary hermit of himself in the South Florida wilds. By placing a strong light in the low window he could easily watch from behind it the creatures which nightly assembled to eat of the scraps thrown out to attract them. "This kind of lamplight scrutiny," he records, "was of never-failing interest. The animals were fresh from the hand of nature and on their native heath. The opossums were particularly interesting; when several females with their broods were on hand, there occurred a mixing of families, for the mother which had secured a bone at once shook off her progeny while she ate it. Her discarded infants would fasten on the nearest female, and sometimes a single mother went about with four families of children hanging to her. When a fox appeared, the incumbered animal at once took to the bushes, the others covering her retreat with wide-open mouths which, with their serried rows of teeth, seemed indeed formidable. Reynard always respected this show of ivory, as the raccoons did also. But in spite of all the precautions taken by the mothers, a strict count of children after home was reached would show loss. When they were shaken off, one would be a little late in regaining a position of safety, and in the hurry consequent on the fox's arrival, this tardy scrambler would prove to be the one not fitted to survive. It left no legacy to its descendants, for it never had any."

The young stay with their dams about two months; nor are these little mothers ever long free from the burden and anxiety of a big family, for hardly has one litter dispersed than another arrives. Thus the multiplication of opossums is almost as rapid as that of mice or rabbits, and they form one of the mainstays in the menu of all the carnivores not only of our woods, but of the countries south of the United States. To attempt to relate the ways and means of the opossum in detail would far overtax my space. Let me better quote a summary by a keen old observer, Dr. Lincecum of Texas, and then pass on to a brief notice of that peculiar behavior which has given our language the expressive verb to play "'possum": —

"They dwell in hollow logs, stumps, and in holes at the root of trees," writes Lincecum in *The American Naturalist* for September, 1872. "They do not burrow or prepare dens for themselves, but find such as are ready made. I have seen them carrying into their holes at the approach of cold weather considerable bundles of dry leaves rolled up in their tail [like rat kangaroos, — see page 499]; they understand the signs of the coming spells of bad weather, and they prepare for it by making themselves a good warm bed. They do not hibernate, but are found out hunting in frosty weather. They possess but little caution. Hence they are often found in the poultry houses, chicken coops, smokehouses, and even in our dining rooms, rattling about in search of something to eat. I have often seen their tracks in the roads and paths, where they had traveled three or four miles to a farmyard, to which they had no doubt been directed by the crowing of the roosters. They will catch a grown hen and drag her off, squalling at the top of her voice, and will not abandon her until the dogs which have been aroused by the uproar have overtaken and begun cracking their bones. They will eat bacon, dry beef, carrion, any kind of fowl, rabbits, any sort of small game, and fruits of every variety. They voraciously devour the muskmelon, and several species of mushrooms; in short, they are nearly omnivorous. . . . During their rutting season the males are very rampant and belligerent. Numbers will collect around a female and fight like dogs."

Often when this animal, or any of its tropical relatives, finds itself cornered or attacked, it will suddenly fall limp and dead; "and when the opossum plays 'possum he invariably **Playing** draws back the gums from his glittering white teeth **'Possum.** until he looks as if he might have been dead a month." You may roll him about with your foot, or pick him up and carry him away by the tail or offer him any indignity you please and he will "keep on sayin' nuffin"; but don't turn your back on him or his little black shoe-button eyes will steal open and he will suddenly spring up and away; and don't let your hand get too near his jaws or a fierce bite is likely to reveal the savage beneath the actor. Foxes and a good many other animals will play the same ruse, and ordinary folks have taken the thing for what it seems, and called it an instinctive feigning of death.

S. M. Lottridge, Phot.

PLAYING 'POSSUM.

Others have asserted that it is really a case of being frightened into a paralysis, — that it is not pretense at all, but an actual swooning from terror. But those who best know the little beast cling to the old notion.

"I have known the 'possum too long," exclaims Professor Sharp, "for a ready faith in his extreme nervousness, too long to believe him so hysterical that the least surprise can frighten him into fits. He has a reasonable fear of dogs; no fear at all of cats; and will take his chances any night with a coon for the possession of a hollow log. He will live in the same burrow with other 'possums, with owls, — with anything in fact, — and overlook any bearable imposition; he will run away from everything, venture anywhere, and manage to escape from the most impossible situations. Is this an epileptic, unstrung, flighty creature? Possibly; but look at him. He rolls in fat; and how long has obesity been the peculiar accompaniment of nervousness?"

A more important question is: Of what good is the ruse? How many enemies are sufficiently deceived by it to go away and leave him undisturbed? Would a cat, a wolf, or a big owl neglect to seize an opossum and eat him because he pretended death? What do they care whether he is dead or not — if it is true, they have been saved some trouble. Lincecum states that in Texas "turkey buzzards will alight near where they find an opossum feeding in the woods, and running up on him will flap their wings violently over him a few times, when the opossum goes into a spasm, and the buzzards very deliberately proceed to pick out its exposed eyes and generally take a pretty good bite from its neck and shoulders; the opossum lying on its side all the time and grunting. I have twice seen a buzzard do as described." Beside this must be placed the universal testimony that a mother opossum will sit up and defend her babies against anything and everything, — no fainting for her! (Is it, I wonder, only the roaming males who "play 'possum"?) It is difficult to see how any animal, friend or foe, that comes near enough to cause an opossum to play dead, or fall into a fit, or whatever it is that he does do, and consequently comes near enough to smell the warmth and odor of the creature's body, could be deceived for a moment; yet if it neither deceives nor defends, of what service is the act? May it not be merely a survival of a practice, now obsolete, involuntary, and really

Copyrt., N. Y. Z. S.   Sanborn, Phot.
MURINE OPOSSUM.

harmful, originating and apt in the remote history of this "last leaf" on the ancestral tree of American zoölogy,— a good habit gone wrong!

In addition to the common opossum no less than 22 species are catalogued in Central and South America. Many of them are no larger than mice,—for example, the murine opossum, which strays across our southwestern border; others are little known, but all seem much alike in their manner of life. The notable exception is the yapock, a water-loving species about the size of a large rat, with webbed hind feet, and aquatic preferences. It inhabits the rivers from Guatemala to southern Brazil, is comparatively rare, and is believed to live chiefly on crustacea, insects, and an occasional fish. "The female has a well-developed pouch, in which the young, usually five in number, are carried for some time; and it will be obvious that during that period the creature must refrain from entering the water. Later on the young accompany their parent to the river, and are exercised by her in swimming and in diving."

This ends the list of eutherian mammals.

RABBIT BANDICOOT.

EGG–LAYING MAMMALS — Subclass, PROTOTHERIA : Order, MONOTREMATA

THERE remain to be accounted for those strange, antique mammals, the duckbill and echidnas, which stand in a group inferior to and widely separated from the remainder of the class. Of their fossil history no evidences have been discovered beyond the most recent past (Pleistocene), yet there can be no doubt that they represent a very primitive type. Their anatomy, fully sketched and discussed in Beddard's [37] and other recent textbooks, displays many very archaic features, some bearing a close resemblance to reptilian modes of structure. There is no question of their generally inferior place in classification; and hence comes their designation Prototheria ("primitive beasts") to take the place of the less precise name "Ornithodelphia." They are often spoken of as "monotremes."

Their most conspicuous peculiarity lies in the method of reproduction : —

All animals begin as eggs; and in all the lower forms of vertebrates (fishes, amphibians, reptiles, and birds) the embryo is formed and remains until far advanced in growth within the protective envelopes (shell) of the egg, **Eggs.** which in most cases is dropped from the body of the parent at an early stage, and among the higher ranks is thereafter warmed and cared for until the embryo is prepared to come forth; and this egg contains a quantity of food material (yolk, etc.). In placental mammals, however, the nutriment necessary for the growth of the embryo is supplied not by the egg but by the mother's blood. In implacental mammals (marsupials) a small amount of material is furnished by the egg, and when this is exhausted the embryo is voided, placed in a protective pouch and thereafter nourished and increased by milk forced into its system. Now in the Prototheria the egg is comparatively large, contains much food yolk, and in fact resembles that of a turtle, even to the parchmentlike shell; and it is laid and brooded in a manner very similar to that of some sea birds, especially the penguins, until the embryo has utilized all its contents and is ready to come out — not as perfect as a young penguin would be, but far more advanced than a marsupial "larva."

This process, then, is outside of the established order of mammalian reproduction, but is remarkable only because of its resemblance to the methods of the inferior vertebrates. Hence it is an indication of low and "generalized" organization and rank in the mammalian scale. Further indication of this is given in the fact that when the embryos come out of the eggs they are not able, as are infant reptiles, birds, and the like, to take general food, but must for a time subsist on milk like other mammals. The provision for nursing, however, in this group, is very imperfect; and for a full explanation of it such text-books as Parker and Haswell's "Zoölogy"[2] should be consulted. Briefly, instead of the milk-secreting glands opening at the surface in teats the skin of that part of the abdomen overlying them is thin and bare and shows no nipples at all; at the time when the young arrive this area will yield milk at two points indicated by tufts of hair, which presumably guide the sensitive nose of the half-witted youngster to the right place at which to suck.

As might be expected, all the Prototheria are Australian; nor is there evidence of their ever having existed in any other part of the world, unless it be conceded that the Mesozoic "multi-tuberculates" were their ancestors.

Existing representatives of this remarkable group are few, — only the duckbill and the spiny ant-eaters.

The duckbill (Ornithorhynchus) is an animal eighteen to twenty inches long, inhabiting the rivers of Australia, Tasmania, and New Guinea, which manifests its aquatic nature in its form, fur, and great paddling feet provided with a webbing two sizes too large. **Duckbill.**

The skin is loose and thickly covered with glossy hair, having an under layer of soft, short, waterproof fur, like that of a beaver. The head is small and round, with small bright eyes, and no external ears, although the internal ears are perfectly developed, and the hearing acute; and in-

DUCKBILL, PLATYPUS, OR ORNITHORHYNCHUS.

stead of the muzzle, mouth, and teeth of an ordinary quadruped, the creature is furnished with a bill like that of a duck, and incloses the jaws within an extremely sensitive naked skin, grayish in color, which is raised into a frill-like fold that protects the eyes when the animal is probing mud; and which in mounted specimens dries hard. The nostrils are at the extremity of the upper mandible; the lower mandible has transverse lamellæ, somewhat like the bill of a duck; and each jaw is furnished with two pairs of horny plates, serving the purpose of teeth for the adults; but true cheek teeth are present in young animals. The tongue is small, partly covered with horny spines, and may direct the food collected into two large cheek pouches, where it can be stored and conveniently carried to the burrow or other eating place. An interesting feature is the strong horny spurs on the heels of the male, which are movable and traversed by a minute canal opening at the point, and connected at the base with the duct from a large venom gland in the back part of the thigh.

A duckbill spends its whole life in or near its chosen river, but with its companions is as shy and hard to get sight of as a beaver. Each pair digs and occupies a long burrow in the bank, entered beneath the water, and bedded in its chambered extremity with grass, where they stay asleep through the daytime, and where the young are hatched. Bennett [263] gave the fullest account of their habits half a century ago.

"The food consists of aquatic insects, small crustaceans and worms, which are caught under water, the sand and small stones at the bottom being turned over with the bill. The creatures appear at first to deposit what they have thus collected in their cheek pouches, and when these are filled they rise to the surface and quietly triturate their meal with the horny plates before swallowing it." This food is discovered in the mud by touch and by smell, of which those studied in captivity show a remarkably high development. The eyes are small and half hidden, but perfect and useful. The animal's voice resembles the growl of a young puppy, but its disposition is gentle.

The duckbill lays eggs which are white, .75 x .50 inch in dimensions, and contain a large amount of food yolk. Only a few eggs are laid at a time, often only one; and it is hatched in a short time. The young are blind and naked at birth, and suck their mother's milk from a little pit in her nippleless breast.

The spiny ant-eaters form a distinct family (Echidnidæ), with probably one highly variable species of the genus Echidna, **Echidnas.** found all over Australia, and a relative (Proechidna) in New Guinea. In both the body is small, 15 to 18 inches long, broad and carried by very short, strong legs terminating in big claws. The head is small, and the nose prolonged into a slender snout covered with a moist black membrane like a dog's nose. The mouth is without teeth, but the palate is studded with recurved spines, and the tongue is slender, extensile, and glutinous. The back is covered with stiff, hedgehoglike spines, mixed with long, coarse hairs; and when danger threatens it outside its burrow, it curls up much like a hedgehog, so as to protect the under parts, which have no spines but are clothed in silky brown hair. The males have spurs on their heels, like the duckbill, but have never been seen to use them. It dwells in burrows of its own digging, and feeds upon ants caught precisely after the manner of other ant-eaters; and in captivity, where it makes a gentle and intelligent pet, is fond of scrambling about whatever it is allowed to climb.[265]

Its Papuan cousin, the nodiak, is larger, with a much more prolonged snout and tongue, and but three front toes.

AN ECHIDNA, OR SPINY ANT-EATER.

The aborigines hunt it for food in the mountain by the aid of dogs which know how to dislodge it from its burrow.

The reproductive process in this family differs somewhat from that among the duckbills; for here, instead of the eggs being laid in a burrow nest, and covered by the mother, like a brooding hen, the echidna's egg is placed by the lips of the mother within two parallel folds of skin which at that season form a deep groove in the abdomen inclosing the nursing area, and is held there until it hatches, the young ant-eater breaking out at last by aid of an "egg tooth," or temporary hard tip on the nose. When the young has attained a certain size the mother removes it from the "pouch," but takes it in from time to time to suckle it. At night it is necessary for her to ramble in search of her own subsistence, and in order to leave her child safe during these absences she digs a small burrow wherever she happens to be and hides the little one within it.

BRAIN OF *Echidna aculeata*, DORSAL VIEW. (NATURAL SIZE.)

AUTHORITIES CITED

The numbers preceding the titles are those by which the books are referred to in the raised figures in the lines of the text.

Those works in the following list which are text-books are numbered 1, 2, 16, 37, 59, 60, 84, 95, 98, and 135.

1. HUXLEY, T. H., Anatomy of Vertebrated Animals. (New York, 1878.)
2. PARKER, T. J., and HASWELL, W. A., Text-book of Zoölogy. (New York, 1897.)
3. FORBES, H. O. A Handbook to the Primates. (*Allen's Naturalist's Library ;* London, 1894.)
4. DUBOIS, EUGENE. Article in *Anatomischer Anzeiger*, Vol. XII, translated into English and reprinted in the Smithsonian Report for 1898. See also Marsh, *Am. Journal of Science*, Vol. I, 1896.
5. HUXLEY, T. H. Man's Place in Nature. (Collected Essays, London,1894.)
6. DU CHAILLU, PAUL. Explorations and Adventures in Equatorial Africa. (New York, 1861.) Gorilla Land. (New York, 1868.)
7. HARTMANN, ROBERT. Anthropoid Apes. (*International Scientific Series*, New York, 1886.)
8. LIVINGSTONE, DAVID. Last Journals ; edited by H. Walter. (London, 1874.) See also Johnston's Livingstone and the Exploration of Central Africa. (London, 1897.)
9. SCHWEINFURTH, GEORG. The Heart of Africa. (London, 1874.)
10. LYDEKKER, RICHARD (editor). The Royal Natural History. (6 vols., London, 1895 +.) Reissued in New York as " The New Natural History."
11. KIPLING, J. S. Beast and Man in India. (London, 1891.)
12. WALLACE, ALFRED RUSSEL. The Geographical Distribution of Animals. (New York, 1875.) Other important authorities on this subject are Murray, Sclater, Newton, Gadow, Beddard, Lydekker, Heilprin, Merriam, and Allen.
13. ROMANES, J. G. Article in *Proceedings Zoölogical Society of London*, 1889.
14. MARTIN, M. Natural History of Mammiferous Animals, with a Particular View of the . . . Monkeys. (London, 1841.)
15. BRODERIP, W. J. Zoölogical Recreations. (Philadelphia, 1849.)

16. FLOWER, W. H., and LYDEKKER, R. Mammals Living and Extinct. (London, 1891.) ☞ Recommended for use with this book.

17. TENNENT, SIR J. E. Ceylon, Physical, Historical, and Topographical. (London, 1859.)

18. JOHNSTON, SIR HARRY H. Kilimanjaro. (London, 1885.)

19. BLANFORD, W. T. Fauna of British India: Mammals. (London, 1888.)

20. INGERSOLL, ERNEST. Articles in *New International Encyclopædia* on subjects cited. (New York, 1903.)

21. DESFONTAINES, RENÉ-LUICHE. Fragmens d'un Voyage dans les Régences d'Alger. (Paris, 1838.)

22. DARWIN, CHARLES. The Descent of Man; and Selection in relation to Sex. (London, 2d ed., 1874.)

23. BLANFORD, W. T. Geology and Zoölogy of Abyssinia. (Lond., 1870.)

24. WATERTON, C. Wanderings in South America. (London, 1828.)

25. BATES, H. W. The Naturalist on the River Amazon. (London, 3d ed., 1873.)

26. BELT, THOS. A Naturalist in Nicaragua. (London, 2d ed., 1888.)

27. WALLACE, A. R. Travels on the Amazon and Rio Negro. (London, 1853.) Reprinted in *Minerva Library*.

28. HAECKEL, ERNEST. The Evolution of Man. Translated by J. McCabe from 5th German edition. (London, 1905.) The Lost Link: our present Knowledge of the Descent of Man, with notes by Hans Gadow. (1898.)

29. BROOKE, RAJAH JAMES. Ten Years in Sarawak. (London, 1866.)

30. HORNADAY, WM. T. Two Years in the Jungle. (New York, 1886.)

31. WALLACE, A. R. The Malay Archipelago. (New York, 1869.)

32. BAIRD, S. F. Zoölogy of the United States and Mexican Boundary Survey. (Washington, 1859.)

33. IM THURN, E. F. Among the Indians of Guiana. (London, 1883.)

34. BROWN, C. B. Canoe and Camp Life in British Guiana. (London, '99.)

35. HUDSON, W. H. The Naturalist in La Plata. (London, 1892.)

36. INGERSOLL, ERNEST. Wild Neighbors: Outdoor Studies in the Natural History of the United States. (New York, 1897.)

37. BEDDARD, F. E. Mammalia. (Cambridge, 1902.)

Volume X of the Cambridge Natural History, a series of treatises covering the whole range of zoölogy. It admirably supplements the present work by giving extensive additional information as to structure and classification. ☞ Recommended for use with this book.

38. HOSE, CHARLES L. Mammals of Borneo. (London, 1893.)

39. CUMMING, GORDON. Wild Beasts and Wild Men. (N.Y., 1888.)

40. BARON, L. Habits of the Aye-Aye. (*Proc. Zoöl. Soc. of London*, 1882.)
41. BARTLETT, A. D. Wild Animals in Captivity. (New York, 1899.)
42. FORSYTH-MAJOR, C. J. Articles in *Novitates Zoölogicæ*.
43. GRANDIDIER, G., and MILNE-EDWARDS, A. Histoire Naturelle de Madagascar: Mammifères. (Paris, 1875.)
44. JERDON, T. C. Mammals of British India. (London, 1865.)
45. FLOWER, STANLEY. Articles in *Proc. Zoöl. Soc. of London*, 1900.
46. DOBSON, GEORGE E. Catalogue of the Cheiroptera of the British Museum; Monograph of Asiatic Bats. (London, 1877.) Special papers, mostly in *Proceedings Zoölogical Society of London*.
47. SPALLANZANI, L. Observations on the Organs of Vision in Bats. (Title of translation by Tilloch, published in the *Philosophical Magazine*, Vol. I, London, 1798.)
48. MERRIAM, C. HART. Natural History of the Adirondacks; in *Transactions Linnæan Society of New York*, Vols. I and II. (1893-6.)
49. ALLEN, H. A Monograph of the Bats of North America. (*Bulletin U.S. Nat. Mus.*, No. 43; Washington, 1893.)
50. MILLER, G. S. A Revision of the North American Bats of the Family Vespertilionidæ. (*N. Am. Fauna*, No. 13; Washington, 1897.)
51. FISHER, A. K. The Mammals of Singsing, N.Y. (*The Observer*, Portland, Conn., 1896.)
52. STONE, WITMER, and CRAM, WM. E. American Animals. (New York, 1902.)
53. GOSSE, P. A Naturalist's Sojourn in Jamaica. (London, 1851.)
54. BURTON, R. F. A Pilgrimage to El Medineh and Mecca. (New York, 1856.)
55. ANDERSON, JOHN. Zoölogy of Egypt. (London, 1898-1902.)
56. KENNICOTT, ROBERT. Quadrupeds of Illinois. (*Ann. Rept. U.S. Dept. Agriculture*, Washington, 1851.)
57. HORSFIELD, THOS. Zoölogical Researches in Java. (London, 1824.)
58. WILKINSON, SIR JOHN. Manners and Customs of the Ancient Egyptians. (London, 1878.)
59. ZITTEL-EASTMAN. Text-book of Paleontology by Karl von Zittel, translated and edited by C. R. Eastman [and other specialists]. Part I, Invertebrates. (1900.) Part II, Fishes, Amphibians, and Reptiles. (New York, 1902.) Part III, Birds and Mammals. (Unpublished.) ☞ Recommended for use with this book.
60. WOODWARD, A. S. Outlines of Vertebrate Paleontology. (New York, 1898.)
61. DOBSON, G. E. A Monograph of the Insectivora. (London, 1886-90.)
62. WHITE, GILBERT. The Natural History of Selborne. (Harting's edition, London, 1888.)

63. WOOD, REV. J. G.   Homes without Hands.   (New York, 1870.)
64. POEY, FELIPE.   Memorias sobre la Historia National de la Isla de Cuba.   (Havana, 1860.)
65. LYDEKKER, R.   Mostly Mammals: Zoölogical Essays.   (London, 1903.)
66. HUMBOLDT, BARON FREDERICK.   Narrative of Voyages.   (Paris, 1804.)
67. MACCURDY, G. C.   The Eolithic Problem: Evidences of a Rude Industry antedating the Paleolithic.   (*American Anthropologist*, n. s. Vol. VII; Washington, 1905.)
68. BAILEY, V.   Biological Survey of Texas.   (*N. Am. Fauna*, No. 25; Washington, 1905.)
69. DARWIN, CHARLES.   Variation of Animals and Plants under Domestication.   (New York, 1896.)
70. KNIGHT, K. W.   The Book of the Rabbit.   (London, 1889.)
71. MORANT, G. F.   Rabbit Farming.   (London, 1890.)
72. SHARPE, D. L.   Wild Life near Home.   (New York, 1901.)
73. PALMER, T. S.   The Jack Rabbits of the United States.   (*Bulletin* No. 8, *U.S. Dept. Agriculture;* Washington, 1896.)
74. TRUE, F. W.   A Revision of the American Moles.   (*Proc. U.S. Nat. Mus.*, Vol. XIX; Washington, 1896.)
75. STANDARD, or RIVERSIDE, NATURAL HISTORY.   Vol. V, Mammals. (Boston, 1884.) Has articles by Theo Gill, Elliott Coues, R. Ramsay Wright, W. B. Scott, W. N. Lockington, J. S. Kingsley.
76. HUDSON, W. H.   Habits of the Vizcachas.   (*Proc. Zoöl. Soc. of London*, 1872.)
77. DARWIN, CHARLES.   Voyage of a Naturalist.   (London, 1860; New York, 1879.)
78. OSGOOD, W. H.   Revision of the Pocket Mice of the Genus Perognathus.   (*N. Am. Fauna*, No. 18; Washington, 1900.)
79. SETON, E. T.   The Kangaroo Rat.   (*Scribner's Magazine*, New York, April, 1900.)
80. COUES, ELLIOTT.   A study of the Genera Geomys and Thomomys. (Powell's Exploration of the Colorado River; Washington, 1875.)
81. MERRIAM, C. H.   Revision of the Pocket Gophers.   (*N. Am. Fauna*, No. 8; Washington, 1895.)
82. BAILEY, V.   The Pocket Gophers of the United States.   (*Bulletin* 5, *U.S. Dept. Agriculture;* Washington, 1895.)
83. DAWKINS, WM. BOYD.   Cave Hunting. (London, 1874.)   British Pleistocene Mammalia.   (London, 1866-7.)
84. BAIRD, SPENCER F.   Zoölogy of Pacific Railroad Reports: Vol. VIII, Mammals.   (Washington, 1857.)

85. MILLER, G. S.   Voles and Lemmings.   (*N. Am. Fauna*, No. 12; Washington, 1896.)

86. PREBLE, E. A.   A Biological Investigation of the Hudson Bay Region. (*N. Am. Fauna*, No. 22; Washington, 1902.)

87. INGERSOLL, ERNEST.   Country Cousins: Short Studies in the Natural History of the United States.   (New York, 1884.)

88. RODWAY, J.   In the Guiana Forest.   (London, 1895.)

89. APLIN, O. V.   Mammals of Uruguay.   (*Proc. Zoöl. Soc. of London,* 1894.)

90. AUDUBON, J. J., and BACHMAN, J.   The Quadrupeds of North America.   (New York, 1846.)

91. GODMAN, JOHN D.   American Natural History.   (Philadelphia, 3d ed., 1836.)

92. MAUNDER, S.   The Treasury of Natural History.   (London, 1862.)

93. BELL, THOS. History of British Quadrupeds. (London, 2d ed., 1874.)

94. INGERSOLL, ERNEST.   Wild Life of Orchard and Field.   (New York, 1902.)

95. HORNADAY, W. T.   The American Natural History: a Foundation of Useful Knowledge of the Higher Animals of North America. (New York, 1904.)

96. WATERTON, C.   Essays on Natural History.   (New York, undated.)

97. COPE, E. D.   Intelligence in Monkeys.   (*Am. Naturalist*, Vol. XI, 1872.)

98. ELLIOT, D. G.   Synopsis of the Mammals of North America.   (Chicago, 1901.)   The Land and Sea Mammals of Middle America and the West Indies.   (Chicago, 1904.)   Both are technical publications of the Field Columbian Museum.

99. ABBOTT, C. C.   Upland and Meadow.   (New York, 1886.)

100. CRAM, W. E.   Little Beasts of Field and Wood.   (Boston, 1899.)

101. AFLALO, B. F.   Sport in Europe.   (London, 1901.)

102. PERKINS, G. H.   Articles on Flying Squirrels, in *Am. Naturalist,* Vol. VII, 1873, pp. 132–138; Vol. XVII, 1883, pp. 36–42.   See also Nos. 48, 52, 56, 90, 99, and 100.

103. GROUND-SQUIRRELS.   For these (Chipmunks and Spermophiles) consult: Allen, J. A., Review of the genus Tamias, *Bulletin Am. Mus. Nat. Hist.*, Vol. III (New York, 1890); Bailey, V., The Prairie Ground-Squirrels or Spermophiles of the Mississippi Valley (U.S. Dept. Agriculture, Washington, 1893); and articles in *Am. Naturalist*, Vol. IV, p. 249; Vol. VII, p. 695.   See also Nos. 48, 52, 56, 90, 91, and 105.

104. INGRAM, J. N.   The Australian Rabbit Plague.   (*Lippincott's Magazine,* Philadelphia, 1893, p. 751.)

105. ABBOTT, C. C.   Wasteland Wanderings.   (New York, 1887.)

106. COUES, E.   The Prairie Gopher, in *Am. Naturalist*, Vol. IX, 1875.

107. SEMPER, CARL.   Animal Life as affected by the Natural Conditions of Existence.   (New York, 1881.)

108. MILLS, WESLEY.   The Nature and Development of Animal Intelligence.   (New York, 1898.)

109. HARTING, J. E.   British Animals extinct within Historic Times. (London, 1880.)

110. BEAVERS.   Consult: Morgan, Lewis H., The American Beaver and his Works (Philadelphia, 1868); Martin, H. T., Castorologia (Montreal, 1892); Hulbert, W. D., Story of the Beaver (*McClure's Magazine*, April, 1901); Dugmore, A. R., Haunts of the Beaver (Nipissing District, Ontario) (*Everybody's Magazine*, December, 1901).

111. ALLEN, J. A.   Seasonal Variations in the Red Squirrel.   (*Bulletin Am. Mus. Nat. Hist.*, Vol. III, 1890.)

112. MERRIAM, C. HART.   The San Francisco Mountain Region.   (*N. Am. Fauna*, No. 3; Washington, 1890.)

113. MERRIAM, C. HART.   Mammals of Idaho.   (*N. Am. Fauna*, No. 5; Washington, 1891.)

114. ALSTON, E.   Biologia Centrali-Americana: Mammals.   (London, 1879–82.)

115. CUMBERLAND, C.   The Guinea Pig: for Food, Fur and Fancy. (London, 1886.)

116. COPE, E. D.   Extinct Rodentia of North America (*Am. Naturalist*, Vol. XVII, 1883, pp. 43, 165, 370); Cope, Tertiary Vertebrata (*U.S. Geol. Survey Territories*, Vol. III, p. 202); Marsh, O. C., (*Am. Jour. Science*, Vol. XI, 1876, p. 249).   See Nos. 60, 98.

117. HUDSON, W. H.   Articles in *Proc. Zoöl. Soc. of London*, 1875.

118. COPE, E. D.   The Creodonta.   (*Am. Naturalist*, Vol. XVIII, 1884, pp. 255, 344, 478.)

119. SCOTT, W. B.   The Evolution of the Mammalia.   (*International Monthly*, June and July, 1901.)

120. OSWALD, FELIX.   Zoölogical Sketches.   (Philadelphia, 1883.)

121. JOHANNA.   For a scientific history, see *Proc. Zoöl. Soc. of London*, 1899.   See also Hartmann, Anthropoid Apes (N.Y. 1886).

122. COPE, E. D.   The Extinct Dogs of North America.   (*Am. Naturalist*, Vol. XVII, 1883, p. 248; also *Proc. Acad. Sciences of Philadelphia*, 1875, p. 447.)

123. COPE, E. D.   Origin of the Specialized Teeth of Carnivora.   (*Am. Naturalist*, Vol. XIII, 1879, p. 171.)

124. CORNISH, C. J.   Animals at Work and Play.   (London, 2d ed., 1897.)

125. JOHNSON, LINDSAY. Observations on the Eyes of Seals and of the Felidæ. (*Proc. Zoöl. Soc. of London*, 1893, p. 719; 1894.)

126. PORTER, J. HAMPDEN. Wild Beasts. (New York, 1874.)

127. SPEARS, J. R. Gold-diggings of Cape Horn. (New York, 1895).

128. ROOSEVELT, THEODORE. Outdoor Pastimes of an American Hunter. (New York, 1905.)

129. PERRY, W. A. Contribution to Shield's Big Game of North America. (Chicago, 1890.)

130. EASTMAN, C. A. The Red Hunters and the Animal People. (New York, 1905.)

131. AZARA, FELIX DE. Natural History of the Quadrupeds of Paraguay and the River La Plata. Translated from the Spanish by Hunter. (London, 1838.)

132. HAMILTON, Dr. E. The Wildcat of Europe. (London, 1896.)

133. WATKINS, M. G. The Natural History of the Ancients. (London, 1896.)

134. ELLIOT, D. G. A Monograph of the Felidæ. (Folio, colored plates; London, 1878.)

135. MIVART, ST. GEORGE. The Cat. (New York, 1892.)

136. NEUMAN, A. H. Elephant Hunting in East Equatorial Africa, etc. (London, 1898.)

137. LANKESTER, E. RAY. Extinct Animals. (London, 1905.)

138. REPPLIER, AGNES. The Fireside Sphinx. (New York, 1901.)

139. BLYTH, E. A Monograph of the Species of Lynx. *Journal Asiatic Society of Bengal.* (Calcutta, 1842.)

140. BALDWIN, J. H. The Large and Small Game of Bengal. (London, 1877.)

141. LA CROIX, PAUL. Mœurs, Usages, et Costumes au Moyen Âge. (Paris, 1871.)

142. CUMMING, R. GORDON. Five Years of a Hunter's Life in South Africa. (New York, 1850.)

143. BAKER, SIR SAMUEL. In the Heart of Africa. (New York, 1884.)

144. DRUMMOND, W. H. The Large Game and Natural History of South Africa. (Edinburgh, 1875.)

145. CAMERON, LIEUT. V. L. Across Africa. (London, 1876.)

146. GIBBONS, A. ST. H. Exploration and Hunting in South Africa. (London, 1898.)

147. BAKER, SIR S. Wild Beasts and their Ways. (New York, 1898.)

148. EL MANGALI, SIDI MOHAMMED. Traité de Vénerie. Traduit de l'Arabe par Florian Pharaon. (Paris, 1880.)

149. ANDERSSON, C. J. Lake Ngami. (New York, 1857.)

150. SELOUS, F. C. A Hunter's Wanderings in Africa. (London, 1895.)

151. DELAMERE, LORD. Lion Hunting. (*Badminton Mag.*, May, 1896.)
152. SCHULZ (and HAMMAR). New Africa. (London, 1897.)
153. STERNDALE, R. A. Mammalia of India. (Calcutta, 1884.)
154. FAYRER, SIR JOSEPH. Royal Tiger of Bengal. (London, 1875.)
155. CAMPBELL, W. My Indian Journal. (London, 1864.)
156. POLLOK, COL. F. T. Incidents of Sport and Travel. (London, 1894.) Wild Sports of Burma and Assam. (London, 1900.)
157. RICE, W. Indian Game: from Quail to Tiger. (London, 1884.)
158. SHAKESPEAR, LT. COL. H. Wild Sports of India. (London, 1865.)
159. MACINTYRE, MAJ. GEN. D. Hindu-Koh; Wanderings and Wild Sports on and beyond the Himalayas. (London, 1892.)
160. KINLOCH, CAPT. A. A. A. Large Game Shooting in Thibet. (Calcutta, 3d ed. 1892.)
161. LEVESON, H. A. Sport in Many Lands. (London, 1880.)
162. SANDERSON, G. P. Thirteen Years among the Wild Beasts of India. (London, 1893.)
163. BEVAN, MAJOR H. Thirty Years in India. (London, 1839.)
164. BROWN, J. MORAY. Shikar Sketches. (London, 1887.) Stray Sport. (1893.)
165. HOLUB, EMIL. Seven Years in South Africa. (London, 1881.)
166. INGLIS, JAMES. Tent Life in Tiger Land, with which is incorporated Sport and Work on the Nepaul Frontier. (London, 1892.)
167. BARRAS, JULIUS. India and Tiger Hunting. (London, 1885.)
168. HALL, BASIL. Voyages and Travels. (London, 1831-3.)
169. FORSYTH, JAMES. Highlands of Central India. (London, 1889.)
170. MORRIS, D. The Mungoose on Sugar Estates in the West Indies.
     Reviewed with extensive comments in *Am. Naturalist*, Vol. XVII, 1883, p. 299. See also *The Field*, London, May 6, 1882, and July 13, 1895.
171. TOPSELL, REV. EDWARD. Historie of Four-footed Beastes. (London, 1607.)
172. MARTIN, MRS. A. Home Life on an Ostrich Farm. (London, 1891.)
173. DALLAS, W. S. Article "Rodentia" in *Cassell's Natural History*.
174. PENNANT, THOS. Arctic Zoölogy. (London, 1787.)
175. COUES, E. Fur-bearing Animals: a Monograph of North American Mustelidæ. (Washington, 1877.)
176. MERRIAM, C. H. Synopsis of the Weasels of North America. (*N. Am. Fauna*, No. 11; Washington, 1896.)
177. EVERITT. Ferrets: their Management. (London, 1897.)
178. POULTON, E. B. The Colors of Animals. (London, 1890.)
179. BEDDARD, FRANK. Animal Coloration. (New York, 1892.)
180. ALLEN, J. A. Change of Color in the Northern Hare. (*Bulletin*

Am. Mus. Nat. His., Vol. VIII, New York, 1894.) Summarized in *Am. Naturalist*, Vol. XVIII, 1894, p. 890.

181. HEARNE, S.   A Journey . . . to the Northern Ocean.   (Lond., 1875.)

182. DE KAY, JAMES E.   Natural History of the State of New York; Part I, Zoölogy.   (Albany, 1842.)

183. RICHARDSON, SIR JOHN.   Fauna Boreali-Americana.   (Lond., 1829.)

184. ROLLESTON, G.   Domestic Cats of ancient and modern times. (*Journal Anat. and Phys.*, Vol. II; London, 1868.)

185. WALLACE, A. R.   Darwinism.   (London, 1889.)   Reprinted in the *Humboldt Library*.

186. HOWELL, A. H.   Revision of the Skunks of the Genus Chincha.   (*N. Am. Fauna*, No. 20;   Washington, 1901.)

187. ROBINSON, R.   In New England Fields and Woods.   (Boston, 1896.)

188. ELLIOTT, H. W.   Report on the Condition of Affairs in Alaska. (Washington, 1875.)

189. SCAMMON, C. M.   The Marine Mammals of the Northwest Coast of North America.   (San Francisco, 1874.)

190. COPE, E. D.   The Japanese Lapdog.   (*Am. Naturalist*, 1879.)

191. HUXLEY, T. H.   The Cranial and Dental Characters of the Canidæ. (*Proc. Zoöl. Soc. of London*, 1880.)

192. MIVART, ST. GEORGE.   Fox-dogs.   (*Proc. Zoöl. Soc. of London*. 1890.)

193. LANTZ, D. E.   Coyotes in their economic Relations.   (*Bulletin* No. 20, *Biological Survey;* Washington, 1905.)

194. SELOUS, EDMUND.   Romance of the Animal World.   (Phila., 1905.)

195. WINDLE and HUMPHREYS.   Cranial and Dental Characteristics of the Domestic Dog.   *Proc. Zoöl. Soc. of London*, 1890.   (Summarized in article "Dog," in *New International Encyclopædia*.)

196. STRUTT, J.   Sports and Pastimes of the People of England.   (London, 1801.)

197. MIVART, ST. GEORGE.   Monograph of the Canidæ.   (Lond., 1870.)

198. SETON, E. T.   Wild Animals I have known.   (New York, 1898.)

199. ADAMS, A. LEITH.   Field and Forest Rambles.   (London, 1873.)

200. BURROUGHS, JOHN.   Winter Sunshine.   (Boston, 1876.)

201. NELSON, E. W.   Report upon Natural History Collections in Alaska. (Washington, 1887.)

202. FEILDEN, H. W.   Articles in *The Zoölogist*, 1877.

203. STELLER, G. W.   Beschreibung von dem Lande Kamtschatka.   (St. Petersburg, 1774.)

204. COPE, E. D.   The Californian Cave Bear.   (*Am. Naturalist*, Vol. XXV, 1891.)

205. GUILLEMARD, F. H. H.   Cruise of the Marchesa to Kamschatka and New Guinea.   (London, 1886.)

206. OSGOOD, W. H. Natural History of the Cook Inlet Region. (*Bulletin* No. 21, *Biological Survey;* Washington, 1901.)

207. HITCHCOCK, ROMYN. The ancient Pit-dwellers of Yezo. (With a bibliography. Smithsonian Report for 1890; Washington, 1891.) See also Ed. Greey's Bear Worshippers of Yezo. (Boston, 1884.)

208. GUBERNATIS, ANGELO DE. Zoölogical Mythology, or the Legends of Animals. (New York, 1872.)

209. BECCARI. Wanderings in the Great Forests of Borneo. (London, 1901.)

210. COPE, E. D. The Condylarthra. (*Am. Naturalist*, Vol. XVIII, 1884.)

211. COPE, E. D. The Amblypoda. (*Am. Naturalist*, Vol. XVIII, 1884; Vol. XIX, 1885.)

212. MARSH, O. C. The Dinocerata. (Washington, 1884.)

213. OSBORN, H. F. The Ancylopoda. (*Am. Naturalist*, Vol. XXVII, 1893.)

214. GERARD, SIR MONTAGUE. Leaves from the Diary of a Soldier and Sportsman. (London, 1903.)

215. STORER, J. Wild White Cattle of Great Britain. (London, 1897.) See also illustrated articles in *The Field* (London) for August 16 and 23, and December 13, 1890; and for November 5, 1904.

216. CATON, J. D. The Antelope and Deer of America. (New York, 1897.)

217. ALLEN, J. A. The American Bisons. (Cambridge, 1876.)

218. HORNADAY, W. T. Extermination of the American Bison. (*Annual Report Smithsonian Institution for* 1887; Washington, 1889.)

219. WHITNEY, WISTER, and others. Musk-ox, Bison, Sheep, and Goat. (*Sportsman's Library;* New York, 1904.)

220. LYDEKKER, R. Wild Oxen, Sheep and Goats of all kinds, Living and Extinct. (London, 1898.)

221. WHITNEY, CASPAR. Jungle Trails and Jungle People. (N. Y., 1905.)

222. HORNADAY, W. T. Mountain Sheep of North America. (*Fifth Ann. Rept., N. Y. Zoöl. Soc.;* New York, 1901.)

223. BUXTON, E. N. Short Stalks. (London, 1898.) See also *Proc. Zoöl. Society London,* 1896.

224. BLANFORD, W. T. Eastern Persia: Zoölogy. (London, 1876.)

225. SHALER, N. Domesticated Animals. (New York, 1895.)

226. BREHM, A. E. Illustrirtes Thierleben. (1st ed., Leipzig, 1863.)

It has had several later editions and English translations; and its illustrations, by Vogt, Specht, and other artists, have been repeatedly copied.

227. BAILLIE-GROHMAN, W. A. Sport in the Alps, Past and Present. (London, 1896.)

228. SCLATER, P. L., and THOMAS, O. The Book of Antelopes. (4 vols., quarto, colored plate of each species; London, 1894–1900.)

229. BAKER, SIR S. Nile Tributaries of Abyssinia. (London, 1867.)

230. HARRIS, CAPT. W. Portraits of Game and Wild Animals in Southern Africa. (Folio, colored plates; London, 1846.)

231. BRYDEN, H. A. Nature and Sport in South Africa. (London, 1879.) Kloof and Karoo. (1886.)

232. MILLAIS, J. G. A Breath from the Veldt. (London, 1895.)

233. ROOSEVELT, THEO., and others. The Deer Family. (*Sportsman's Library;* New York, 1902.)

234. ALLEN, J. A. History of North American Pinnipeds. (Wash., 1880.)

235. MORGAN, LLOYD. Animal Sketches. (London, 1891.)

236. LYDEKKER, R. Deer of all Lands. (Four vols., quarto, colored plates of all species; London, 1898.)

237. DEER STALKING. Scrope, Days of Deer Stalking in the Scottish Highlands (London, Hamilton's ed., 1883); St. John, Sportsman and Naturalist in Sutherlandshire (London, 1891); Jeffries, Red Deer (London, 2d ed., 1892); Grimble, Highland Sport (London, 1896); and volumes in the *Badminton* and similar libraries of books for sportsmen.

238. MAYER, A. M. Sport with Gun and Rod in American Woods and Waters. (New York, 1883.)

239. WORTMAN, J. L. Extinct Camelidæ of North America. (*Bulletin Am. Mus. Nat. Hist.*, Vol. X, 1898.)

240. CUNNINGHAM, R. O. Natural History of the Straits of Magellan. (London, 1871.)

241. TSCHUDI, J. J. VON. Travels in Peru. (New York, 1854.)

242. BEEBE, C. WM. Two Bird Lovers in Mexico. (Boston, 1905.)

243. HUXLEY, T. H. American Addresses. (London, 1877.)

244. SCHMIDT, OSCAR. Mammalia. (New York, 1886.)

245. TEGETMEIER, W. B. Horses, Asses, and Mules. (London, 1895.)

246. EWART, COSSAR. The Penecuik Experiments. (London, 1899.)

247. OSBORN, HENRY F. Evolution of the Horse. (New York, 1907.)
     With this may well be read Professor Ridgway's Origin and Influence of the Thoroughbred Horse. (London, 1905.)

248. Living Animals of the World. (London and New York, 1902.)

249. LUCAS, F. A. Animals of the Past. (New York, 1901.)

250. NORDENSKJOLD, BARON N. A. Voyage of the Vega. (Lond., 1881.)

251. STEJNEGER, L. Articles in *Proc. U.S. Nat. Mus.*, Vol. VI (Washington, 1884); and in *Am. Naturalist*, Vol. XXI, 1887.

252. BIGG-WITHER, T. P. Pioneering in South Brazil. (London, 1878.)

253. DAMPIER, WILLIAM. Voyages to Campeachy. (London, 1729.)

254. WILSON, THOS. The Swastika, the earliest known Symbol, etc. (*Ann. Rept. U.S. Nat. Mus.;* Washington, 1894.)

255. BEDDARD, F. The Book of Whales. (London, 1900.)

256. BULLEN, F. T. Denizens of the Deep. (New York, 1904.)

257. SACK, A. VON. Narrative of a Voyage to Surinam. (London, 1810.)

258. LYDEKKER, R. A Handbook to the Marsupialia and Monotremata. (*Allen's Naturalist's Library ;* London, 1894.)

259. WALLACE, A. R. Island Life. (New York, 1880.)

260. MORGAN, T. H. Evolution and Adaptation. (New York, 1903.)

261. WHEELWRIGHT, H. Bush Wanderings of a Naturalist; or Notes on the Field Sports and Fauna of Australia Felix. By an old Bushman. (London, 2d ed., 1865.)

262. GOULD, JOHN. The Mammals of Australia. (London, 1863.)

> This is a magnificent work in three folio volumes with colored plates. Other notable illustrated works on Marsupials are Waterhouse's Mammalia (Vol. I, London, 1848), and Krefft's Mammals of Australia (Sydney, 1871). Both have excellent drawings, in some editions colored. See also No. 258.

263. BENNETT, G. F. Gatherings of a Naturalist. (London, 1866.)

264. KREFFT, G. Mammals of Australia. (Sydney, 1871.)

265. SAVILLE-KENT, W. The Naturalist in Australia. (London, 1897.)

266. BENSLEY, B. A. A Theory of the Origin and Evolution of the Australian Marsupials. (*Am. Naturalist,* Vol. XXXV, 1901 ; see also in this connection *Ibid.,* pp. 117 and 139.)

267. COUES, E., and ALLEN, J. A. Monographs of North American Rodentia; with Bibliography of N. Am. Mammals to 1877. (U.S. Geological Survey; Washington, 1877.)

268. LORD, J. K. The Naturalist in Vancouver Island and British Columbia. (London, 1866.)

269. SCHILLINGS, C. G. Flashlights in the Jungle. (New York, 1906.)

> This is the authorized rendering into English of Schilling's German work, and is the most instructive book on the zoölogy of East Africa published within recent years. It appeared too late to enable the author of the present book to take advantage of its store of information, and its numerous and remarkable photographic illustrations; but it does not compel any changes of statement or view, except, perhaps, that it shows that certain of the large game animals are still more numerous than had been supposed.

270. MATSCHIE, PAUL. Saugethiere Deutsch Ost-Afrika. (Berlin, 1895.)

Index of Authorities Cited

References are to numbers preceding the various entries, pp. 527-538.

Abbott, 99, 105.
Adams, 199.
Aflalo, 101.
Allen, H., 49.
Allen, J. A., 111, 180, 217, 234.
Alston, 114.
Anderson, 55.
Andersson, 149.
Aplin, 89.
Audubon, 90.
Azara, 131.

Bailey, 68, 82.
Baillie-Grohman, 227.
Baird, 32, 84.
Baker, 143, 147, 229.
Baldwin, 140.
Baron, 40.
Barras, 167.
Bartlett, 41.
Bates, 25.
Beaver, Literature, 110.
Beccari, 209.
Beddard, 37, 179, 255.
Beebe, 242.
Bell, 93.
Belt, 26.
Bennett, 263.
Bensley, 266.
Bevan, 163.
Bigg-Wither, 252.
Blanford, 19, 23, 224.
Blyth, 139.
Brehm. 226.
Broderip, W. J., 15.
Brooke, 29.
Brown, C. B., 34.
Brown, J. M., 164.

Bryden, 231.
Bullen, 256.
Burroughs, 200.
Burton, 54.
Buxton, 223.

Cameron, 145.
Campbell, 155.
Caton, 216.
Cope, 97, 116, 118, 122, 123, 190, 204, 210, 211.
Cornish, 124.
Coues, 80, 106, 175.
Cram, 52, 100.
Cumberland, 115.
Cumming, G., 39.
Cumming, R. G., 142.
Cunningham, 240.

Dallas, 173.
Dampier, 253.
Darwin, 22, 69, 77.
Dawkins, 83.
Deer Stalking, 237.
De Kay, 182.
Delamere, 151.
Desfontaines, 21.
Distribution of Animals, 110.
Dobson, 46, 61.
Drummond, 144.
Dubois, 4.
Du Chaillu, 6.

Eastman, 59, 130.
Elliot, D. G., 98, 134.
Elliott, H. W., 188.
El Mangali, 148.
Everitt, 177.
Ewart, 246.

Fayrer, 154.
Feilden, 202.
Fisher, 51.
Flower, S., 45.
Flower, W. H., 16.
Flying Squirrels, 102.
Forbes, 3.
Forsyth, 169.
Forsyth-Major, 42.

Gerard, 214.
Godman, 91.
Gosse, 53.
Gould, 262.
Grandidier, 43.
Ground Squirrels, 103.
Gubernatis, 208.
Guillemard, 205.

Haeckel, 28.
Hall, 168.
Hamilton, 132.
Harris, 230.
Harting, 109.
Hartmann, 7.
Hearne, 181.
Hitchcock, 207.
Holub, 165.
Hornaday, 30, 95, 218, 222.
Horsfield, 57.
Hose, 38.
Howell, 186.
Hudson, 35, 76, 117.
Humboldt, 66.
Huxley, 1, 5, 191, 243.

Im Thurn, 33.
Ingersoll, 20, 36, 87, 94.
Inglis, 166.
Ingram, 104.

Jerdon, 44.
Johanna, 121.
Johnson, 125.
Johnston, 18.

Kennicott, 56.
Kinloch, 160.
Kipling, 11.
Knight, 70.
Krefft, 264.

La Croix, 141.
Lantz, 193.
Leveson, 161.
Living Animals of the World, 248.
Livingstone, 8.
Lucas, 249.
Lydekker, 10, 16, 65, 220, 236, 258.

Macintyre, 159.
Marsh, 212.
Martin, H. T., 110.
Martin, M., 14, 172.
Maunder, 92.
Mayer, 238.
Merriam, 48, 81, 103, 112, 113, 176.
Millais, 232.
Miller, 50, 85.
Mills, 108.
Mivart, 135, 192, 197.
Morant, 71.
Morgan, C. L., 235.
Morgan, L. H., 110.
Morgan, T. H., 260.
Morris, 170.

Nelson, 201.
Nordenskjold, 250.

Osborn, 213, 247.
Osgood, 78, 206.
Oswald, 120.

Palmer, 73.
Parker and Haswell, 2.
Pennant, 174.
Perkins, 102.
Perry, 129.

Poey, 64.
Pollok, 156.
Porter, 126.
Poulton, 178.
Preble, 86.

Repplier, 138.
Rice, 157.
Richardson, 183.
Riverside Natural History, 75.
Robinson, 187.
Rodway, 88.
Rolleston, 184.
Romanes, 13.
Roosevelt, 128, 233.
Royal Natural History, 10.

Sack, 257.
Sanderson, 162.
Scammon, 189.
Schmidt, 244.
Schulz, 152.
Schweinfurth, G., 9.
Sclater, 228.
Scott, 119.
Selous, E., 194.
Selous, F. C., 150.
Semper, 107.
Seton, 79, 198.
Shakespear, 158.
Shaler, 225.

Sharp, 72.
Spallanzani, 47.
Spears, 127.
Standard Natural History, 75.
Stejneger, 251.
Steller, 203.
Sterndale, 153.
Stone and Cram, 52.
Storer, 215.
Strutt, 196.

Tegetmeier, 245.
Tennent, 17.
Topsell, 171.
True, 74.
Tschudi, 241.

Wallace, 12, 27, 31, 185, 259.
Waterton, 24, 96.
Watkins, 133.
Wheelwright, 261.
White, 62.
Whitney, 219, 221.
Wilkinson, 58.
Wilson, 254.
Windle, 195.
Wood, 63.
Woodward, 60.
Wortman, 239.

Zittel-Eastman, 59.

INDEX

Aard vark (*Orycteropus capensis*), 485.

Aard wolf (*Proteles cristata*), 158.

Ælurodon, 188.

Æluropus (*Æ. melanoleucus*), 210.

Agouti (*Dasyprocta agouti*), 418.

Ai, or two-toed sloth, 473.

Alacdaga (*Alactaga jaculus*), 424.

Alluates or arguatoes, 43.

Alpaca, domesticated, 338, 340.

Amblypoda, 232.

Ammon or argali, 255.

Amphicyon, primitive carnivore, 85, 86, 188, 210.

Ancylopoda, 234.

Animals alike in northern hemisphere, 461.

Animals, domesticated by prehistoric man, 195, 200, 340, 359, 483.

Animals, sacred.—*See* Superstitions.

Anoa (*Anoa depressicornis*), 243.

Anomalurus, or scaletail, 446.

Ant-eater, banded (*Myrmecobius fasciatus*), 510.

Ant-eater, great (*Myrmecophaga jubata*), 469.

Ant-eater, lesser (*Tamandua tetradactyla*), 472, 473.

Ant-eater, little two-toed (*Cycloturus didactylus*), 473.

Ant-eaters, Old World, 485–487.

Ant-eaters, scaly, or pangolins, 486.

Ant-eaters, spiny, 524.

Antelope, addax (*Addax nasomaculatus*), 272.

Antelope, American, or pronghorn, 286.

Antelope, Angas's (*Tragelaphus angasi*), 271.

Antelope, beatrix (*Oryx beatrix*), 272.

Antelope, beisa (*Oryx beisa*), 272.

Antelope, harnessed (*Tragelaphus scripta*), 276.

Antelope, Indian, or blackbuck, 277.

Antelope, nilgai (*Boselaphus tragocamelus*), 272.

Antelope, roan (*Hippotragus equinus*), 273.

Antelope, sable (*Hippotragus niger*), 273.

Antelope, Speke's or sitatunga, 272.

Antelope, zebra (*Cephalophus doriæ*), 282.

Antelopes, ancestry of, 268.

Anthropoid apes, characterized, 10.

Aoudad (*Ovis tragelaphus*), 257.

Apar, or three-banded armadillo, 478.

Ape of Gibraltar (*Macacus inuus*), 31.

Apes, anthropoid, 7–23.

Apes and monkeys, intelligence of, 13, 19, 20, 22, 30, 33, 34, 40, 46.

Apes and monkeys using missiles, 19, 29, 35, 43.

Arctotherium, 210, 211.

Argali, true (*Ovis ammon*), 255.

Armadillo, Brazilian (*Scleropeura bruneti*), 476.

Armadillo, giant (*Priodon giganteus*), 476.

Armadillo, peludo (*Dasypus sexcinctus*), 476.

Armadillo, three-banded (*Tolypeutes tricinctus*), 478.

543

Armadillos, mail of, 476.
Arsinoëtherium, 375.
Artiodactyla, 234, 235.
Ass, African (*Equus [Asinus] africanus*), 366, 369.
Ass, Asiatic (*Equus [Asinus] onager*), 367.
Aurochs (*Bos taurus*), 238.
Axis, or spotted Indian deer, 303, 308.

Babakoto, or indris, a lemur, 51.
Babirussa (*Babirusa alfurus*), 350.
Baboon, characteristics of, 32.
Baboon, Arabian or sacred (*Papio hamadryas*), 33, 36.
Baboon, Celebean black (*Cynopithecus niger*), 32.
Baboon, chacma (*Papio porcarius*), 33.
Baboon, gelada (*Theropithecus gelada*), 35.
Baboon, hamadryad, sacred in Egypt, 36.
Baboon, mandrill (*Papio maimon*), 32, 34.
Baboon, yellow (*Papio babuin*), 35.
Badger, American (*Taxidea americana*), 177.
Badger, European (*Meles taxus*), 176.
Badger, ferret (genus Helictis), 175.
Badger, sand, 176.
Badger, stinking, 176.
Balisaur (*Arctonyx collaris*), 176.
Bandicoots (family Peramelidæ), 506.
Banteng or tsine (*Bos sondaicus*), 241.
Barbary or Gibraltar ape, 31.
Barrigudo or caparro monkeys, 41.
Bat, brush-tongued, 63.
Bat, little (*Myotis lucifugus*), 59.
Bat, lyre (*Megaderma lyra*), 67.
Bats (order Chiroptera), 58.
Bats, color protection for, 63.
Bats, fruit-eating, 64.

Bats, superstitions as to, 62, 67.
Bats, vampire (genus Desmodus), 61.
Bats, wing and membranes, 59.
Bear, American black (*Ursus americanus*), 212, 215.
Bear, Glacier (*Ursus emmonsi*), 220.
Bear, grizzly (*Ursus horribilis*), 212, 218.
Bear, Malayan sun (*Ursus malayanus*), 220.
Bear, party-colored (*Æluropus melanoleucus*), 210, 212.
Bear, polar (*Ursus [Thalassarctos] maritimus*), 212, 218.
Bear, sloth (*Ursus [Melursus] labiatus*), 212, 216.
Bear, spectacled (*Ursus [Tremarctus] ornatus*), 211.
Bears, ancestry of, 210, 211.
Bears, characteristics of, 211–220.
Bears, classification of, 212.
Bears, methods of fishing, 214.
Bears, prehistoric cave, 211.
Beaver, American (*Castor canadensis*), 460–468.
Beaver, European (*Castor fiber*), 460.
Beaver rat (*Hydromys chrysogaster*), 431, 494.
Bengal or Rhesus monkey, 30.
Bezoar goat or pasan, 259.
Bharal or nahura (*Ovis nahura*), 257.
Bighorn, American (*Ovis cervina*), 255, 256.
Binturong (*Arctitis binturong*), 154.
Bison, American (*Bos americanus*) 250.
Bison, European (*Bos bonasus*), 249.
Bison, fossil, 248.
Bison, Indian, or gaur, 240.
Blackbuck, Indian (*Antilope cervicapra*), 277.
Blacktail, or mule deer, 330.
Blacktail, Columbian (*Odocoileus columbianus*), 332.

Blessbok (*Bubalis [Damaliscus] albifrons*), 284.

Boar, wild (*Sus scrofa*), 345, 347.

Bobac (*Arctomys bobac*), 457.

Bobcat (*Felis ruja*), 143, 144.

Bouquetin or ibex (*Capra ibex*), 260.

Bovidæ, family of, 238.

Brain, of man compared with that of apes, 9, 11, 19.

Buansuah or dhole, 197.

Buffalo, American, 257.

Buffalo, Indian (*Bos bubalus*), 244.

Buffalo, S. African (*Bos caffre*), 246.

Buffalo, W. African (*Bos pumilus*), 246.

Buffalo-runner, 191.

Bushbucks (genus Tragelaphus), 269.

Cacomistle (*Bassariscus astutus*), 225.

Camel, Arabian (*Camelus dromedarius*), 336.

Camel, Bactrian (*Camelus bactrianus*), 337.

Camel tribe (Tylopoda), 334.

Camels, ancestry of, 334.

Capybara (*Hydrochœrus capybara*), 420.

Caracal (*Felis caracal*), 146, 148.

Carcajou, or wolverine, 166.

Caribou, Barren Grounds (*Rangifer arcticus*), 321.

Caribou, woodland (*Rangifer caribou*), 324.

Carnivora, place in nature, 82.

Carnivora, primitive, 80, 85.

Cat, Angora or Persian, 137, 139.

Cat, Bengal (*Felis bengalensis*), 132.

Cat, Caffre, Libyan or gloved, 135, 139.

Cat, desert (*Felis ornata*), 137, 139.

Cat, Egyptian (*Felis libyca*), poem upon, 134, 139.

Cat, fishing (*Felis viverrina*), 132.

Cat, flat-headed (*Felis planiceps*), 131.

Cat, golden-haired (*Felis rutila*), 131.

Cat, grass or Pampas (*Felis pajeros*), 103.

Cat, Indian jungle (*Felis chaus*), 138.

Cat, leopard, 101, 132.

Cat, mechanism of sheathed claws, 107.

Cat, Mediterranean, 138.

Cat, mummies of, 134.

Cat, Pampas or grass, 103.

Cat, ring-tailed or cacomistle, 221.

Cat, rusty (*Felis rubiginosa*), 132.

Cat, serval (*Felis serval*), 133.

Cat, Siamese, 131.

Cat, steppe (*Felis caudata*), 137, 139.

Cat, wild, of Europe (*Felis catus*), 137.

Cats (family Felidæ), 90.

Cats, origin of group, 90.

Cats, origin of domestic, 138.

Cats trained for sport, 146, 148.

Cattle (family Bovidæ), 238.

Cattle, British white, 239.

Cattle, Galla or sunga, 243.

Cattle, humped (*Bos indicus*), 241.

Cattle, Pembroke, 240.

Cattle, sacred, of India, 242.

Cave bears, 211.

Cave lion (*Felis spelæus*), 121.

Cavy family (Caviidæ), 421.

Cavy, Patagonian (*Dolichotis patachonica*), 418.

Cetacea, order of, 403.

Chacma (*see* Baboon, chacma), 33.

Chalicotherium, 234.

Chamois (*Rupicapra tragus*), 263.

Chaus, or Indian jungle cat, 138.

Cheeta (*Cynælurus jubatus*), 146, 148, 149.

Chevrotain, African (*Dorcatherium aquaticum*), 342.

Chevrotain, East Indian (*Tragulus meminna*), 343.

Chimpanzee (*Anthropopithecus troglodytes*), 11, 20.

Chimpanzee, bald (*A. calvus*), 12.

Chinchilla (*Chinchilla laniger*), 416.

Chipmunk, eastern (*Tamias striatus*), 448, 453.

Chipmunk, western (*Tamias quadrivitatus*), 452.

Chiroptera, order of Bats, 58.

Chiru or orongo (*Pantholops hodgsoni*), 277.

Civet cat, African (*Viverra civetta*), 152.

Civet cat, American, 221.

Coaita, a spider monkey, 41.

Coati, brown (*Nasua nasica*), 227.

Coati, red (*Nasua rufa*), 227.

Coloration, protective, 172, 364.

Coloration, warning, 174.

Colpeo (*Canis azaræ*), 194.

Colugo or kaguan (*Galeopithecus volans*), 69.

Condylarthra, 231.

Conies or rock-badgers, 232.

Coon-bear, or panda, 221.

Corsac (*Canis corsac*), 209.

Cougar, or puma, 90–97.

Coyote (*Canis latrans*), 192.

Coypu, or nutria (*Myopotamus coypu*), 422.

Creodonta, order of, 79.

Cuscuses (genus Cuscus), 501.

Cutia, or agouti, 419.

Cynodictis, 187.

Cynogale, 154.

Dædicurus, a glyptodon, 482.

Daman (*Procavia syriaca*), 232.

Dasyure, common or native cat (*Dasyurus viverrinus*), 509.

Dasyures (family Dasyuridæ), 507.

Deer (family Cervidæ), 298–333.

Deer, American, 325.

Deer, American red (*Cervus canadensis*), 312.

Deer, ancestry of, 302.

Deer, antlers, types of, 326.

Deer, antlers, service of, 301.

Deer, antlers, structure of, 299, 300.

Deer, axis or chital (*Cervus axis*), 303, 308.

Deer, barking or kakar, 305.

Deer, Chilean (*Odocoileus chilensis*), 333.

Deer, Chinese water (*Hydropotes inermis*), 304.

Deer, coloration of, 302.

Deer, common Virginian, or willow, 326, 329. — *See* Deer, white-tailed.

Deer, Costa Rican (*Odocoileus clavatus*), 333.

Deer, Eld's or thamin (*Cervus eldi*), 306.

Deer, fallow (*Cervusdama*), 303, 309.

Deer, gigantic Irish, 302.

Deer, hog, or para (*Cervus porcinus*), 305.

Deer, Japanese (*Cervus sika*), 307.

Deer, marsh (*Odocoileus palustris*), 333.

Deer, mule or blacktail (*Odocoileus hemionus*), 330.

Deer, musk (*Moschus moschiferus*), 304.

Deer, Pampas (*Odocoileus campestris*), 333.

Deer, Peking Park (*Cervus davidianus*), 303, 306.

Deer, red (*Cervus elephas*), 309.

Deer, roe (*Capreolus caprea*), 305.

Deer, sambar (*Cervus unicolor*), 303, 307.

Deer, tufted (*Elaphodus cephalolophus*), 304.

Deer, white-tailed (*Odocoileus americanus*), 326.

Deer, winter "yards" of, 318, 327.
Dermoptera, 69.
Desmans (genus Myogale), 72.
Dhole (*Cyon dukkunensis*), 197.
Diana monkey (*Cercopithecus diana*), 28.
Diceratherium, 374.
Dingo (*Canis dingo*), 195.
Dinocerata, 233, 234.
Dinotherium, 391, 392.
Dog, Azara's (*Canis azaræ*), 194.
Dog, crab-eating (*Canis cancrivorus*), 194.
Dog family (Canidæ), 187.
Dog, hunting or hyena (*Lycaon pictus*), 196.
Dog, Lalande's or long-eared (*Otocyon megalotis*), 196.
Dogs, ancestry of, 187.
Dogs, Asiatic wild (*Cyon*), 197.
Dogs, origin of domestic, 198, 210.
Donkey, origin and traits of, 369.
Dormouse (*Muscardinus avellanarius*), 441.
Douroucolis (monkeys), 45.
Dromedary camel, 336.
Dryopithecus, fossil ape, 19.
Duckbill (*Ornithorhynchus anatinus*), 523.
Dugong (*Halicore dugong*), 402.
Duikerboks, or bluebucks (genus Cephalophus), 281.
Dziggettai, or Asiatic ass, 367.

Echidna (*E. aculeata*), 525.
Edentata, order of, 469–484.
Egg-laying mammals, 521.
Eland, common (*Oreas canna*), 269.
Eland, Derbian (*Oreas derbiana*), 270.
Elasmotherium, 377.
Elephant, African (*Elephas africanus*), 397.
Elephant, evolution of, 388, 392.

Elephant, Indian (*Elephas indicus*), 393.
Elephant, past and present, 386–399.
Elk, American, or wapiti, 312.
Elk, European (*Alces machlis*), 315.
Endrina lemurs (subfamily Indrisinæ), 51.
Entellus monkey (*Semnopithecus entellus*), 24.
Eohippus, Eocene horse, 353, 354.
Eolithic man, 10.
Epanorthidæ, 505.
Ermine, 169, 170.
Eutheria, subclass of, 490.
Eyra (*Felis eyra*), 104.

Face, the human, 9.
Felidæ (cat family), 90.
Fennec (*Canis [Fennecus] zerda*), 209.
Ferret, black-footed (*Putorius nigripes*), 168.
Ferrets (tamed polecats), 168.
Fisher, or pekan (*Mustela pennanti*), 164, 165.
Fitch fur, 168.
Flying-foxes, or fox-bats, 65.
Flying-squirrel, *see* Squirrels, Flying, 445.
Fodientia, order of, 485.
Food storage; evolution of habit, 449.
Fossane (*Fossa daubentoni*), 153.
Foumart, or polecat, 168.
Foussa (*Cryptoprocta fossa*), 151.
Fox, American red (*Canis virginianus*), 203.
Fox, Arctic (*Canis lagopus*), 207.
Fox, big-eared (*Canis megalotis*), 204.
Fox, blue, or white Arctic, 207.
Fox, corsac (*Canis corsac*), 209.
Fox, East-Indian (*Canis bengalensis*), 209.

Fox, European red (*Canis vulpes*), 203.

Fox, fennec or zerda, 209.

Fox, gray (*Canis [Urocyon] cinereoargenteus*), 206.

Fox, kit or swift (*Canis velox*), 204.

Fox, sagacity of, 202.

Fox-bats, or flying-foxes, 65.

Fox-dogs (genus Lycalopex), 193.

Fur bearers (*Mustelidæ*), 162–187.

Galago, great, or palm rat (*Galago crassicaudata*), 53.

Galago lemurs (genus Galago), 53.

Galecynus, 188.

Ganesha, elephant god, 394.

Ganodonta, order of, 484.

Gaur (*Bos gaurus*), 240.

Gayal or mithan (*Bos frontalis*), 241.

Gazelles, dorcas (*Gazella dorcas*), 275.

Gemsbok (*Oryx gazella*), 273.

Gemse, or chamois, 263.

Genet, Mediterranean (*Genetta vulgaris*), 153.

Gerbilles (*Gerbillinæ*), 441.

Ghorkhar, or Asiatic ass, 367.

Gibbons (genus Hylobates), 21–23.

Giraffe, five-horned, 294.

Giraffe (*Giraffa camelopardalis*), 292–295.

Glutton (*Gulo luscus*), 166.

Glyptodons, club-tailed, 482.

Glyptodons, ring-tailed, 483.

Gnu, brindled (*Connochætes taurinus*), 284.

Gnu, white-tailed (*Connochætes gnu*), 284.

Goat, Persian (*Capra ægagrus*), 259.

Goat, Rocky Mountain white (*Oreamnus montanus*), 263.

Goat, Spanish (*Capra pyrenaica*), 259.

Goats, domestic, 260.

Gopher, prairie (*Geomys bursarius*), 427.

Gopher, small gray (*Thomomys talpoides*), 428.

Gopher, southern (*Geomys tuza*), 427.

Gophers, habits of, 426.

Gorilla (*Gorilla savagei*), 15.

Grison or huron (*Grisonia vittata*), 167.

Grivet monkey (*Cercopithecus sabæus*), 28.

Ground hog or woodchuck, 458.

Ground sloths, 480.

Guanaco.—*See* Huanaco.

Guemal deer, 333.

Guenon monkeys (genus Cercopithecus), 28.

Guereza, white-tailed (*Colobus caudata*), 27.

Guinea pigs, 421.

Guljar (*Ovis poli*), 253, 254.

Hair, green, of sloths, 474.

Hair of mammals, 3.

Halitherium, fossil Sirenian, 400.

Hangul, or Kashmir red deer, 310.

Hanuman, monkey-god, 24.

Hare, wood or cottontail (*Lepus sylvaticus*), 408, 412.

Hare, southern marsh (*Lepus palustris*), 413.

Hare, southern water (*Lepus aquaticus*), 413.

Hare, varying (*Lepus americanus*), 413.

Hares and rabbits, 407.

Harrisbuck or sable antelope, 273.

Hartbeests (genus Bubalis), 282.

Hedgehog (*Erinaceus europæus*), 75.

Hedgehog superstitions, 76.

Helladotherium, 298.

Hemicyon, 210.

Hemigales, 154.

Heraldic lion considered, 89.

Hibernation, assisted by lack of air, 452.

Hibernation of bear, 219.

Hibernation, phenomena of, 459.

Hippopotamus (*Hippopotamus amphibius*), 350.

Hippopotamus, evolution of, 350, 352.

Hoolock gibbon (*Hylobates hoolock*), 22.

Horns, treatise on, 237.

Horse, evolution of, 352–360.

Horse, Przewalsky's, 360.

Horses, ancestry of modern (*Equus caballus*), 359, 361.

Horses, migration of Tertiary, 357.

Horses of prehistoric man, 359.

Howlers, or howling Monkeys, 43.

Huanaco (*Lama huanacos*), 338.

Hunting-leopard, or cheeta, 146, 148.

Huron or grison, 167.

Hutia, Cuban (*Capromys melanurus*), 422.

Hyænarctus, 210.

Hyænodons (creodonts), 81.

Hyena, spotted (*Crocuta maculata*), 159, 161.

Hyena, striped (*Hyæna striata*), 159.

Hyohippus, Miocene horse, 354.

Hyracoidea, 231.

Hyracotherium, 353.

Ibex, European (*Capra ibex*), 260.

Ibex, Himalayan (*Capra sibirica*), 261.

Ichneumon, Abyssinian (*Herpestes albicauda*), 157.

Ichneumon, Egyptian (*Herpestes ichneumon*), 154, 156.

Ictithere, primitive carnivore, 85, 159.

Indris or babakoto, a lemur (*Indris brevicaudatus*), 51.

Insectivora, order of, characterized, 68.

Inyala, or Angas's antelope, 271.

Ivory, fossil, and living, 389, 399.

Izard, or atchi, 263.

Jackals, African, 194, 196.

Jackals, Indian (*Canis aureus*), 195.

Jack rabbits, American, 410.

Jaguar (*Felis jaguar*), 97–101, 345.

Jaguar, methods of hunting, 100.

Jerboa, Egyptian (*Dipus hirtipes*), 423, 424.

Jumping deer, or mule deer, 331.

Jumping mouse (*Zapus hudsonius*), 424.

Kanchil or napu, 343.

Kangaroo, brush, or wallabies, 498.

Kangaroo, great gray (*Macropus giganteus*), 495.

Kangaroo rat (genus Potorous), 499.

Kangaroo rats and mice, 424.

Kangaroo, red (*Macropus rufus*), 496.

Kiang or kulan, 367.

Kinkajou (*Cercoleptes caudivolvus*), 227.

Klipspringer (*Oreotragus saltator*), 281.

Koala (*Phascolarctos cinereus*), 501.

Koodos (*Strepsiceros kudu*), 269, 275.

Langurs, 25.

Lar gibbon (*Hylobates lar*), 22.

Lemming, habits of, 433.

Lemming, Scandinavian (*Lemmus lemmus*), 433.

Lemmings, migratory, 433–436.

Lemur, flying, or colugo, 69.

Lemur, ring-tailed (*Lemur catta*), 52.

Lemur, ruffed (*Lemur varius*), 52.

Lemurs (suborder Lemuroidea), characterized, 48, 51.

Lemurs, dwarf (genus Microcebus), 54.

Lemurs, fat-tailed (genus Opolemur), 54.

Lemurs, mouse (genus Chirogale), 54.

Lemurs, slow (subfamily Lorisinæ), 54.

Lemurs, superstitions in regard to, 51, 55.

Lemurs, typical (subfamily Lemurinæ), 52.

Leopard-cat, of Texas, 101; of Bengal, 132.

Leopard, clouded (*Felis nebulosa*), 131.

Leopard, hunting, 146.

Leopard, or panther (*Felis pardus*), 127.

Leopard, snow (*Felis uncia*), 130.

Leporidæ, hare family, 407.

Linsang, 153.

Lion (*Felis leo*) in fact and fable, 105–123.

Lion and buffalo, etc., 114.

Lion in Asia, 122.

Lion, man-eating, 116, 118.

Lion, prehistoric, 121.

Lion, superstitions as to, 116.

Litopterna, a fossil equine, 370.

Llama, Peruvian, 339.

Llamas, ancestry of, 335.

Loris, slender (*Loris gracilis*), 54.

Loris, slow (*Nycticebus tardigradus*), 54, 56.

Loxolophodon, 234.

Lucivee (*i.e. loup cervier*), 142.

Lynx, Canada (*Felis canadensis*), 141, 143.

Lynx, European (*Felis lyncus*), 142, 148.

Macaque, Bengal or rhesus monkey (*see* Rhesus), 30.

Macaque, Japanese (*Macacus fuscatus*), 30.

Macaque, leonine (*Macacus leoninus*), 30.

Macaque, lion-tailed (*Macacus silenus*), 31.

Macaque, pig-tailed (*Macacus nemestrinus*), 30.

Macrotherium, 234.

Magot (*see* Ape of Gibraltar), 31.

Malmag or tarsier (*Tarsius tarsius*), 49, 55.

Mammals, hoofed (*Ungulata*), 231, 236.

Mammals, marine (*Pinnipedia*), 230.

Mammals, name of, 1.

Mammals, origin and history of, 5.

Mammals, rank of, 2.

Mammals, teeth (dental formula), 51.

Mammoths, Siberian, 389.

Man (*Homo sapiens*), 7.

Manatee, Florida (*Manatus americanus*), 403.

Manatee, South American (*Manatus inunguis*), 402.

Mandrill (*see* Baboon), 32, 34.

Mangabey monkeys (genus Cercocebus), 29, 31.

Manigordo, or ocelot, 101.

Mapurito (*Conepatus mapurito*), 182.

Maral, or Persian red deer, 310.

Margay (*Felis tigrina*), 103, 104.

Markhor, Himalayan (*Capra falconeri*), 261.

Marmosets and tamarins (family Hapalidæ), 46.

Marmot, alpine (*Arctomys marmotta*), 457.

Marsupialia, order of, 488–520.

Marsupials, adapted types, 493.

Marsupials, ancestry of, 490, 505, 513.

Marsupials, distribution of, 491, 513.
Marsupials, reproduction in, 488.
Marten, American pine (*Mustela americana*), 164.
Marten, beech (*Mustela foina*), 164.
Marten, domesticated in Greece, 139.
Marten, European pine (*Mustela martes*), 164.
Marten, Pennant's, 164.
Mastodons (genus Mastodon), 390, 394.
Meerkat (*Suricata tridactyla*), 157.
Megatherium (*M. robustus*), 480.
Merycodus, 286.
Mesohippus, Oligocene horse, 353, 354.
Mesonyx, a creodont, 78, 81.
Metatheria, subclass of, 490.
Mias, Dyak name for orang-utan, 17, 19.
Mice and rats (Muridæ), 423, 428.
Mi-lou, or David's Peking Park deer, 303, 306.
Mink (*Putorius vison*), 172.
Mithan or gayal, 241.
Mœritherium, 392, 394.
Mole, marsupial (*Notoryctes typhlops*), 506.
Mole, star-nosed (*Condylura cristata*), 74.
Moles, golden (genus Chrysochloris), 74.
Moles, habits and homes of, 72, 73.
Monkeys and allies, 23–48.
Monkeys and apes, fossil, 10, 19, 37, 48.
Monkeys, barrigudo or woolly (genus Lagothrix), 41.
Monkeys, Capuchin (genus Cebus), 38.
Monkeys, howling (genus Mycetes or Allouatta), 43.
Monkeys, night (genus Nyctipithecus), 45.

Monkeys, ooakari (genus Uakaria), 44.
Monkeys, of New World, characterized, 37.
Monkeys, sacred, 24, 30, 36.
Monkeys, saki (genus Pithecia), 44.
Monkeys, spider (genus Ateles), 41.
Monkeys, squirrel (genus Chrysothrix), 46.
Monkeys, teetee, or titi (genus Callithrix), 45.
Monotremata, order of, 521–526.
Moose (*Alces machlis*), 316.
Mountain lion, the puma, 90.
Mouse, harvest (*Mus minutus*), 430.
Mouse, house (*Mus musculus*), 428.
Mouse, meadow (*Microtus pennsylvanicus*), 432.
Mouse, pine (*Microtus pinetorum*), 433.
Mouse, white-footed (*Peromyscus leucopus*), 440.
Mungoos (*Herpestes mungoos*), 155.
Muntjac, Indian (*Cervulus muntjac*), 305.
Musk, of musk deer, 304.
Musk-hog, javeline, tajacu, or peccary (*Ovibos moschatus*), 344.
Musk ox, 265–268.
Muskrat (*Fiber zibethecus*), 436.
Mustelidæ (fur bearers), 162–187.
Mylodons, 480.

Nahura, sheep, 257.
Native bear, or koala, 501.
Necrolestes (fossil insectivore), 506.
Neohipparion, Miocene horse, 355.
Night monkeys, 45.
Nilgai or blue cow, 272.
Nodiak (*Proëchidna bruijnii*), 525.
Nyan (*Ovis hodgsoni*), 255.

Ocelot (*Felis pardalis*), 101.
Okapi (*Ocapia johnstoni*), 296–298.

Oligobunis, 188.

Onager, or Asiatic ass, 367.

Onka, or agile gibbon (*Hylobates agilis*), 22.

Ooakaries (monkeys), 44.

Oorial or sha (*Ovis vignei*), 251, 252.

Opossum family (Didelphidæ), 513.

Opossum, Australian, 500, 502.

Opossum, evolution of habits, 519.

Opossum, murine (*Didelphis murina*), 519.

Opossum, of United States (*Didelphis virginianus*), 514.

Opossum, water (*Chironectes minima*), 520.

Opossum-rat (*Cænolestes obscurus*), 505.

Orang-utan (*Simia satyrus*), 17, 20.

Ornithorhynchus or duckbill, 523.

Orohippus, Eocene horse, 353.

Oryx antelopes (genus Oryx), 272.

Otter, Brazilian (*Pteronura brasiliensis*), 184.

Otter, European (*Lutra vulgaris*), 183.

Otter, North American (*Lutra canadensis*), 184.

Otter, sea (*Latax lutris*), 185.

Ounce (*Felis uncia*), 130.

Oxen or cattle, 238.

Paca (*Cælogenys paca*), 419.

Pack-rat, bushy tailed (*Neotoma cinereus*), 439.

Pajero, or grass cat, 103.

Palæomastodon, 392, 394.

Palhyæna, 159.

Palm rat, a galago, 53.

Pampas cat (*Felis pajeros*), 103.

Panda (*Ælurus fulgens*), 221.

Pangolin, West African (*Manis gigantea*), 487.

Panther (puma or leopard), 94, 127.

Pantolambda, 233.

Paradoxures or tree-cats, 153.

Parahippus, Miocene horse, 355.

Peccary, collared (*Tayassu angulatum*), 344.

Peccary, white-lipped (*Dicotyles labiatus*), 345.

Pekan or Pennant's marten, 164.

Peludo armadillo, 476, 477.

Perissodactyla, 234, 236, 352.

Phalanger, long-snouted (*Tarsipes rostratus*), 503.

Phalanger, opossum (*Trichosurus vulpecula*), 502.

Phalanger, yellow, flying (*Petaurus australis*), 502.

Phenacodus, 230.

Pigs, intelligence of, 346.

Pigs, source of domestic, 346.

Pinnipedia, order, 230.

Pisoti, or coati, 227.

Pithecanthropus (*P. erectus*), 10.

Platypus, or duckbill, 523.

Playing 'possum, considered, 518, 519.

Plesictis, 162.

Pliohippus, Miocene horse, 355.

Pocket mice and gophers, 426, 427.

Polecat (*Putorius fœtidus*), 168.

Porcupine, artistic use of quills, 415.

Porcupine, Brazilian tree (*Sphingurus prehensilis*), 416.

Porcupine, Canada (*Erethizon dorsatus*), 414.

Porcupine, European (*Hystrix cristata*), 413.

Porcupine, yellow-haired (*Erethizon epixanthus*), 415.

Potto, Bosman's (*Perodicticus potto*), 54.

Pouch, evolution of marsupial, 512.

Prairie dog (*Cynomys ludovicianus*), 454.

Primates, characteristics of order, 7.

Proboscidea, elephant order, 386–399.

Pronghorn (*Antilocapra americana*), 286–292.

Protective coloration, 295, 303.

Protohippus, Miocene horse, 354, 355.

Protorohippus, Eocene horse, 353.

Prototheria, subclass of, 490, 521–526.

Pudu deer (*Pudua humilis*), 333.

Puma (*Felis concolor*), 90–97.

Puma, behavior toward man, 95.

Puma, methods of hunting, 96.

Puss and her ancestors, 133–141.

Quagga (*Equus quagga*), 363.

Rabbit, cottontail, or wood hare, 411.

Rabbit, domestic (*Lepus cuniculus*), 408.

Rabbit, plague of, in Australia, 409.

Rabbit, use of the word, 408.

Raccoon (*Procyon lotor*), 221.

Rat, bamboo (genus Rhizomys), 431.

Rat, beaver (*Hydromys chrysogaster*), 431.

Rat, black (*Mus alexandrinus*), 429.

Rat, brown house (*Mus rattus*), 429.

Rat, crested or webber (*Lophiomys imhausi*), 441.

Rat, kangaroo (Perodipus and Dipodomys), 424.

Ratel, African (*Mellivora capensis*), 175.

Ratel, East Indian (*Mellivora indica*), 176.

Rats as sources of disease, 430.

Ravine deer or blackbuck, 277.

Recognition colors, 287.

Reindeer, European (*Rangifer tarandus*), 321, 325.

Restoration of fossil animals, 87.

Rhesus monkey (*Macacus rhesus*), 30.

Rhinoceros, African black (*R. bicornis*), 381.

Rhinoceros, ancestry of, 374.

Rhinoceros, hairy-eared (*R. lasiotis*), 380.

Rhinoceros, horn of, 375, 376, 377.

Rhinoceros, Indian (*Rhinoceros indicus*), 378.

Rhinoceros, Sumatran or Sondaic (*R. sondaicus*), 381.

Rhinoceros, white or square-mouthed (*R. simus*), 382.

Rhinoceros, woolly or tichorine, 377.

Rhytina or Arctic sea-cow, 400.

Rock-badgers or rock-rabbits, 232.

Rodentia, order of Gnawers, 404.

Rodents, ancestry of, 406.

Roebuck (*Capreolus caprea*), 305.

Ruminantia, 236–334.

Ruminants, digestion in, 273.

Saber-toothed tigers, 86–90.

Sable, American (*Mustela americana*), 164.

Sable, European (*Mustela zibellina*), 164.

Saiga, or kiik (*Saiga tartarica*) 278.

Saimiris (monkeys), 46.

Sakis or ooakaries (monkeys), 44.

Salamander (*Geomys tuza*), 427.

Sambar deer (*Cervus unicolor*), 303, 307.

Samotherium, 298.

Sapajou, or Capuchin monkey, 38.

Sapi-utan, or anoa, 243.

Scaletails (Anomaluris), 446.

Sea-cows (Sirenia), 400.

Sea-otter (*Latax lutris*), 186.

Seals and sea-bears, 230.

Serval (*Felis serval*), 133.

Set, symbolized by okapi, 297.

Sha or oorial, 251, 252.

Sheep, Barbary, 257.

Sheep, blue (*Ovis nahura*), 257.

Sheep and goats, 251.

Sheep, Marco Polo's, 253, 254.

Sheep, Rocky Mountain or bighorn, 256.

Shou, or Thibetan red deer, 312.

Shrew, elephant, 74.

Shrew, long-tailed (*Sorex personatus*), 70.

Shrew, short-tailed (*Blarina brevicauda*), 69.

Shrews, superstitions as to, 71.

Shrewmole, western (*Urotrichus gibbsi*), 70.

Siamang (*Hylobates syndactylus*), 21.

Sifaka lemurs (Propithecus), 51.

Siffleur or whistler (*Arctomys pruinosus*), 458.

Sika deer, 307, 308.

Sirenia, order of, 400–403.

Sitatunga or Nakong (*Tragelaphus spekei*), 272.

Sivatherium, 292, 298.

Skunk, eastern (*Mephitis mephitica*), 179.

Skunk, scent glands, 175, 182.

Skunk, striped (Spilogale), 182.

Skunk, white-backed or mapurito, 182.

Sladang, or Malayan gaur, 240.

Sloth, three-toed (*Bradypus tridactylus*), 473.

Sloth, two-toed (*Cholœpus didactylus*), 473.

Sloths, greenness of hair on, 474.

Smilodon, a saber-tooth, 87, 88.

Snow leopard, 130.

Speech, human, 8.

Spermophiles and sousliks, 454.

Spider monkey, or coaita, 41.

Springbok (*Antidorcas euchore*), 279.

Squirrel, Abert's (*Sciurus aberti*), 444.

Squirrel, Douglas's (*Sciurus douglasi*), 444.

Squirrel, European (*Sciurus vulgaris*), 443.

Squirrel, flying (*Pteromys volans*), 445, 447.

Squirrel, Fremont's (*Sciurus fremonti*), 444.

Squirrel, golden-backed (*Callospermophilus chrysodeirus*), 453.

Squirrel, gray (*Sciurus carolinensis*), 442.

Squirrel, Malabar (*Sciurus maximus*), 445.

Squirrel, red (*Sciurus hudsonius*), 443.

Squirrels, ground, or Spermophiles, 452.

Stegodon, a primitive elephant, 390.

Steinbok antelope (*Nanotragus campestris*), 281.

Steinbok, or ibex (*Capra ibex*), 260.

Straw, or pampas, cat, 103.

Sugar squirrel (*Petaurus sciureus*), 503.

Suina, non-ruminants, 236, 345.

Superstitions relating to animals, 24, 30, 36, 51, 55, 62, 67, 71, 76, 116, 125, 134, 160, 192, 242, 378, 390, 487.

Suricate or meerkat, 157.

Swine family (Suidæ), 345.

Taguan or tooan (*Petauroides volans*), 502.

Tahr (*Hemitragus jemlaicus*), 262.

Tail, the prehensile, 38.

Tait, or long-snouted phalanger, 503.

Takin, Thibetan (*Budorcas taxicolor*), 262.

Tamandua assu, 469, 473.

Tamarao (*Bos mindorensis*), 243.

Tapir, American (*Tapirus terrestris*), 373.

Tapir, ancestry of, 371.

Tapir, Malayan (*Tapirus indicus*), 372.

Tardo or two-toed sloth, 473.

Tarsier, spectral (*Tarsius tarsius*), 49.

Tasmanian devil (*Sarcophilus ursinus*), 508.

Tasmanian wolf or thylacine, 511.

Tayra (*Galictis barbara*), 167.

Teetee, or titi, monkeys, 45.

Teeth of a carnivore, 82.

Teludu (*Mydaus meliceps*), 176.

Tenrecs (family Centetidæ), 75.

Thamin or Eld's deer, 306.

Thylacine (*Thylacinus cynocephalus*), 511.

Tiger (*Felis tigris*), 123-127.

Tiger, man-eating, 125.

Tiger, superstitions as to, 125.

Tiger-cat, American, 101, 103.

Tigre or onça, the jaguar, 97.

Tillodontia and Tillotherium, 406.

Tinoceras, 234.

Titanotherium, 375.

Toddy cat or palm civet, 153.

Toxodon, 234.

Tree-tiger, or clouded leopard, 131.

Tremarctus, 211.

Trilophodon, 393, 394.

Tsine, or banteng, 241.

Tuco-tuco (*Ctenomys magellanica*), 422.

Tupias or tree-shrews, 75.

Turs (*Capra cylindricornis*, etc.), 258.

Uintatherium, 234.

Unau, or three-toed sloth, 473.

Ungulata, order, 231, 235.

Unicorn, origin of fabled, 273.

Urus, or aurochs, 238.

Veneration for animals, 394.

Vicunia (*Lama vicugna*), 338, 341.

Viscacha (*Lagostomus trichodactylus*), 417.

Viverridæ (civet family).

Voles and water rats, 431.

Wallaby, rock (*Petrogale xanthopus*), 489, 498.

Webber (*Lophiomys imhausi*), 441.

Whistler, or siffleur, 458.

Winter, how animals endure it, 449.

Wolf, gray (*Canis lupus*), 188.

Wolf, prairie, or coyote, 192.

Wolverine (*Gulo luscus*), 166.

Wombat (*Phascolomys wombat*), 504.

Woodchuck, eastern (*Arctomys monax*), 458.

Wood-rats (genus Neotoma), 439.

Yak or duank (*Bos grunniens*), 246.

Yapock, or water opossum, 520.

Zebras, African, 369.

Zebra wolf, or thylacine, 511.